A GUIDE TO

PALMS
& CYCADS
of the
WORLD

LYNETTE STEWART

CASSELL

Cassell Publishers Limited
Villiers House
41/47 Strand
London WC2N 5JE
Copyright © Lynette Stewart 1994
Illustrations copyright © Margaret Hodgson 1994

This edition first published in the United Kingdom 1994 by arrangement with
HarperCollins*Publishers* Pty Limited, Sydney, Australia.

First published in Australia in 1994 by
Angus & Robertson, an imprint of
HarperCollins*Publishers*
25 Ryde Road, Pymble, Sydney NSW 2073, Australia.

British Library Cataloguing-in-Publication Data:
A catalogue record for this book is available from the British Library.

ISBN 0 304 34415 X

Cover Photograph by Lynette Stewart
Back cover Photograph by Ken Hill
Printed in Hong Kong

FOREWORD

It is with great pleasure that I write the foreword to this book. Historical perspective places this work in an interesting position, as it presents information about palms and cycads which has not previously been available to the general reader. Recent advances in taxonomy have been carefully checked; additionally, details of distribution and the habitats in which the species occur naturally, allow a greater understanding of the plants' biotic preferences and needs, and thus portray them as dynamic, living organisms rather than collectible objects, as so often they have been treated in recent publications on the same subject.

Another innovative inclusion in the work is the conservation rating of most of the species described. A cursory glance will reveal that many palms and cycads are threatened, being either 'endangered', 'vulnerable' or 'rare', and therefore in urgent need of protective action. The chapter on conservation includes some suggestions for resolution of this problem.

The superb photographs, particularly those of palms and cycads in their natural habitats, artistic arrangement of distribution maps and illustrations, and a well researched and informed text, make this work an important addition to the general literature on palms and cycads.

John Dowe
The Palmetum, Townsville
August 1993

A double-headed *Lepidozamia peroffskyana*: North Brother Mountain, east coast of New South Wales, Australia. The habitat is wet sclerophyll forest.

ACKNOWLEDGMENTS

My special thanks go to John Dowe, Botanic Collections Officer of the Townsville Botanic Gardens, Australia. As a friend he has been most encouraging to me in what seemed a daunting task. As my botanical editor he has been enormously generous in his time and effort with the work of advising, checking and correcting the manuscript as it lurched along the road to final completion.

Australia John Dowe, Townsville; Stan and Jane Walkely, Brisbane; Dr Ken Hill, National Herbarium, Sydney; The Library of the National Herbarium, Sydney; Dr Peter Byrne, Sydney; Craig Thompson, Sydney; Paul Kennedy, Sydney; Lyn and Peter Kristensen, Sydney; Len Butt, Brisbane; Roly Paine and Margaret Hodgson, Grafton; Dusan Balint, Cairns; Curt Butterfield, Port Douglas; A. Suria Kumaran, Sydney
Costa Rica Jim Mintkin, San José
Indonesia Gregory Hambali, Bogor, West Java
Malaysia Alex Joseph, Sungei Choh Estate; Mustapha Mohamad, Garden Superintendent, Rimba Ilmu, Kuala Lumpur; Mr Rajadurai, The Incorporated Society of Planters, Kuala Lumpur; Dr Ruth Kiew, Kuala Lumpur; Datuk Lim Chong Keat, Penang; Alim Bium, Park Ranger, Mt Kinabalu, Sabah; Dr Tim Hatch, Sarawak
New Zealand Bryan Laughland, Auckland; Keith Boyer, Auckland
Singapore Mohamad Shah and his assistant Nora, Singapore Gardens; Raffles Hotel, Singapore; Sentosa Development Corporation, Sentosa Island
South Africa Dr Roy Osborne, Durban; Cynthia Giddy
Thailand Cmdr. Watana Sumawong, Bangkok; Poonsak Vatcharakorn and Kampon Tansacha, Nong Nooch Village, Sattahip Cholburi
UK Dr John Dransfield and Martin Gibbons, London
USA Loran Whitelock, California; Dr Knut Norstog, Illinois; Don Hodel, California; Chuck Hubbach, Florida; Dr Andrew Henderson, New York
Botanic Gardens The Royal Botanic Gardens, Sydney; The Mt Coot-tha Botanic Gardens, Brisbane; The Brisbane Botanic Gardens, Brisbane; The Flecker Botanic Gardens, Cairns; The Botanic Gardens and Palmetum, Townsville; The Singapore Botanic Gardens, Singapore; The Bogor Gardens, Bogor, Java, Indonesia; The Palm Oil Research Institute of Malaysia, Kuala Lumpur, Malaysia; The Forest Research Institute, Kuala Lumpur, Malaysia; Rimbi Ilmu, Kuala Lumpur, Malaysia; Nong Nooch Village, Sattahip Cholburi, Thailand; Ho'omaluhia Botanical Garden, Hawaii; The Robert and Catherine Wilson Botanical Garden, San Vito, Costa Rica; Royal Botanic Gardens, Kew, UK; The Virginia Robinson Gardens, California, USA; The Los Angeles and State Arboretum, California, USA; The Huntington Botanical Gardens, California, USA; The Fairchild Tropical Gardens, Florida, USA.

PALM AND CYCAD SOCIETIES

Readers interested in learning more about palms and cycads may wish to join the following societies to become involved with their activities and receive their excellent journals.

The International Palm Society
PO Box 1897
Lawrence
Kansas   66044
USA

Palm and Cycad Societies of Australia
PO Box 1134
Milton   QLD   4064
Australia

The European Palm Society
c/o The Palm Centre
563 Upper Richmond Road West
London   SW147ED
England

Cycad Society of Southern Africa
PO Box 189
Port Elizabeth   6000
South Africa

Palm and Cycad Society of New Zealand
PO Box 3871
Auckland
New Zealand

CONTENTS

Preface

The popularity of palms has been on an upswing for at least the past fifteen years. Cycads have been sought-after garden specimens in South Africa, the USA and Europe for several decades and enthusiasm has spread to Australia and New Zealand, particularly in the last ten years. A handful of palm books have been published over this period, with cycad books now appearing to satisfy the newly-curious. With this book I hope to give more than just a taste to the reader of the fascination of both these wonderful plant groups and to spur them on to visit the plants in their natural habitat.

In an endeavour to contribute new and up-to-date information, several palm genera have been included which have previously received little attention in books of this style. The palm enthusiast may find the genera of *Asterogyne, Calamus, Iguanura, Johannesteijsmannia, Linospadix, Pinanga, Raphia, Salacca, Trachycarpus* and *Wodyetia* provide some fresh material. Some palm genera, such as *Archontophoenix, Areca, Arenga, Dypsis, Iguanura, Licuala, Pinanga* and *Trachycarpus* badly need revision and thus the information supplied here is of interim value while we await the re-evaluation by botanists of the known species and of those species as yet unpublished. All eleven cycad genera with a selection of the species are described and pictured. For the reader who is new to cycads the selection here offers a broad introduction with sufficient detail to gain an understanding of the diversity amongst this most unusual plant group.

The classification, evolution, botany and cultivation of palms and cycads are large subjects and are covered in an introductory way. More detailed information can be gained from a number of specialist references listed in the bibliography. The International Palm Society's journal, *Principes*, and the journal of the Cycad Society of Southern Africa, *Encephalartos*, often publish articles on cultivation experiences as well as updating the enthusiast on the latest botanical research and taxonomic changes.

The subject of the conservation of palms and cycads receives focused attention in the early chapters and I hope will fuel debate and a wider sense of awareness of conservation issues amongst palm and cycad devotees. The IUCN conservation status categories are given for most species but in some cases further information is given which will help to give the reader an indication of the species' chances for survival in the wild. The conservation status ascribed relates to the plant at the world level unless only regional information was available and is identified as such. I have taken advice from several palm and cycad experts who have experience of the population status of the species in the field. Several entries are thus written as the probable or likely status on the basis of this information. Any conservation status assigned to a plant species is, at best, from whatever source, an informed estimate, subject to change as new information becomes available.

Maintaining the natural habitats of plants is vitally important to their future survival on this planet. Cultivation of plant species in botanical gardens and private collections is no substitute for maintaining them in the wild. The genetic diversity within a species is not possible to maintain in cultivation although we are forced to try this route with some economically important plant species which are perilously close to extinction in the wild. I hope that my chapters on habitats and conservation will sway those people as yet unconvinced of the merits of maintaining plant habitats. Some of the photographs shown amongst these pages of palms and cycads in their natural habitat will, I hope, convince the reader of, at the very least, the aesthetic value of *in situ* conservation.

Lynette Stewart
August 1993

CLASSIFICATION

The similarity between palms and cycads is, botanically, a superficial one. In terms of their relative positions within the plant world, palms and cycads could not be further apart.

Palms are flowering plants, thus belonging to the angiosperms. Cycads, on the other hand, do not produce flowers, but have their reproductive organs within cones or cone-like structures. They are gymnosperms, i.e. the plants bear exposed or naked seeds, not seeds which are enclosed in an ovary as are the seeds of angiosperms. For this reason, cycads have a greater affinity with conifers and ferns than they do with palms.

The current classification of palms, formalised by John Dransfield and Natalie Uhl in 1986, is built on the work of H. E. Moore and botanical taxonomists before him, such as Martius, Griffith, Hooker, Beccari and Burret. With the current surge of interest in palms amongst botanists, the rate of change in palm taxonomy has increased. As new species are discovered and described, others are reduced to synonymy. Sometimes two or more genera (or species) are reduced to one when they are recognised as being more closely related than was previously believed. In Madagascar, for example, recent work on the palms in the subtribe Dypsidinae has shown a close relationship between species of that subtribe. Closing gaps between the species, gaps that allowed the separation of genera, makes it likely that several genera will be combined into one. The current state of palm taxonomy provides us with approximately 205 genera and 2800 species.

The current classification of cycads represents a culmination of previous work by Chamberlain (1935), Johnson (1959) and Johnson and Wilson (1990). Interest in cycads has been growing over the past 10 to 15 years, with considerable work on their biology and physiology being undertaken, as well as the description of many new species. Cycads are generally regarded as rare plants and are displayed as valued oddities in botanical garden collections. Currently the number of genera is 11 and the total number of species is estimated as 187 (Stevenson and Osborne, 1993).

The following tables give the current classification within the cycad order and within the palm family.

CLASSIFICATION OF THE ORDER CYCADALES
according to Stevenson (1992)

SUBORDER	FAMILY	SUBFAMILY	TRIBE	SUBTRIBE	GENUS
Cycadineae	Cycadaceae				Cycas
Zamineae	Stangeriaceae	Stangerioideae			Stangeria
		Bowenioideae			Bowenia*
	Zamiaceae	Encephalartoideae	Diooeae		Dioon
			Encephalarteae	Encephalartinae Macrozamiinae	Encephalartos Lepidozamia, Macrozamia
		Zamioideae	Ceratozamieae Zamieae	Microcycadinae Zamiinae	Ceratozamia Microcycas Zamia, Chigua

* Johnson and Wilson (1990) place *Bowenia* in its own family, Boweniaceae.

CLASSIFICATION OF THE FAMILY PALMAE[*]
according to Dransfield and Uhl (1986)

SUBFAMILY	TRIBE	SUBTRIBE	GENUS
Coryphoideae	Corypheae	Thrinacinae	Trithrinax, Chelyocarpus, Cryosophila, Itaya, Schippia, Thrinax, Coccothrinax, Zombia, Trachycarpus, Rhapidophyllum, Chamaerops, Maxburretia, Guihaia, Rhapis
		Livistoninae	Livistona, Pholidocarpus, Johannesteijsmannia, Licuala, Pritchardiopsis, Pritchardia, Colpothrinax, Acoelorraphe, Serenoa, Brahea, Copernicia, Washingtonia
		Coryphinae	Corypha, Nannorrhops, Chuniophoenix, Kerriodoxa
		Sabalinae	Sabal
	Phoeniceae		Phoenix
	Borasseae	Lataniinae	Borassodendron, Latania, Borassus, Lodoicea
		Hyphaeninae	Hyphaene, Medemia, Bismarckia
Calamoideae	Calameae	Ancistrophyllinae	Laccosperma, Eremospatha
		Eugeissoninae	Eugeissona
		Metroxylinae	Metroxylon, Korthalsia
		Calamineae	Eleiodoxa, Salacca, Daemonorops,, Calamus, Calospatha, Pogonotium, Ceratolobus, Retispatha
		Plectocomiinae	Myrialepsis, Plectocomiopsis, Plectocomia
		Pigafettinae	Pigafetta
		Raphiinae	Raphia
		Oncocalaminae	Oncocalamus
	Lepidocaryeae		Mauritia, Mauritiella, Lepidocaryum
Nypoideae			Nypa
Ceroxyloideae	Cyclospatheae		Pseudophoenix
	Ceroxyleae		Ceroxylon, Oraniopsis, Juania, Louvelia, Ravenea
	Hyophorbeae		Gaussia, Hyophorbe, Synechanthus, Chamaedorea, Wendlandiella

[*] Palmae, also known as Arecaceae.

Genus changes since 1986 (not all published):

New genera: *Aphandra, Voaniola* and *Lemurophoenix.*

Lost genera: *Bismarckia* to be included in *Medemia; Louvelia* to be included in *Ravenea; Halmoorea* to be included in *Orania; Vonitra, Chrysalidocarpus, Neodypsis* and *Phloga* to be included in *Dypsis; Prestoea* to be included in *Euterpe; Jessenia* to be included in *Oenocarpus; Scheelea, Orbignya* and *Maximiliana* to be included in *Attalea; Marojejya* to be included in *Masoala; Palandra* to be included in *Phytelephas; Carpoxylon* to be included in subtribe Iguanurinae.

Subfamily	Tribe	Subtribe	Genus
Arecoideae	Caryoteae		*Arenga, Caryota, Wallichia*
	Iriarteeae	Iriarteinae	*Dictyocaryum, Iriartella, Iriartea, Socratea*
		Wettiniinae	*Catoblastus, Wettinia*
	Podococceae		*Podococcus*
	Areceae	Oraniinae	*Halmoorea, Orania*
		Manicariinae	*Manicaria*
		Leopoldiniinae	*Leopoldinia*
		Malortieinae	*Reinhardtia*
		Dypsidinae	*Vonitra, Chrysalidocarpus, Neophloga, Neodypsis, Phloga, Dypsis*
		Euterpeinae	*Euterpe, Prestoea, Neonicholsonia, Oenocarpus, Jessenia, Hyospathe*
		Roystoneinae	*Roystonea*
		Archontophoenicinae	*Archontophoenix, Chambeyronia, Hedyscepe, Rhopalostylis, Kentiopsis, Mackeea, Actinokentia*
		Cyrtostachydinae	*Cyrtostachys*
		Linospadicinae	*Calyptrocalyx, Linospadix, Laccospadix, Howea*
		Ptychospermatinae	*Drymophloeus, Carpentaria, Veitchia, Balaka, Normanbya, Wodyetia, Ptychosperma, Ptychococcus, Brassiophoenix*
		Arecinae	*Loxococcus, Gronophyllum, Siphokentia, Hydriastele, Gulubia, Nenga, Pinanga, Areca*
		Iguanurinae	*Neoveitchia, Pelagodoxa, Iguanura, Brongniartikentia, Lepidorrhachis, Heterospathe, Sommieria, Bentinckia, Clinosperma, Cyphokentia, Moratia, Clinostigma, Alsmithia, Satakentia, Rhopaloblaste, Dictyosperma, Actinorhytis, Lavoixia, Alloschmidia, Cyphophoenix, Campecarpus, Basselinia,Cyphosperma, Veillonia, Burretiokentia, Physokentia, Goniocladus*
		Oncospermatinae	*Deckenia, Acanthophoenix, Oncosperma, Tectiphiala, Verschaffeltia, Rocheria, Phoenicophorium, Nephrosperma*
		Sclerospermatinae	*Sclerosperma, Marojejya*
			Genera of the tribe Areceae, but of uncertain affinity, *Masoala, Carpoxylon*
	Cocoeae	Beccariophoenicinae	*Beccariophoenix*
		Butiinae	*Butia, Jubaea, Jubaeopsis, Cocos, Syagrus, Lytocaryum, Parajubaea, Allagoptera, Polyandrococos*
		Attaleinae	*Attalea, Scheelea, Orbignya, Maximiliana*
		Elaeidinae	*Barcella, Elaeis*
		Bactridinae	*Acrocomia, Gastrococos, Aiphanes, Bactris, Desmoncus, Astrocaryum*
	Geonomeae		*Pholidostachys,Welfia, Calyptronoma, Calyptrogyne, Asterogyne, Geonoma*
Phytelephantoideae			*Palandra, Phytelephas, Ammandra*

CONSERVATION STATUS KEY

THREATENED CATEGORIES

Extinct: No longer exists in the wild.

Endangered: In danger of extinction. Survival unlikely if causal factors continue.

Vulnerable: Likely to become endangered in the near future if causal factors continue.

Rare: Only small world populations exist. Either localised in a restricted area or thinly scattered over a greater range.

Indeterminate: Known to be one of the above threatened categories but not enough information to decide which category is most appropriate.

UNKNOWN CATEGORIES

Status unknown: No information.

Candidate: Being assessed and suspected as belonging to a threatened category.

Insufficiently known: Suspected as belonging to a threatened category but insufficient information available for assessment.

NOT THREATENED CATEGORY

Not threatened: Neither rare nor threatened. Safe.

Chamaedorea amabilis: with male inflorescence. This palm is found in Costa Rica, Panama and Colombia and has the conservation status of 'endangered'.

PRONUNCIATION GUIDE

A phonetic guide to the pronunciation of scientific names has been given for every genus within both the palms and cycads Genera and Species sections. This follows simple principles regarding length of vowels and emphasis on syllables.

˙ short vowel
˘ medium or 'regular' length vowel
‾ long vowel
ˈ major stress
ˌ secondary stress

EVOLUTION AND DISTRIBUTION

EVOLUTION

PALMS

Palms first appear in the fossil record in the late Mesozoic Era, about 85 million years ago, after Gondwana, one of the earth's two supercontinents, had started to break into pieces which were drifting apart. Palm fossils are more numerous about 20 million years later, and by 55 million years ago they appear to have been abundant in many parts of the world, including areas where they do not occur today. The earliest palm leaf fossils are of the costapalmate form, pinnate and palmate forms appearing later in the fossil records. Fossil fruit, seeds, stems, leaves and pollen have been found, some with close affinities to modern palm genera.

Nypa is one of the first recognisable modern genera appearing in the fossil records — about 65 million years ago. Its pollen is relatively easy to recognise and its natural mangrove habitat is one that lends itself to fossil formation. Other palms that may have existed at the same time are less easily identified and less likely to have been fossilised. Palm fossil records should, with further study, lead to an expanded understanding of the evolution of the palm leaf and floral structure as well as other morphological characters in the family and the early monocots in general.

CYCADS

Cycads are believed to be amongst the earliest seed plants. The generally-accepted theory is that they arose from the now-extinct 'seed ferns' (the pteridosperms). Botanists have postulated that there was an early

Attalea rostrata: near San Vito, Costa Rica. This palm is one of the few survivor species from felled rainforest.

separation amongst the cycads into several evolutionary lines of descent. The modern diversity in the Cycadales is thought to be a reflection of the slow evolution of these separate lines over a long period of time. Today's cycads are thus thought to be the survivors of a long period of evolution, many relatives having been lost along the way. A fossil of a cycad-like plant from the Triassic period has been found in Antarctica, but it cannot be placed in any of the modern cycad genera.

Of the fossil cycads belonging to the Tertiary period which have been found, a number have close affinities to modern cycad genera. These include *Lepidozamia* and *Macrozamia* from the Oligocene epoch, which commenced 39 million years ago. *Bowenia papillosa* and *B. eocenia* are two species discovered from the Eocene epoch of about 45 million years ago. Their leaflets appear very similar to modern *Bowenia*. Fossilised *Cycas* species from the Eocene epoch have also been found in China and Japan.

DISTRIBUTION

PALMS

Modern palms are widely distributed throughout the world in the humid tropics and subtropics. They are, however, absent from hot arid zones unless they have access to permanent underground water. A few species occur in temperate regions but very few are tolerant of cold climates. Of the current total of 205 genera, only a small number have numerous species and are widespread in their distribution. *Calamus* is the largest genus, with about 400 species and a distribution across the Old World tropics. *Chamaedorea* has about 100 species and is distributed throughout southern Mexico, Central America and northern South America. There are many monotypic palm genera (i.e. a genus consisting of one species only). These are frequently endemic to a small area, a unique and isolated ecological niche, often on an island. The island of Madagascar is a special case in this regard; becoming separated from Africa about 100 million years ago, it has developed a rich and diverse palm flora mostly unrepresented in Africa. The benign climate on

Livistona decipiens grows as scattered individuals and in small groups in Bowling Green National Park in northeastern Australia.

Madagascar appears to have encouraged palms to evolve while, on continental Africa, adverse conditions of climate and other ecological factors have reduced the chances of survival and evolution of palms.

An interesting discussion of present-day palm distribution and its evolutionary origins is found in *Genera Palmarum* by Uhl and Dransfield (1987).

CYCADS

The various cycad genera tend to be endemic to particular continents. *Cycas* is the exception, being widely distributed throughout Southeast Asia, and extending east to Australia and the western Pacific Ocean islands, and west to eastern Africa and the Indian Ocean islands. This wide distribution may be explained by the fact that some *Cycas* species produce seeds with a spongy layer, enabling them to float on water, and thus allowing dispersal by sea currents. *Bowenia*, *Lepidozamia* and *Macrozamia* are found only on the Australian continent. *Microcycas* is endemic to Cuba. *Dioon, Ceratozamia, Chigua* and *Zamia* species are found from Florida and Mexico to Brazil and Chile. *Encephalartos* species are found in southern, western and central Africa and *Stangeria* is restricted to southern Africa.

Macrozamia communis with trunk, growing in dry sclerophyll forest on sandy soil, in eastern Australia.

STRUCTURE

THE STRUCTURE OF PALMS

Palms belong to the monocotyledons and thus are characterised by having an embryo with one cotyledon, an adventitious root system, a vascular system of scattered bundles throughout the stem, leaves with usually parallel venation and a sheathing leaf base, and flowers with parts often in multiples of three. Palms often also have a sympodial habit (new shoots developing from axillary buds near the base of the stem) considered characteristic of monocotyledons. The diversity of form among palms is very wide and reflects the diversity found among all the monocots.

The basic growth form is of the solitary erect stem with a crown of leaves at the aerial growing end, adventitious roots at the subterranean growing end and inflorescences produced in the leaf axils (see opposite).

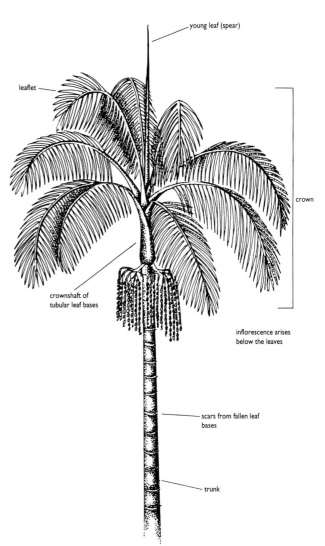

BASIC GROWTH FORM IN PALMS

Hyphaene thebaica 'Doum Palm' has a dichotomously branching trunk.

Not all palms have solitary stems or trunks. In fact, many have a clustering or clumping habit. New shoots develop from axillary buds, which are usually located near the base of the stem. As the new shoot develops into a stem it also produces axillary buds that develop into new shoots. Many palm genera include species that exhibit a monopodial (solitary) habit and species that exhibit a sympodial (clustering) habit (e.g. *Licuala, Phoenix, Metroxylon, Arenga, Caryota, Chamaedorea, Areca, Heterospathe, Chrysalidocarpus, Neodypsis, Pinanga, Geonoma* and *Bactris*). Some individual species exhibit both a monopodial and sympodial habit. Two well-known examples are *Chrysalidocarpus madagascariensis* and *Laccospadix australasica*, in which some individuals are solitary while others are clustering.

Corypha utan: leaf bases are split just below the petiole.

The persistence of leaf bases is another important characteristic of palms, as is the form and pattern of leaf scars that cover the trunk once the leaf bases have abscised. *Borassus* and *Corypha* exhibit split leaf bases, which form a characteristic pattern on the trunk. The trunk of *Arenga pinnata* is characterised by the thick mass of spine-like fibres which results from the disintegration of leaf sheaths. *Zombia* and *Trithrinax* also have leaf sheaths that disintegrate, leaving fibres which have the appearance of long stiff spines.

Armature is an important aspect of palm structure used in characterising taxa. Many palms are armed with spines on the leaf sheaths, petioles and leaf blades. *Phoenix* has spines at the basal portion of the blade. *Calamus*, *Aiphanes* and *Bactris* may have spines on the leaf blade surface itself, while *Livistona* and *Sabal* have teeth along the margins of the petioles. Even some roots can be spiny as with the stilt roots of *Socratea*. In the genera *Calamus* and *Daemonorops*, spines on the leaf sheaths may form elaborate galleries that ants colonise.

Within these two basic growth forms, solitary or clustering, there is a variety of growth patterns. Stems may be prostrate or decumbent. *Elaeis oleifera*, for example, has a prostrate trunk and erect crown. It thus appears to grow along the ground surface with the crown directed skywards. Some palms, particularly those found in rainforests, like *Chamaedorea*, grow along the ground, producing roots from some of the nodes, and directing their leafy growing point upwards. Some palms, such as *Serenoa repens*, can produce either vegetative shoots or inflorescences in the leaf axils along a prostrate stem.

A few palms exhibit dichotomous branching of their stems. *Nypa fruticans* has a dichotomously branching stem, which is prostrate under the surface or on the surface of the soft mud in which it grows. *Hyphaene* is characterised by dichotomous branching, and other examples are to be found among such palms as *Chamaedorea cataractarum* and *Allagoptera arenaria*. Some palms (e.g. most *Salacca* and all but one species of *Johannesteijsmannia*) are acaulescent, meaning they have no above-ground trunk though they may have a subterranean trunk. Others have adopted a climbing habit (e.g. *Chamaedorea elatior*, *Calamus* spp., *Korthalsia* spp., *Daemonorrops* spp., *Plectocomia* spp.) and some have developed specialised climbing organs such as flagella and cirri.

Amongst palms there is a wide variation in the size and appearance of the stem. A few miniature species such as *Chamaedorea tenerrima* have stems that may be as small as 0.6–1 cm (¼–½ in) in diameter and 25 cm (10 in) tall. At the other end of the spectrum, the giants such as *Jubaea chilensis* can have a trunk over 1 m (3 ft) in diameter. Some tall palms, such as *Ceroxylon*, can tower up to 60 m (200 ft) high.

Zombia antillarum has a characteristic pattern of spines on the trunk.

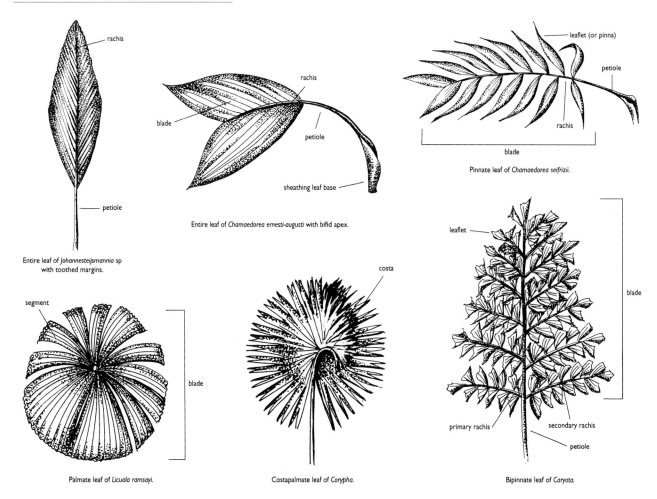

Entire leaf of *Johannesteijsmannia* sp with toothed margins.

Entire leaf of *Chamaedorea ernesti-augusti* with bifid apex.

Pinnate leaf of *Chamaedorea seifrizii*.

Palmate leaf of *Licuala ramsayi*.

Costapalmate leaf of *Corypha*.

Bipinnate leaf of *Caryota*.

THE BASIC TYPES OF PALM LEAVES AND THEIR STRUCTURES

The basic types of palm leaves and their structures are shown above. The petiole is the leaf's stalk or that part of the leaf from the trunk or stem to the start of the blade or first leaflet. The upper surface of the petiole may be grooved, concave, flat or convex, and the margins may be smooth, toothed or spined. The basal part of the petiole expands into a sheathing and clasping structure, called the leaf sheath. It can completely encircle the stem, forming a tubular structure called a crown shaft (as in *Archontophoenix*), or it may encircle the stem only at the basal end of the sheath. In some palms it is split at the base (as in *Corypha*). Sometimes the leaf sheath and petiole are covered in a furry, hairy or woolly growth, or sometimes a waxy coating which gives a whitish bloom to the surface. That whitish bloom may also cover the undersurface of the blade itself, and in some species the wax is thick and covers both upper and lower blade surfaces. The rachis is the central axis of the leaf and that part from which the leaflets arise. It is well developed in pinnate leaves. It is, however, absent in palmate leaves and takes the form of the central rib or costa in costapalmate leaves.

The leaf blade may be entire and undivided except at the apex or sometimes the margins. *Asterogyne martiana*, for example, has undivided leaves except for the short notch at the tip and its leaf is described as entire and bifid at the apex. Entire leaves are often marked with pinnate ribs and if the leaf is split by the force of wind or some other agency, the tear usually runs along one of the ribs. Palm leaves may be divided into groups, with several variations in form to be found:

pinnate — with one-ribbed or several-ribbed units called leaflets or pinnae arranged somewhat like a feather along the rachis

bipinnate — with a double pinnate arrangement of leaflets

palmate — with the blade shaped like the palm of a hand, with ribs or veins radiating from one point. The blade may be shortly, deeply or completely divided into units called segments, which follow the pattern of ribs

costapalmate — with the blade more or less palmate but with a pronounced midrib or costa.

Pinnate leaves can be found with a range of leaflet arrangements. The leaflets may be of fairly equal size or they can differ in size. They may be opposite or alternate in their placement on the rachis, or may be irregularly placed with no repeating pattern. Sometimes leaflets are arranged in groups and they may arise from the rachis at differing angles or in rows. In some palms, the basal leaflets are reduced to spines (as in *Phoenix*). In others, the terminal leaflets are united into a fan shape (as in *Iriartea*) or a fishtail shape (as in *Ptychosperma elegans*). There is also a wide range of shapes in the tips of leaflets. They may be acutely pointed or gently taper to a point (acuminate). Some are abruptly cut off at the tip and may be described as 'truncate'. Jagged-toothed or ragged, chewed-looking leaflet ends are described as 'praemorse'. In cross-section, leaflets are either reduplicate (upside-down 'V'), or induplicate (upright 'V'). Most palms in the subfamily Coryphoideae (except the genus *Guihaia*) and genera of the tribe Caryoteae (subfamily Arecoideae) are characterised by induplicate leaflets or leaf segments. The diagram below shows a range of leaflet arrangements and leaflet shapes.

LEAFLET SHAPES AND ARRANGEMENTS

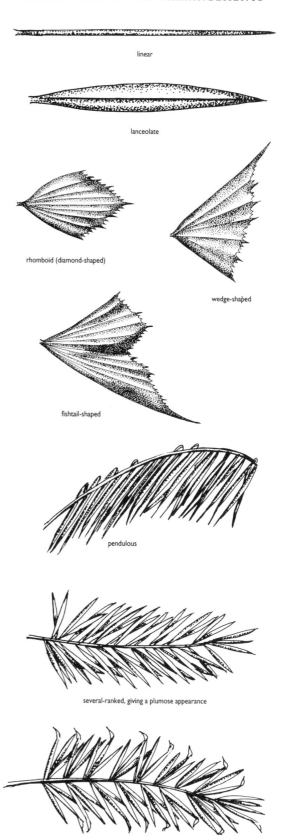

linear

lanceolate

rhomboid (diamond-shaped)

wedge-shaped

fishtail-shaped

pendulous

several-ranked, giving a plumose appearance

grouped or clustered

LEAFLET TIPS

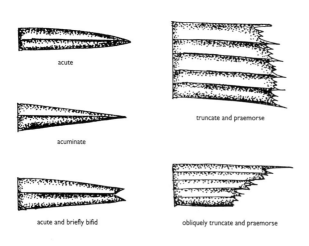

acute

acuminate

acute and briefly bifid

truncate and praemorse

obliquely truncate and praemorse

LEAFLET SECTIONS

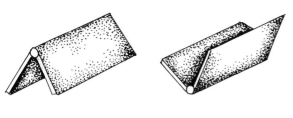

section of a reduplicate leaflet

section of an induplicate leaflet

Aiphanes aculeata has fishtail-shaped leaflets.

The first-formed leaf of a seedling palm is termed the 'eophyll'. This is most commonly a simple linear to elliptical leaf, but may also be bifid or, occasionally, a more complex form such as pinnate or palmate.

Another part of the leaf structure of interest, and often important in identifying palm species, is the hastula. It is a projection of tissue that is at the junction of the petiole and the blade. It may be thin and fragile or thick and tough.

Rhopalostylis sapida: in various stages of flowering and fruiting. Inflorescences arise below the crownshaft.

The inflorescence is the axillary branch that carries the flowers. It appears either among the leaves (interfoliar), as in *Phoenix*, or below the leaves (infrafoliar), as in *Archontophoenix*, where it is exposed after the subtending leaf falls. In a few cases, such as *Metroxylon* and *Raphia*, inflorescences are terminal and above the leaves (suprafoliar). Some palms have inflorescences that arise among the leaves, but, because of the time taken for fruit development, several leaves die and fall and the inflorescence branch is below the leaves by the time the fruit is ripe. Most inflorescences are solitary but some palms have multiple inflorescences arising from one leaf axil (e.g. the male plants of *Chamaedorea deckeriana*, *C. oreophila* and several other *Chamaedorea* spp.). Some small palms flower when just two or three years old, while other palms, particularly those growing into tall trees, may not flower until they are several decades old.

Most palms exhibit pleonanthy: they produce flowers continually throughout the whole mature life of the plant in association with continual vegetative growth. A number of palms exhibit hapaxanthy. This is where the stem, after years of vegetative growth, produces one or more inflorescences and then dies immediately after flowering and fruiting are complete. Solitary-stemmed palms that flower in this way are termed monocarpic. If the palm has a clumping habit then the individual stem dies after flowering but the plant as a whole lives on with new shoots replacing the old ones. *Corypha*, *Nannorrhops*, *Plectocomia*, *Arenga*, *Caryota*, *Wallichia*, *Korthalsia*, *Raphia* and most *Metroxylon* are among the genera that exhibit hapaxanthy. *Metroxylon sagu* produces clusters of hapaxanthic stems. A few palms

Licuala ramsayi: the large palmate leaf is divided into wedge-shaped segments with truncate toothed tips.

Various Plam Inflorescences

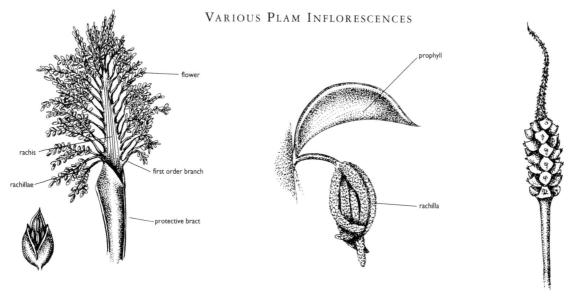

Inflorescence of *Phoenix roebelinii*.

Simple-branched inflorescence (branched to one order) of *Bactris acanthocarpa*.

Spike of *Allagoptera arenaria* flowers.

(e.g. *Corypha*) produce a single terminal inflorescence and then die once fruiting is completed. Most species of the tribe Caryoteae (e.g. *Caryota mitis, Caryota urens, Arenga pinnata, Wallichia disticha*) flower sequentially from the top of the trunk towards the base (basipetal sequence of flowering) whilst a few flower in an acropetal sequence, i.e. from the base to the top of the trunk (e.g. *Arenga hastata*).

The developing inflorescence is always protected by one or more sheathing bracts. These usually completely enclose the inflorescence in bud. The number and position of these bracts is important to the botanist in palm classification. The most basal bract on the inflorescence peduncle (the lower unbranched stalk of the inflorescence) is called the prophyll. There may be other bracts present that are attached further along the peduncle. These are termed peduncular bracts and, when the inflorescence is in bud, they are generally fully enclosed by the prophyll. Also of diagnostic significance is whether the prophyll and peduncular bracts persist or not after the inflorescence opens.

In many palms, the inflorescence is a 'panicle', a much-branched structure in which successive branches become smaller. The ultimate branches on which the flowers are borne are termed 'rachillae'. The number of branches and degree of branching of the inflorescence varies amongst palms and is also of diagnostic importance (see Glossary for the terms used (in this book) for the degree of branching). Some palms have an unbranched inflorescence, which is termed a spike. In *Chamaedorea deckeriana*, for example, the spike is solitary at the node in the female, but there are several spikes per node in the male plant. The diagram above shows the basic structure of the palm inflorescence and several common variations.

Palm flowers are usually small, numerous, rather inconspicuous and short-lasting. However, as with so many other palm features, the variation in floral structure is wide. Flowers are bisexual (hermaphrodite) in many palms but can be unisexual in some species. *Chamaedorea*, for example, has male and female flowers borne on separate plants and is thus said to be dioecious. In other palms flowers are unisexual but are borne on the same inflorescence. When male and female flowers are borne on the same plant it is said to be monoecious. In *Archontophoenix*, for example, male and female flowers are in triads, one female flower flanked by two male flowers. Pairs of male flowers or single male flowers are also present on the distal portion of the rachillae. Some palms have male and female flowers in pairs, termed 'dyads'. Others have flowers in rows (acervuli) along the rachillae. Some species have both unisexual and bisexual flowers present on the same inflorescence and these are said to be polygamous.

Metroxylon warburgii has pear-shaped fruit covered with rows of scales.

Palm flowers may be sweet smelling, but they occasionally have an offensive odour. Flower colours are most often white to cream, and sometimes yellow, mauve, pink or red. Pollination is sometimes by wind, but usually by insects such as beetles, flies, weevils or bees.

Palm fruits may be multi-seeded or single-seeded. They are sometimes brightly coloured and for that reason may be the eye-catching feature of a palm that makes it most attractive. Palm fruits are sometimes conspicuous for their size and shape. The huge fruit of *Lodoicea maldivica* is one which is popular amongst collectors for its exotic (and some say erotic) shape and size. The skin (epicarp) of palm fruit may be smooth and shiny, or dull and waxy, or sometimes rough, scaly, warty and corky or spiny. The mesocarp may be thin or thick, is often fleshy, sometimes fibrous, and sometimes oily. The fleshy and oily mesocarp of the fruit of *Elaeis guineensis* provides a major source of edible oil. A different quality oil is also extracted from the endosperm of the seed. Palm fruits are often edible and, in some parts of the world, form an important component of people's diet. Some examples of popular edible palm fruits are the coconut, *Cocos nucifera*; the date, *Phoenix dactylifera*; the pejibaye, *Bactris gasipaes*; and the salak, *Salacca zalacca*.

BOTANICAL DIFFERENCES BETWEEN THE SUBFAMILIES OF PALMS

CORYPHOIDEAE

Leaves are palmate or costapalmate, rarely entire and usually induplicate. Flowers are solitary or clustered, but not in triads (groups of three).

Washingtonia robusta

CALAMOIDEAE

Distinguished by spines on many organs, tubular inflorescence bracts, small bracts for each flower, climbing organs (cirrus and flagellum), flowers in dyads (pairs), fruit with closely overlapping scales and a specialised three-part gynoecium.

NYPOIDEAE

Contains only one genus which is distinguished by its unique erect inflorescence, which bears a terminal head of female flowers and lateral spikes of male flowers. It is also unusual for its prostrate, dichotomously branching stem.

CEROXYLOIDEAE

Characterised by pinnate, reduplicate leaves, several peduncular bracts covering the inflorescence, flowers that are usually unisexual with a specialised syncarpous, triovulate gynoecium. Flowers are solitary and arranged in spirals or in rows. They produce relatively small fruit, mostly developing from one of three carpels.

ARECOIDEAE

Characterised by unisexual flowers in triads (groups of three in which the female flower is surrounded by two male flowers) or in clusters derived from triads.

Cyrtostachys renda

PHYTELEPHANTOIDEAE

Appears to be without other palm relatives. It is characterised by having large female flowers borne in a head on a short peduncle. Flowers are multi-parted, stamens are numerous and centrifugal in development. Fruits are extremely heavy and many-seeded.

THE STRUCTURE OF CYCADS

Cycads superficially resemble many palms in that they often have erect trunks and a terminal crown of pinnate leaves. Beyond that the similarities end, and in reality they could not be morphologically further apart. The growth habit of cycads may be either arborescent, i.e. like a tree with an aerial and columnar trunk, or subterranean, i.e. underground and tuberous. *Lepidozamia* and *Microcycas* are arborescent. In *Encephalartos, Ceratozamia, Cycas, Dioon, Macrozamia* and *Zamia*, the stem is above ground in some species and subterranean in others. *Bowenia, Stangeria* and *Chigua* have subterranean stems. The diagram below shows the basic growth habit of an arborescent cycad.

The stem of a cycad has a very thick fleshy pith and cortex. This is surrounded by a relatively narrow vascular cylinder of cells, sometimes in concentric woody rings. The rapidly-dividing cells which differentiate into the various specialised cell types are concentrated at the top of the stem. The outer trunk of some arborescent cycads may be covered with a persistent layer of old leaf bases (e.g. arborescent

species of *Dioon* and *Cycas*), or it may be smooth (e.g. *Microcycas* and the arborescent species of *Zamia*). The stem of the subterranean and tuberous form of cycad lacks the outer layer of persistent leaf bases. This is characteristic of the genera *Bowenia, Stangeria* and *Chigua*.

Cycad stems are usually unbranched but are sometimes branched as a result of injury. Bulbils can often form on the outside of cycad trunks, a common occurrence in *Cycas revoluta*. These bulbils are formed from spongy callus tissue of the leaf bases on the outside of the stem. In contrast, the branches that occur as a result of injury to the plant grow from the meristematic tissue at the top of the stem. Branches and bulbils are thus adventitious in origin (i.e. they arise from stem tissues). Unlike palms, cycads do not have axillary buds and thus do not produce any of the axillary structures of palms.

Cycad seedlings produce one tap root which branches and produces small fibrous roots. Generally, new leaves are produced continually for the first two or

BASIC GROWTH HABIT OF THE ARBORESCENT CYCAD.

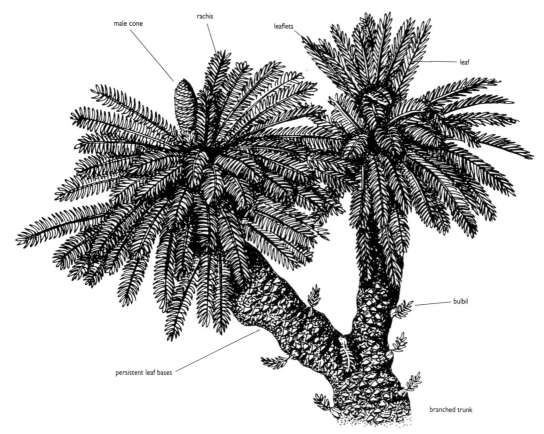

Basic growth habit of the arborescent cycad, *Cycas revoluta*

three years, after which leaves are seasonal in production. Leaf bases build up in number to cover the crown and the tap root contracts, pulling the plant down further into the ground. This appears to be a protective measure for those cycads that grow in dry habitats. Species of cycads with underground stems also have contractile stems, which can be recognised by the wrinkled appearance of the surface. The mechanism appears to be that some of the cortex and pith cells collapse, thus decreasing the total length of the stem or root. Many species produce annual flushes of fleshy contractile roots which swell and push the soil back, then contract and draw the plant down into the space so made. Underground stems and the tuberous roots of cycads store water and carbohydrate.

A secondary root system is also formed which is apogeotropic, growing outwards and upwards towards the soil surface. It produces fleshy outgrowths or nodules in a coral-like form (coralloid roots) near, or sometimes just above, the soil surface and usually within a few centimetres of the stem. These roots contain cyanobacteria, which are able to fix nitrogen from the air and make it available to the plant. Because of the probable nutritional value of these fragile coralloid roots to the plant, they are best not disturbed.

Cycads produce two types of leaves, scale leaves (cataphylls) and foliage leaves. *Stangeria* and *Bowenia*

are the exceptions in that they do not produce cataphylls. Other than *Bowenia*, cycads have pinnate leaves, usually with strong leathery leaflets and no terminal leaflet. The central rachis and petiole are sturdy and the leaf base is swollen or expanded. In some species the petiole is well developed and in others it is apparently absent. Often there are spines or prickles on the petiole and rachis. *Bowenia* is unique in that the rachis itself branches and the leaf is bipinnate. The shape and margins (lobed, toothed or serrated) of leaflets often help identify the species. The broadest leaflets are usually found in the central portion of the blade, with the shorter, narrower leaflets in the proximal and distal portions. Leaflets are most often oval to oblong or lanceolate in outline. The diagrams below and opposite shows a variety of cycad leaflet shapes. The way in which the leaflets attach to the rachis is variable. Decurrent leaflets extend along the rachis parallel to it and thus reinforce their attachment. Articulate leaflets have a narrowed base at the point of attachment to the rachis and they tend to abscise from the rachis before the leaf itself abscises. Articulate leaflets occur in *Ceratozamia*, *Chigua*, *Microcycas* and *Zamia*.

Young leaves are soft and delicate when they emerge and take some time to toughen. New leaves emerge in an interesting manner with similarities to the way fern leaves emerge. The shape of the emerging leaf before it

SOME CYCAD LEAFLET SHAPES

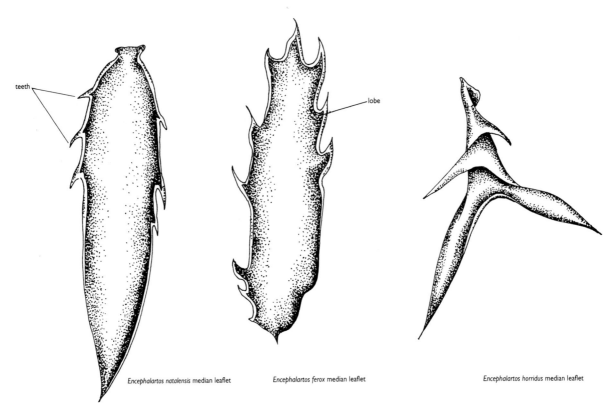

teeth

lobe

Encephalartos natalensis median leaflet   *Encephalartos ferox* median leaflet   *Encephalartos horridus* median leaflet

JUVENILE LEAVES

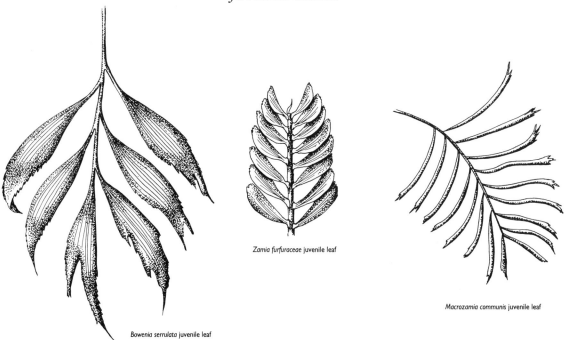

Zamia furfuraceae juvenile leaf

Macrozamia communis juvenile leaf

Bowenia serrulata juvenile leaf

expands is either folded (bent inwards) or rolled inwards (circinate). *Cycas* leaflets are circinate or coiled inwards while the leaf itself emerges erect. *Stangeria* leaves are bent in an inverted 'J' shape as they emerge while *Bowenia* are circinate. The bent and coiled forms of newly-emerging leaves appear to be an adaptation to protect the succulent leaf (particularly of seedlings and plants with no aerial stem), as it pushes its way through the soil.

Cycads appear to grow slowly in the first few years. Much of their energy at this early stage goes into storing carbohydrate in their root system. Once the plant has established and has reached a certain maturity it then produces leaves in whorls. The whorl of leaves, up to fifty in some species, appears in an apparent flush of growth. New leaves may appear each year, sometimes more often, sometimes less often. The frequency of new leaf production is very dependent on climatic conditions. Sometimes a bushfire can destroy all foliage in a location, including cycad foliage. The fresh flush of new bright green leaves on top of the charred trunks of the cycads may be the first sign of plant recovery and regeneration in the habitat.

Cycads are dioecious, the male and female reproductive organs being carried on separate plants. It is impossible to differentiate between male and female plants without the presence of their cones. Female cones bear the ovules, which, once fertilised, develop into fertile seeds. Male cones produce the pollen

Cycas revoluta: bulbils on the trunk surface.

Emerging leaf of *Stangeria eriopus*

required for the fertilisation process. The cones are composed of a large number of modified leaves called sporophylls, which carry the sexual organs. In the female cone, the sporophylls are called megasporophylls and they carry the ovules. In the male cone, they are called the microsporophylls and they carry the pollen.

Cycas does not have a true female cone, but instead has a terminal aggregation of seed-bearing leaves (megasporophylls) curving over and enveloping the apex of the stem. Each megasporophyll bears several ovules, which develop into seeds after fertilisation. After pollination (probably by insects) the megasporophylls, in most species, relax and fold down around the stem sides and a new whorl of leaves may be produced from the apex.

In general, the megasporophyll carries two ovules, but may carry four to eight or more in *Cycas*. Female cones in some species of *Encephalartos* may carry as many as 500 seeds. Male cones are usually narrower and longer than the female of the same species and usually carry more sporophylls than the female. As the cones mature, the compactly-held sporophylls begin to separate. Pollen is released (usually plentifully) from sacs on the undersides of the microsporophyll and is carried by wind and/or insects to the female cone.

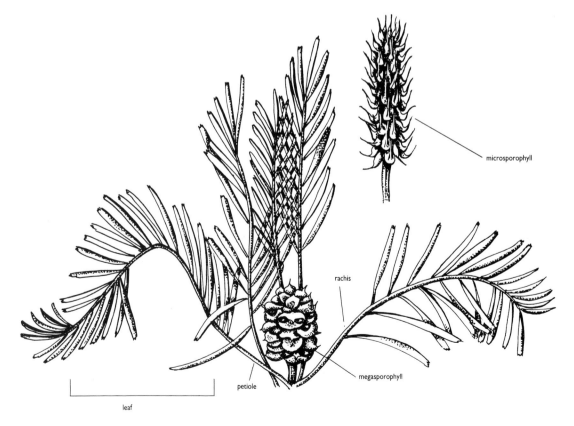

Detail of *Macrozamia fawcetti*

Pollen enters the gaps, usually towards the top of the cone, between the megasporophylls and finds its way (sometimes via an insect such as a weevil) down the interior chamber of the cone to settle on the ovule. The pollen grain is drawn into the ovule with the aid of a sticky fluid and a pollen tube grows down to the chamber where the egg is fertilised. The seed develops over several months before the cone falls apart, releasing all its seeds. There may be a further maturation period before the seeds are ready to germinate. This may be six months or more in *Macrozamia*, for example, and sometimes over one year in *Cycas*.

The structure of the cone is an important diagnostic feature in cycads. The outer surface of the sporophylls, compressed together, as they are, to form the cone, often form a characteristic pattern that is helpful in identification. The seeds of most cycads are covered with brightly-coloured flesh, perhaps to attract the small animals and birds who will aid in dispersal. Colours vary but are usually fairly consistent within a species. They are commonly brown to green, yellow to orange, or dark or bright red. The diagram opposite shows detail of the female and male cones of *Macrozamia fawcettii*.

Cycad seeds, foliage and stems contain toxins that can damage the human central nervous system if ingested. The seeds of several *Cycas* species are used by indigenous peoples to make flour. Preparation procedures always include a careful washing of the starch to remove toxins. Less than a century ago a mill in Florida was extracting flour from wild *Zamia* to process arrowroot flour. Similarly, the pith of *Cycas* and *Encephalartos* species have been used to produce a tapioca-type edible starch. Not withstanding these uses, all parts of the cycad should be handled with care and treated as though they may be poisonous if eaten. When removing the fleshy outer layer of the seed it is also wise to protect the skin of the hands with rubber gloves. Similarly, when hand-pollinating from the male cone to the female, it is best to take precautions against inhaling pollen.

Cycas revoluta: displaying the aggregation of megasporophylls (seed-bearing leaves) and ripening seed.

HABITAT

THE HABITATS OF PALMS

Palms are most abundant in the tropics and subtropics. The warm moist conditions of tropical rainforests provide the growing conditions which are ideal for 75% of palm species. The lowland rainforests (below about 1000 m (3300 ft) of Southeast Asia, including southern Thailand, Peninsular Malaysia, the Philippines, Borneo, Indonesia and New Guinea, and the lowland rainforests of Mexico, Central America and South America are the richest in palm species. Some island rainforests, such as those found on Madagascar and New Caledonia, also offer a rich diversity of palms. In these habitats palms have evolved a diversity of growth habits and specialised features adapted to their particular ecosystem, and there are often many species to be found growing side by side in a small area. Other habitats range from seacoasts, mangroves and swamp forests to desert oases, open grasslands, savannas and woodlands. The warm temperate zones of the world also provide some habitats for palms, particularly in coastal and near-coastal rainforests.

Braulio Carrillo National Park in Costa Rica is one such lowland tropical rainforest (pictured here) that provides an ideal habitat for a large number of palms. Various species of *Geonoma*, *Chamaedorea*, *Asterogyne* and *Bactris* grow in the moist, rotting debris which forms the nutritionally-rich growing medium of the forest floor. The huge bifid leaves of *Asterogyne martiana* and *Geonoma cuneata* grow in close

Braulio Carrillo National Park, Costa Rica: lowland tropical rainforest provides a habitat for palms.

proximity to the large, deeply-divided palmate leaves of *Cryosophila albida* and the comparatively diminutive, delicate, bifid leaves of *Chamaedorea amabilis*. Scattered throughout the undergrowth is a variety of seedling palms, just a few surviving to finally reach the canopy as tall individuals such as *Socratea exorrhiza* and *Iriartea deltoidea*. Occasionally the deep red new leaf of the sub-canopy palm *Welfia georgii* contrasts against the rich green of other leaves. In the soft ground of the forest floor, particularly beside creeks and on slopes where a firm foothold for roots is not guaranteed, these tall-growing palms and some other mid-storey palms, such as *Chamaedorea tepijilote*, develop stilt roots to buttress their stems against shifting ground. Other palms, unable to remain upright in the loose leaf litter, develop roots from nodes along the stem, which give the plant a further hold.

Some palms occur in large, dense stands, completely dominating the forest. The Licuala State Forest at Mission Beach in northeast Queensland, Australia, is one such location (pictured here), where *Licuala ramsayi* dominates the forest. The rattans *Calamus australis* and *C. moti* form thickets in the forest undergrowth and climb up amongst the trees. Individuals of the small understorey *Linospadix minor* and the cycad *Bowenia spectabilis* are to be found in the deep shade of the forest floor. Occasionally a scattered individual or small clump of *Hydriastele wendlandiana* is to be found struggling against the taller growing Licualas in competition for light. And on the edges of the Licuala State Forest, in more open and uninhibited eucalypt scrub, *Livistona drudei* grows in groups and as scattered individuals.

The hot dry desert lands of the world grow few palms. Those that do survive have adapted to these harsh environments. In north Africa there is *Phoenix dactylifera*, and in the Californian desert, *Washingtonia filifera*. Both have deep root systems which can tap into underground water when the surface soil has dried out and the hot summer sun seems relentless. The glaucous leaves of *Hyphaene*, *Brahea*, *Thrinax*, *Butia*, *Nannorrhops* and others are an adaptation to a hot dry climate. A waxy layer protects the surface of the leaf, often both sides, from water loss. The wax often delivers a bloom to the leaf surface and gives the leaf a bluish hue.

In the Old World tropics, *Nypa fruticans* often forms dense colonies on mud banks of natural and constructed waterways. This palm is only found in brackish water and is capable of spreading quickly by repeated branching of the prostrate stems. It can establish in new localities when its buoyant fruit float away on the tide or flood water. In parts of Borneo and Sumatra, *Nypa* covers hundreds of hectares in pure stands and has the

Licuala ramsayi dominates the forest near Mission Beach in northeast Queensland, Australia.

same stabilising effect in river estuaries as do other mangrove species.

In New Guinea, *Metroxylon sagu* grows abundantly in freshwater swamps. It can form pure stands like *Nypa*, and in Borneo and Indonesia it is exploited for the starch it stores in its clumping stems. As a starch crop with multiple uses, it has a growing economic importance in Southeast Asia.

Coastal sand dunes are a favoured habitat for some palms. *Allagoptera arenaria* has a branching underground stem and forms low-growing thickets along the sandy foreshores of Brazil and Uruguay. It is also found in dry grassland areas away from the sea. The bangalow palm, *Archontophoenix cunninghamiana*, grows in a range of soil types including virtually pure sand on Fraser Island off the east coast of Australia.

Once rainforest habitats are cleared or partially cleared for timber or to make way for agriculture or pasture land, very few palms can survive. The increased light of partially-felled forest encourages the growth of some plants while destroying others. Only a few palms are colonisers of disturbed habitats. The fast-growing large palm *Pigafetta filaris* is one such opportunistic coloniser in the Celebes, while *Acrocomia vinifera* and *Attalea rostrata* are other tall-growing palms found dotting the pasture lands of Costa Rica where rainforests once grew.

THE HABITATS OF CYCADS

Cycads occupy various woodland, grassland and forest (including rainforest) habitats. They are characterised by their ability to survive in harsh environments and much of their morphology is adapted to conserving water, and energy, in the form of starch. The few examples that follow give an idea of the range of their habitats.

The genus *Encephalartos* is comprised of about 52 species, all found in western, central and southern Africa. Habitats range from open grassland to closed forest. *E. laevifolius*, for example, grows in exposed rocky slopes at altitudes of 1800 m (5000 ft). These slopes receive high summer rainfall, more than 1250 mm (50 in) each year, and are subject to frosts in winter. *E. ferox*, in contrast, grows in sandy coastal bushland where it receives almost as much summer rain but no frosts. *E. horridus* grows on near-coastal, dry, fertile soil and in association with Karoo scrub, but also grows inland on the infertile soil of rocky ridges where it may receive less than 400 mm (16 in) of summer rain. The trunk is mostly below ground, probably an adaptation for water conservation, and its glaucous blue leaves indicate a hardiness to a dry summer climate and cold winter temperatures.

Cycas media has a wide distribution with habitats ranging from open or closed forest to (occasionally) rainforest. Seen here it is growing on steep slopes near the coast of northeastern Australia. The area receives a high summer rainfall and is not subject to frosts. As with many cycads they are tolerant of occasional bushfires, the stored starch of their trunks and roots providing the necessary reserves for a new flush of growth.

Zamia are found in a variety of habitats from coastal sand dunes to steep mountain slopes in rainforests, from sea level to elevations of 2500 m (8200 ft). One species, *Z. roezlii*, can grow in mangrove swamps, while another, *Z. pseudoparasitica*, is an epiphyte.

Perhaps the characteristic that appears most often among the cycads is good drainage in the soil. Whether on the steep rocky slopes in a dry inland location or the moist rotting plant material of the rainforest floor, good drainage that provides aeration around the roots seems to be fundamental to the cycad ecosystem.

Cycas media: growing on steep slopes in open eucalypt forest near the coast in northeastern Australia. Note the new flush of leaves after a recent bushfire has burned the area.

PALM AND CYCAD CONSERVATION

There are a variety of reasons for the loss or endangerment of palm and cycad species. Loss of habitat is the main threat, but over-collection of plants and seeds also poses a threat to some horticulturally desirable species.

Among the most imperilled ecosystems of the world are the tropical rainforests which contain the greatest diversity of plant life on earth. The vast majority of the world's palm species and many of the world's cycad species are found in these rainforests. Pressure on these habitats derives mainly from the need for more agricultural and pastoral land. Forestry, mining, urbanisation, roads and hydroelectric developments have all taken their toll. Unfortunately, the agricultural exploitation of the rich soil of rainforests often leads to its structural degradation and loss of fertility. Once destabilised by clearing, the soil easily erodes and loses its fertility, thus resulting in irreparable damage in both the short and long term.

Reduction of habitat often places pressure on specific palms and cycads for their very survival. Most palms appear to require precise conditions for seed germination and seedling establishment. Many of the rainforest species exist as scattered individuals amongst a wide variety of other plants. They are typically reliant on certain conditions of moisture, temperature and light for the establishment and survival of new generations. In the few ecological studies done on these plants, we often learn that insects, birds and small animals that share the same habitat are important in one or more aspects of a species's survival (e.g. flower pollination and seed dispersal). Those species that are normally found in low densities, but widely spread, may be threatened if the area of their natural habitat is severely reduced. Some species are already restricted in their distribution. Maintaining small pockets of rainforest as remnant samples of what was once present can often mean the reduction of opportunities for reproduction. The broken continuity of replenishment of a population, particularly if that population carries the last remaining individuals of the species, can result in the loss of that species from the wild. Leaving a few individuals as remnants of the forest is often as good as total destruction. Tall palms left standing when the forest is cleared will often not regenerate because the conditions for seed germination and regrowth are no longer

The restored Palm House at Kew Gardens, England.

present. Selective logging can sometimes mean the overgrowth of opportunistic plant species, which take advantage of the newly-created extra light penetrating the forest. Other less robust plants are totally swamped by the competition and disappear from the felled localities.

Cultivation of species in botanical gardens and private collections is no substitute for maintaining the plant in the wild. Chazdon (1988) pointed out the dangers of relying on *ex situ* propagation and cultivation for the survival of species. The genetic diversity within a species cannot be maintained in cultivation. A species's genetic diversity will deteriorate, especially if the original collections were restricted in number and from only one or just a few habitat locations. She writes:

> ... *continuing evolution and adaptation to natural conditions, which provide the only real hope for long-term survival of species, are possible only within natural habitats.*

CONSERVATION STATUS OF PALMS AND CYCADS

The conservation status of a particular plant species represents an estimation of the degree of threat to the plant's survival in the wild. The IUCN conservation status categories are used in this book and these require some explanation.

Founded in 1948, the International Union for the Conservation of Nature and Natural Resources (IUCN) is a network of government and non-government organisations, scientists and conservationists, who have united to promote the protection and sustainable use of living resources. Amongst its many roles, the IUCN monitors the status of ecosystems and species throughout the world and plans conservation programmes for sustainable development and the maintenance of living species. One of the six commissions of the IUCN is the Species Survival Commission and, together with the World Wide Fund for Nature (WWF), it has funded special projects aimed at both palm conservation and cycad conservation that identify the conservation status of these plants around the world. The conservation status ascribed to the palm species depicted in the genera section of this book is derived from several projects of the IUCN and WWF, and from work currently being conducted (but unpublished at the time of printing). The conservation status ascribed to the cycads is derived from several sources, including a WWF project report by Gilbert (1984). The conservation status ascribed is the World Conservation Category, unless only regional information was available. This is identified as such. I have also taken advice from several palm and cycad experts who have experience of the population status of species in the field. Several entries are thus written as 'probable' status on the basis of this information. Any conservation status assigned to a plant species is, at best, from whatever source, an informed estimate which must be

Calamus penicullatus is endemic to a small area of rainforest on Penang Hill, Malaysia.

subject to change as new information becomes available. The continuing pressures on forest areas and the change in the state of knowledge of species mean that the conservation status of many palms and cycads will alter from time to time.

RESTRICTION OF TRADE IN PROTECTED PLANTS

Certain species are now also protected under the Convention on International Trade in Endangered Species of Wild Fauna and Flora (CITES). This international agreement binds the signatory countries to place restrictions on the import, export and re-export of listed species. Those species listed on the CITES Appendix I require permits from both the importing and exporting countries. Artificially-propagated plants on Appendix I are able to be given special consideration, depending on whether they are propagated for commercial purposes. Plants listed on a second list, Appendix II, require a permit for export (or re-export) from the country from which they are to be exported.

Appendix I includes all cycads in *Ceratozamia*, *Encephalartos*, *Microcycas*, *Chigua* and *Stangeria*. Appendix II includes all *Bowenia*, *Cycas*, *Dioon*, *Macrozamia*, *Lepidozamia* and *Zamia*. Currently there is no permitted trade in plants or seed of Appendix I cycads collected in the wild.

To reduce the pressure of illegal collection of wild plants and seed, there is a proposal to register selected nurseries to collect wild seed and to grow it (under monitoring) for trade purposes. Another proposal to protect seedlings of threatened palms collected in the wild by adding them to the CITES Appendix II list is also being developed.

Encephalartos horridus growing on the edge of the Little Karoo Desert, South Africa, with *Aloe ferox* (right and background) and *Aloe striata* (left). *E. horridus* is classified as 'vulnerable', being much diminished in numbers because of removal of plants for sale.

THE IUCN CONSERVATION STATUS CATEGORIES
(Definitions of the IUCN Conservation (Red Data Book) Categories.)

A. THREATENED CATEGORIES

Extinct: Taxa that are no longer known to exist in the wild after repeated searches of their type localities and other known or likely places.

Endangered: Taxa in danger of extinction and whose survival is unlikely if the causal factors continue to operate. Included are taxa whose numbers have been reduced to a critical level or whose habitats have been so drastically reduced that they are deemed to be in immediate danger of extinction.

Vulnerable: Taxa that are likely to move into the endangered category in the near future if the causal factors continue to operate. Included are taxa of which most or all of the populations are decreasing because of large-scale exploitation, extensive destruction of habitat or other significant environmental disturbance; taxa with populations that have been seriously depleted and whose ultimate security is not yet assured; and taxa with populations that are still abundant, but which are under threat from serious adverse factors throughout their range.

Rare: Taxa with small world populations that are not at present endangered or vulnerable, but are at risk. These taxa are usually localised within restricted geographical areas or habitats or are thinly scattered over a more extensive range.

Indeterminate: Taxa known to be extinct, endangered, vulnerable or rare, but where there is not enough information to say which of the four categories is appropriate.

B. UNKNOWN CATEGORIES

Status unknown: No information.

Candidate: Taxa whose status is being assessed and which are suspected but not yet definitely known to belong to any of the above categories.

Insufficiently known: Taxa that are suspected, but not definetely known, to belong to any of the above categories following assessment (because of the lack of information).

C. NOT THREATENED CATEGORIES

Not threatened: Neither rare nor threatened. Safe.

Pritchardia affinis ssp. *gracilis*

There are 45 palm species listed as endangered in the New World. Five genera account for 20 of this total. These are *Attalea* (5), *Ceroxylon* (5), *Coccothrinax* (4), *Chamaedorea* (3) and *Copernicia* (3). Four palms (*Itaya*, *Jubaea*, *Neonicholsonia* and *Schippia*) are monotypic, that is, they contain just one species. In the Old World, the conservation status of palms is only partly studied. A list published by Johnson (1988) gave 45 endangered and one extinct species. Seventeen of the 46 are found in just two genera, those being *Pritchardia* (13) and *Hyophorbe* (4). The Hawaiian Islands account for 13 endemic species on the list, Madagascar has 12 and Mauritius four. The Old World has nine endangered palms that are monotypic. Since the publication of WWF

Project No. 3325, which gave more information on the conservation status and utilisation of palms in India, Indonesia, the Philippines and Malaysia, the list of endangered palms in the Old World has grown to over 50. Countries with significant palm populations such as Bangladesh, Myanmar (Burma), China, Cambodia, Laos, Thailand and Vietnam have not been studied.

At last count (Johnson and Wilson, 1990), 26 species of cycads were listed as endangered worldwide. Those listed include *Microcycas calocoma*, *Cycas chamberlainii*, seven species of *Encephalartos*, two of *Dioon*, five of *Ceratozamia* and nine of *Zamia*. Twenty-eight species are listed as vulnerable. Many cycads have an unknown conservation status.

SOME CASE STUDIES

A few specific examples are presented here of palms and cycads under threat. The reasons for their endangerment vary; the reactions of governments and individual citizens also vary. The list of species under threat continues to grow and the solutions are not straightforward.

PALMS

Chamaedorea spp. — Found in the New World tropical rainforests, 19 species are listed by Hodel (1992) as endangered, 17 species as vulnerable, 9 as rare, 23 as indeterminate and 10 as insufficiently known. With tropical rainforests continuing to disappear quickly, the Chamaedoreas are under threat. These understorey palms will not reproduce in secondary rainforest. Their future in the wild is linked to that of primary, undisturbed rainforest. A number of Chamaedoreas are highly desirable plants to collectors. Not only are they ornamental, but due to the climatic nature of their low and mid-montane habitats, they are often adaptable to cultivation in subtropical and warm temperate climates. Loss of habitat is thus not the only threat to some of these palms. As Hodel (1992) points out, 'another more acute threat is overcollecting by acquisitive and zealous hobbyists, many with commercial interests, who do not hesitate to strip seeds and plants from the forest in great numbers.' Populations of the following species, Hodel reports, have already declined from overcollecting — *Chamaedorea tuerckheimii* in Mexico and Guatemala, *C. amabilis* and *C. sullivaniorum* in Panama, and *C. tenella* in Mexico.

Calamus manan — This is the premier quality, large diameter rattan for furniture making. It is a single-stemmed plant and thus cutting the stem results in the death of the plant. It has been overcollected from its wild habitats, the lowland rainforests of Peninsular Malaysia, Sumatra and Kalimantan. It is now listed as vulnerable in those regions. The collection of rotan manau (*C. manan*) by the Orang Asli, an indigenous cultural group in Peninsular Malaysia, has been an activity of significant economic importance to them for several decades. In the 1970s, rotan manau was plentiful and easy to collect. Today it is depleted from logged and accessible forest areas and is only to be found in inaccessible virgin rainforest. Many other rattan species have also been reduced by overcollecting. Other Southeast Asian countries producing rattans have banned the export of the raw and partially-processed product in an effort to develop all stages of the industry for the benefit of their own country and to conserve the resource in the wild. In Malaysia, a high export tax on the partially-processed rattans was aimed at reducing rattan collected for export and encouraging the development of the processing and manufacturing end of the industry within the country. It is hoped the strategy will help to develop a long-term sustainable industry with a renewable resource. Research is underway for the development of plantations of various rattan species including *C. manan*. However, the genetic base for commercial development of a plantation rattan industry has already been severely depleted through overcollection in the wild.

Ptychosperma bleeseri — Endemic to just a few locations in the Northern Territory of Australia, this palm has a very restricted distribution and is listed as endangered. This species is closely related to *P. macarthurii*. There are approximately 350 individual plants surviving with more than 50 plants and good numbers of juveniles in only two locations. Recent conservation measures have included fencing off these two populations to protect them from feral and grazing animals.

Wodyetia bifurcata: growing in the Melville Ranges, Cape York Peninsula, Australia. It has a restricted distribution and a 'rare' conservation status.

Johannesteijsmannia altifrons

Wodyetia bifurcata — A beautiful, fast-growing palm from Australia's southeastern Cape York Peninsula, this species has the conservation status of rare. The palm was only discovered in 1975 and formally described in 1983. Despite the fact that collection of seed is prohibited because the palm only occurs within the confines of a national park, *Wodyetia* is now grown widely throughout eastern Australia and many millions of seed have been exported to other countries. Some seed was collected in 1982 under a CSIRO Botanical Collection Permit, the only one issued for seed collection of this species, and this seed was distributed to a few botanical gardens. Advanced specimens of *Wodyetia* can today be found in botanical gardens and private collections from the tropics to warm temperate areas throughout the world. The exportation of illegally-collected seed has proven lucrative for some unscrupulous agents. Such was the demand for this forbidden palm that poachers entered the park and knocked down trees to harvest seed. Several northern Australian nurseries have been raided and had

thousands of seedlings confiscated by the authorities. A recent High Court appeal in Australia allowed a nursery grower to go free from prosecution on the basis that the illegal growing of the palm was so widespread that it was unfair to single out one person for prosecution. As a result of the High Court's decision, all *Wodyetia* under cultivation are now being considered for an amnesty. *Wodyetia bifurcata* provides an example of how legislation can be meaningless when implementation is weak and impractical. Controlled collection and distribution of seed by national parks authorities or licensed persons would surely have alleviated the black market demand for this magnificent palm. 1993–95 should see a reduction in black market demand for seed from the national park as sufficient *Wodyetia* trees in cultivation will be producing fruit.

Johannesteijsmannia spp. — These magnificent palms are under threat because of loss of habitat by clearing and logging, and by overcollection of plants and seed by, and for, foreign collectors. *Johannesteijsmannia magnifica* and *J. lanceolata* have restricted distribution in Peninsular Malaysia and are considered endangered. *J. altifrons* has a more patchy distribution in Peninsular Malaysia, and is considered vulnerable in both Peninsular Malaysia and Sarawak (Borneo). *J. altifrons* leaves are collected and sold by indigenous communities (the Orang Asli and Orang Hulu) for making house walls and roof thatch. Eight to ten leaves can be cut from a single plant and it will recover provided that two to three leaves remain. *Johannesteijsmannia* species are well represented in collections in Australia, England and the USA, but are poorly represented in Malaysian collections. The Malayan Nature Society has placed seed of all *Johannesteijsmannia* species on the list of plants that require permission to export from the Ministry of Agriculture. The society is further considering a proposal to have *Johannesteijsmannia* species added to the CITES appendices.

Euterpe edulis — This species is found in northern Argentina, Paraguay and Brazil and is considered vulnerable. This single-stemmed palm is considered one of the best for the succulent palm heart (cabbage) and it has been the mainstay of the palmito industry. The bulk of the populations in the southernmost range of *Euterpe edulis* have disappeared through overcollection of palm hearts. The result has been that those genotypes adapted to colder, more temperate climates have all but been lost. Now over 96% of the palmito is obtained from other species. Research is being carried out to facilitate the active recuperation of remnant native populations and the planting of domesticated populations. Unless this is successful, this species will soon be extinct in the wild from overexploitation.

CYCADS

Encephalartos dyerianus — This species was first discovered in the early 1970s and not formally described until 1988. The delay in naming it was at least partly because botanists thought there would be a rush by collectors to procure specimens. It has an extremely restricted distribution, growing mainly on one low granite hill in northeastern Transvaal of South Africa, where there are about 600 specimens growing very densely. The conservation of this species in the wild is secure for the moment with the site fenced and a guard on duty 24 hours a day. Pressure from collectors has been alleviated by the fact that the Transvaal Nature Conservation Department raised hundreds of seedling several years ago and sold them to the public under the name *Encephalartos eugene-maraisii*. Now recognised as *E. dyerianus*, it is well established in cultivation with seed coming from cultivated plants. The Transvaal Nature Conservation Department for many years attempted to satisfy the public demand for cycads by hand-pollinating many garden plants and germinating seed in their nurseries for sale of five-year-old plants at a more-or-less cost price. They no longer provide this service because it was considered to represent unfair competition to private cycad nurseries.

Encephalartos woodii — Extinct in the wild, the remaining specimens are all male plants. No female plant has been discovered and thus all living plants are male clones. One solitary clump was discovered in Zululand in 1895 by Medley Wood, a celebrated South African botanist. The several hundred specimens in collections around the world are all clones of the original offshoots collected by Wood and his assistant James Wylie. The rarity of *Encephalartos woodii* lends great attraction to the collector. Luckily it has been fairly easy to propagate as it suckers freely and grows relatively quickly. Spontaneous sex change in cycads is rare but does happen, and is a hoped-for event for the future of *E. woodii*. Another possibility for its future is to obtain female plants that are very near pure *E. woodii*. Repeated back-crossing using *E. woodii* pollen with *E. natalensis* should produce plants more like *E. woodii* with each generation of females so produced. After five generations, the resultant female is theoretically 97% 'woodii'. Another possibility is through tissue culture and experimentation with plantlets using hormones to try to obtain a gender change.

Ceratozamia spp. — This species is now listed on the CITES Appendix I which restricts trade in wild-collected plants and plant parts including seed. Distributed in Mexico, Guatemala and Belize, there are only ten species recognised. Populations are widely dispersed and some isolated. Many have been seriously reduced by collection of live plants. The high prices obtained for plants in the USA have fuelled the overcollection of *Ceratozamia* species, particularly in Mexico. Ranchers and farmers have also destroyed plants because of their toxicity to cattle. In 1982, over 3000 specimens were imported legally to the USA from Mexico with a marked adverse effect on the wild populations. The USA re-exported 550 to the Republic of South Africa. In 1983, 2500 specimens of the newly described *C. norstogii* were exported to the USA, with the result that one of the two known populations in the wild was eliminated. The extent of illegal trade is unknown, but very little is thought to derive from plants cultivated from seed in nurseries.

CONSERVATION STRATEGIES FOR PALMS AND CYCADS

Attention has been drawn to the need for a global action plan for palms (Johnson, 1991). Conservation research projects in the New World and Old World tropics have improved our state of knowledge on palms and their *in situ* (wild habitat) conservation status. Much work still remains to be done in those countries not studied or barely studied. Humankind's link with the palms is of major importance to the future of some species. Any conservation strategy must take full cognisance of the economic value of palm products that are of subsistence or commercial value to many indigenous cultures, whether plants are gathered from the wild or cultivated.

Measures which are underway to promote the protection of threatened palms and cycads include:

- legal protection under CITES aimed at controlling the country to country trade of threatened plants

- conservation research projects aimed at identification of the conservation status of plant taxa and the evaluation of the economic importance of palm products to community groups

- the dissemination of information gained in these research projects to the general public in order to raise the awareness of people to conservation in general and the plight of individual species in particular

- the development of germplasm banks of threatened species recognised to be of economic importance to humans. Such collections of plants and seed are aimed at actively conserving the genetic diversity of the species in question and providing an ongoing reserve of material for plant breeding. Some commercially important palms, such as *Elaeis guineensis, Cocos nucifera, Acrocomia* spp., *Salacca* spp., *Bactris gasipaes*, *Euterpe edulis* and some of the rattan palms, are already receiving this type of attention.

- the establishment of botanical garden collections and horticultural nurseries to maintain populations of palms and cycads outside their native habitat.
- the development of forestry practices aimed at sustaining the diversity of plant species within the forests; that is, creating sustainable forests rather than destroying forests for short-term use of resources.

The conservation status of cycads is at a more critical stage than palms because of their greater rarity and lesser diversity. The *in situ* status of some cycads is perilously close to extinction. Attempts to stop poaching of plants and seed for sale on the black market by the apprehension of marketeers often appears to be an exercise in frustration and futility. In South Africa, some conservation authorities refuse to provide permits for the export of seed of indigenous cycads even when the seed has been derived from garden plants that have been artificially pollinated. Because it is becoming too difficult to identify artificially produced seed from wild-collected seed, the authorities are tending to prohibit all export, no matter what the origin of the seed may be. This has tended to antagonise some growers and enthusiasts, and is perceived as counterproductive to the cause of conservation because it fuels the demand for contraband plants and seed.

Grobbelaar (1992) argues:

> *authorities must also concede that it is an admirable and normal human trait to admire, collect and study plants and animals. In addition to conserving plants and animals, the authorities must also make it easy for the public to see and acquire specimens of such plants and animals.*

He suggests that restrictive legislation should be kept to a minimum and instead the cooperation of groups interested in participating in conservation projects should be sought. There is significant support for the proposition that if efforts could be directed to increasing the propagation of endangered species *ex situ* and making plants available to the public, the pressure on wild populations would decrease. The idea of 'conservation through cultivation' is an attractive one. It may, however, be overoptimistic as a strategy to solve the conservation problems of some of the threatened cycads. Whether seed is collected from the wild by commercial nurseries or government organisations, if it is collected extensively, the result is detrimental to normal regeneration of the wild population.

There is a great need for public education as to the current legislation and regulations relating to plant and seed collection from the wild. Much of the damage done

Rainforest along the Rio Sarapiqui in Costa Rica provides an ideal habitat for many palms.

in the depletion of palm and cycad populations in the wild is done directly or indirectly through the enthusiastic amateur collector who is ignorant or ill-informed. In their unfettered eagerness to possess the plants, they can unwittingly rob the habitat of the critical numbers of plant or seed needed for natural replenishment of the population. Indirectly, their acquisitive need creates a market price for the plant which in turn provides the economic motivation for less scrupulous people who become the plant and seed strippers of the plant's habitat. Conservation measures need to recognise these forces and deal with them constructively.

CONSERVATION-CONSCIOUS GUIDELINES FOR PALM AND CYCAD COLLECTORS

Chazdon (1988) listed 'conservation guidelines for palm collectors and growers'. Hodel (1992) also put forward some constructive ideas. The following list builds on the themes they put forward.

1. Do not collect living plants from the wild unless permitted by the controlling authority to so do. Permission for collection of plants for herbaria identification and botanical research should also be obtained. Find out what is required before going on the collection trip. Seed collection from the wild of CITES Appendix I species should be only under licence from the controlling authority. Other palms and cycads listed in threatened categories may also be prohibited from collection by government authorities. Palm and cycad interest groups should regularly publicise current information on regulations to their members.

2. Collect seed in preference to plants. Do not kill the plant in order to collect the seed. Collect a few seed from several individuals rather than many seed from one individual. If the species is rare, collect only a small proportion of the fruit crop. If there is only one fruiting individual in the vicinity, do not collect any seed. Collect only the amount you intend to germinate and distribute to others. Keep collections from each species separate to avoid wrong identification and/or hybridisation. Document your collection as to location (including elevation).

3. Whenever possible, use seed from wild palms to establish stock plants for breeding purposes rather than for direct sale. Distribute palm and cycad seed to botanical gardens and the seed banks of the palm and cycad societies. Collect pollen of male cycad plants in cultivation for the pollen banks of the cycad societies. Use the pollen banks to make sure rare cycad female plants in cultivation produce fertile seed.

4. Become involved in conservation activities relating to threatened plants. Use the knowledge you have gained of plant habitats and threatened species to promote the conservation of particular species and populations. Take photographs of plants in their habitat to help publicise this information. Work with special interest groups, local conservation groups and international organisations such as the Nature Conservancy International Program or the World Wide Fund for Nature towards these aims.

Howea forsteriana is endemic to Lord Howe Island, off the east coast of the Australian continent.

CULTIVATION OF PALMS AND CYCADS

Cultivation is a large subject that can only be covered here in a cursory way. The further references given at the end of the book will provide more detailed information. The information provided here is designed to give an overview to the hobbyist.

PROPAGATION OF PALMS

Palm propagation may be from seed or by division of vegetative plant parts. The majority of palms are grown from seed. Vegetative propagation is not commercially viable for palms except in a very few special cases, such as *Rhapis humilis*.

Fresh seed, collected as ripe palm fruits, is usually readily germinated given a warm, moist growing medium. Those palms that have a reputation for difficult germination have often been so credited because the seed obtained has, with time, lost some of its viability. Even *Phytelephas aequatorialis*, which has the reputation of being extremely slow to germinate (one to two years or more), has been reported as germinating within two months of sowing. Seed storage conditions are of prime importance in maintaining seed viability. A cool temperature and moist environment help retain viability, while a warm, dry environment promotes loss of water and thus also of viability. Seeds may go into dormancy under these conditions or lose their viability altogether.

In general, palm seed requires a temperature of 22°–35°C (72°–95°F), the range varying depending on the species. In commercial nurseries this requires the application of 'bottom heat' in the form of heating cables under the propagating medium. There are various methods the hobbyist can use to achieve the same result. The top of a water heater is a favourite location for heating trays of seed. At cooler temperatures, germination is slower and the percentage of seed that germinates is usually less. A few palms (e.g. *Elaeis guineensis*) need higher temperatures to break dormancy.

Seed should be cleaned to remove any remaining flesh on the outside of the hard shell. Some palms will require immersion in water or being enclosed in a plastic bag with extra moisture for a day or two to start the flesh rotting and make it loose enough to remove easily.

Propagating media vary, and may include coarse sand, peat moss, vermiculite, perlite, pine bark, sawdust, peanut husks, rice husks etc. Often a combination of media is used, usually coarse sand plus a water-holding component such as peat moss or sawdust. Unlike cycad seeds, palm seeds should be covered to about 2 cm (¾ in) depth, or at least their own thickness. A deep tray is best, but hobbyists can improvise with plastic ice cream trays or shallow plastic growing pots. It is also possible to place the seed in a plastic bag with plenty of moistened peat moss or sphagnum moss, hang the bag in a warm cupboard, and wait for germination to occur. Germinating seeds can be individually removed and potted into a growing container.

When the first leaf (eophyll) has expanded, the seedlings are ready to pot. Seedling palms should generally be potted into smallish containers that are deeper than they are wide. Enough room should be available for development of the first, often long, root and the quickly following adventitious roots. Commercial potting mixtures vary greatly but many hobbyists will prefer to purchase a ready-made potting mixture. Many are soil-less mixtures and will require the addition of extra fertilisers after a few months. For a homemade mixture, equal parts of coarse sand, peat moss or mushroom compost, well-rotted cow manure and a good garden loam are a tried and true combination.

Potted palms should be kept in a shaded position such as a bush house, a shade house, a verandah, or under trees in the garden. Regular watering is a necessity, and extra applications of fertiliser in summer months are advisable to promote growth.

Vegetative propagation can be achieved by removing basal suckers from clumping palms. This is a good way of dividing *Rhapis* palms, a number of the *Chamaedorea* palms and the golden cane palm (*Chrysalidocarpus lutescens*). To divide suckers from the parent plant use a knife or saw and remove as much root material and soil as possible. Suckers that have not developed roots of their own are more difficult to grow. One approach is to partially wrench or twist the sucker away from the parent. Another is to cut halfway across the

Sentosa Island resort near Singapore. Mature coconut palms have been transplanted onto the beachfront and given wooden supports while they re-establish.

underground part of the sucker and leave it attached to the parent plant for several weeks. The cut should be dusted with fungicide powder to prevent fungal rot. Roots should develop above the cut, the sucker needing an extra path to obtain nutrients. Once these new roots have developed the sucker can be completely removed and planted or potted.

A good variety of palms are suitable for indoor cultivation. The most successful indoor palms have been the kentia palms, *Howea forsteriana* and *H. belmoreana*, *Rhapis excelsa* and *R. humilis*, *Chamaedorea elegans* and *Phoenix roebelenii*. They have all proved to be tolerant of low light intensities and a fairly dry atmosphere. Regular watering of indoor palms is necessary but it must be according to the plant's needs. A potting mix kept soggy may kill the plant. An annual (or more regular) rest and recuperation period outside in a bush house or greenhouse, or under trees,

preferably in the warm months of the year, promotes new growth.

A much wider range of palms can be grown outside in the garden or in containers. Young palms do best if they obtain shade or at least partial shade from the sun for most of the day. Some palms (e.g. *Copernicia, Sabal* and *Phoenix*) will tolerate open sunlight from an early age. Young palms can be progressively 'hardened off' by placing them in a little more sun each day while keeping them well watered. This acclimatises the plants to a more open location, a process likely to be needed for palms purchased from a nursery where they have been growing under shady conditions. Palms usually do not tolerate frost and windy conditions. The cultivation notes for many species in the genera section of this book relate to a suitable climate for growing the plants and to their ability to tolerate cold and other variable factors of the environment.

PROPAGATION OF CYCADS

Fertile cycad seed should be prepared for germination by removal of the fleshy layer covering the seed. In fresh seed this can be more easily done by soaking the seed in water to begin the rotting process which loosens the tissue. Fresh cycad seed is usually not ready to germinate immediately. It may be several months after the cone has fallen open and dropped the seed before the embryo is mature and germination can begin. Furthermore, not all the seed may be fertile because not every ovule is necessarily successfully pollinated. Even if male plants are close to the female, pollen may not reach every ovule of the female cone.

Artificial pollination (hand pollination) of cycads is not only possible but is now gaining popularity as a means of producing stocks of cycad seed. It is particularly useful as a means of building the numbers of surviving plants of the rarer species. Generally, when the male cone starts shedding pollen it is about the right time to hand pollinate the female cone. Hand pollination can ensure a higher rate of successful fertilisation of ovules than the natural agencies of wind and/or insects. To hand pollinate, one of the scales near the top of the female cone is removed with a knife, thus revealing the open space around the central axis of the cone. A small quantity of dry pollen is puffed into the hole using a small kitchen syringe or eye dropper with a rubber bulb attached to the end. In some species the scales on the outside of the female cone begin to separate and pollen can be puffed between the scales. In *Cycas* the male pollen cone (when releasing pollen) can be shaken over the megasporophylls of the female plant. The most receptive period for the megasporophylls of *Cycas* appears to be within a few days after they open outwards from the tightly-held inwards position. The process of applying the pollen needs repeating over several days.

The period between pollination and the release of seed from the cone varies from species to species. For example, *Macrozamia lucida* takes about 7–8 months, while *Stangeria eriopus* takes 10–11 months, *Encephalartos hildebrandtii* only 4–6 months, and *Dioon spinulosum* may take 15–16 months. For many species, the embryo within the seed requires a further period of a few months for maturation after the seed has been released from the cone. During this time seed can be stored (after cleaning) in a cool moist environment, such as in a plastic bag with moistened peat moss or sphagnum moss. The seed radicle emerges from a star-shaped hatch in the end of the seed in all but *Cycas* seeds, which split in half. Cycad seedlings can develop for several months using only the nutrients reserved in the seed.

Fruit of *Cycas media*.

Seeds should not be buried in the growing medium, but should be pressed into the surface so that about one-half to two-thirds of the seed is above the surface. Already-germinating seeds should be placed so that the radicle is pointing down towards the growing medium. Sterile media are preferable, but ordinary potting mixtures can be used. Commercial nurseries may use heated seed beds to germinate cycad seeds, but this is not necessary for the hobbyist. Germinating seed is best placed in a 'community' pot so that a number of seedlings utilise the potting medium. Once the tap root is well established the leaves will develop more rapidly. Seedlings with two or three leaves can be transferred into their own pots. Great care should be given to repotting seedlings as the root system is very brittle. The potting mix may have to be washed off the roots in order to remove seedlings from their community pot with minimum damage.

A warm environment with high humidity promotes growth in cycads. A shade house or shaded hot house providing about 40% shade are preferred locations for growing cycad seedlings. They have a reputation for slow growth but under optimum conditions they can achieve growth rates comparable to other foliage plants. Giddy (1990) reports that seedlings grown in a plastic tunnel in a controlled environment with temperatures 28°–30°C (82°–86°F), a relative humidity of 60–70% and with weekly applications of liquid fertiliser (N:P:K of 3:1:5 in a dilution of 1:1000) grew tubers weighing 250–300 g (8–9 oz), and with six to eight leaves within 18 months of germination. Recent research suggests that higher light conditions for longer hours promotes more leaves. Severing the long tap root (which generally requires a deep pot for development) just below the leaf crown and dipping it in a growth hormone (indolebutyric acid) solution promotes callus formation and subsequent adventitious roots, which are better able to utilise the medium. Plants treated this way have an increased growth rate and can be grown in shallower pots than cycads usually require.

Potting mixes should be chosen so that good drainage is achieved. After watering, the medium must be able to drain quickly, so it stays damp but well aerated. Composted pine bark is one recommended medium but many other media have been successful. Mixtures can be tried using coarse sand with peat moss, ground pine bark and vermiculite or perlite. Media without soil will require regular additions of fertiliser.

Cycads can also be propagated from suckers which grow from the base of the plant and from 'bulbils', which sometimes grow on the trunk itself. The suckers may already have some roots, but the bulbil will not. Suckers and bulbils can be removed cleanly from the parent with a sharp knife. The severed area should be dusted with fungicide and allowed to dry and form some callus tissue. Planted in moist coarse sand they should form roots within a few months. Large suckers with established roots may be directly planted into the garden.

TRANSPLANTING LARGE PALMS AND CYCADS

Both palms and cycads generally transplant well as mature plants. Palms, because of their adventitious root system, can be removed from the ground with a large root ball intact. The plant can be prepared for removal by cutting around the trunk at a distance which corresponds to the size of the root ball required. Palms over 3 m (10 ft) tall need a root ball at least 60–100 cm (2–3 ft) in diameter. The optimal size of the root ball will vary from species to species and from soil to soil. Once the cut has been made (by spade or a mechanical cutting tool) the root ball should be kept well watered for a few weeks to promote fresh root growth within the root ball. Then the plant can be removed (using suitable equipment such as a backhoe or crane if necessary) and the root ball wrapped with hessian or placed in a plastic tub. The palm can be further prepared by reducing the number of leaves and thus reducing transpiration while it is between its old and new home and while the roots are re-establishing themselves in the new location. Usually palms are best transplanted when the weather is warming up in early summer so that there are several months of suitable growing conditions ahead once the palm is in its new location.

Cycad morphology is better adapted than that of the palm to cope with the shock of transplantation. Cycads can be, and often are, treated roughly when they are removed from one location to another. This is because it is difficult to remove the whole of the underground root system, which can be very large and tuberous, intact. Nevertheless, as much of the tuber should be removed as is possible and practical. If the roots are trimmed or the tuber severed the plant will take longer to recover. Callus tissue should be allowed to form on damaged areas to reduce the chance of fungal rot. The base of the plant should be buried to about the same depth as in the old location and the soil around the trunk should be kept moist but freely draining. Some leaves can be removed to reduce transpiration while the plant is adapting and re-establishing in its new location. In a garden situation cycads are best planted on a slope or mound, with the soil being improved for drainage by the addition of gravel or crushed rock. Water should not be allowed to build up around the plant, otherwise there is a danger of its root system rotting.

Transplantation of a large clump of *Phoenix reclinata* from the Royal Botanic Gardens in Sydney, Australia, across the harbour to a private garden.

Palm Genera
and Species

Nypa fruticans

ACOELORRAPHE

a-'sē-lŏ-,rā-fē

*A*coelorraphe (syn. *Paurotis)* has only one representative, the popular ornamental, *Acoelorraphe wrightii*. Often seen in botanical garden collections, this handsome fan-leaf palm will form large thick clumps. Naturally found in brackish swamps in South Florida, the West Indies and the Caribbean coast of Central America, the palm forms dense multi-stemmed clumps.

The slim brown trunks usually have persistent leaf bases attached except in older stems, which are clean but marked by the leaf scars. The leaf crowns are compact, with the stiffly-held fan leaves almost orbicular in shape. Each is silvery on the underside and is deeply divided (to more than halfway) into narrow, single-fold segments which are split at the tips.

This popular ornamental likes moist or wet areas, but will grow at a slower rate in drier locations. It is hardy in a range of climates from tropical to warm-temperate. Propagation is from seed or by stem division.

Acoelorraphe wrightii

Acoelorraphe wrightii

syn. *Paurotis wrightii*

COMMON NAME: Paurotis palm, silversaw palm, Everglades palm.

SIZE: Dense multi-stemmed clumps, 3–8 m (10–26 ft) tall, up to 6 m (20 ft) or more wide.

HABITAT: Brackish swamps.

DISTRIBUTION: South Florida, the West Indies, Central America.

CONSERVATION STATUS: Not threatened.

DESCRIPTION: Leaf bases persistent on young stems. Compact crown of stiffly-held palmate leaves. Leaf blade is about 1 m (3 ft) wide, silvery on the underside, and deeply divided (to more than halfway) into narrow, single-fold segments which are split at the tips. Petioles have spines. Has well-branched inflorescences among the leaves. Fruit are small, round to oval, black, about 1.2 cm (0.5 in) in diameter.

CULTIVATION: Moist soil conditions are best.

Acoelorraphe wrightii

AIPHANES
'ī-făn-ēs

Aiphanes (syn. *Martinezia)* has approximately 38 species, most of which are found in northern South America, while a few species are found in the West Indies. *Aiphanes* palms form part of the understorey of rainforests from low elevations to mountain regions up to 2000 m (6500 ft). Trunks are usually single and slender, sometimes short, armed with leaf scars and bearing horizontal rows of long spines. Other plant parts are also usually spined, including the leaf bases, petioles, midribs and leaflets, inflorescence peduncle and bracts. In some species, even the fruit carries spines. Leaves are pinnate, or entire and bifid in shape. Leaflets vary in shape and arrangement from one species to another, but all have the jagged-toothed tips characteristic of the genus. Some species have leaflets arranged in groups at regular spaces along the rachis. Inflorescences are usually simple-branched, occasionally unbranched, and arise from among the leaves. The long cylindrical bract enclosing the unopened inflorescence persists after flowering and hangs down below the inflorescence. Male and female flowers are usually borne in triads of two male and one female flower. Fruit of these palms is a bright red when ripe, and more or less globose.

Despite their spiny nature, *Aiphanes* palms are popular as ornamentals. They can be grown in various soil conditions, but achieve fast, luxuriant growth in sheltered positions with plenty of water. Shaded conditions are best when the plants are young.

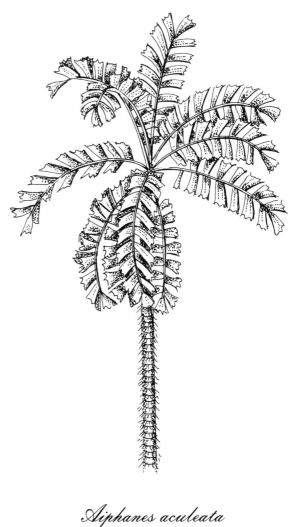

Aiphanes aculeata

Aiphanes aculeata

syn. *Aiphanes caryotifolia, Martinezia caryotifolia*

COMMON NAME: Coyure palm.

SIZE: Single trunk, 10–12 m (33–40 ft) tall.

HABITAT: Tropical rainforest, in partial shade to fully-shaded locations.

DISTRIBUTION: Colombia, Venezuela, Ecuador.

CONSERVATION STATUS: Unknown.

DESCRIPTION: Trunk is ringed with strong black spines of various lengths up to 10 cm (4 in). Arching pinnate leaves are approximately 2 m (6.5 ft) long with fishtail-shaped leaflets held most attractively in groups. Leaflets are broad-ended and frilled or ruffled, with spines on both surfaces. Fruit are round, about 1.5 cm (0.6 in) in diameter and bright red when ripe.

CULTIVATION: Readily grown from seed in protected shade or partial shade. Should be kept well watered. Tropical to subtropical climate is required. Plants will tolerate more sun as they get older.

Aiphanes aculeata

Aiphanes erosa

Aiphanes erosa

syn. *Martinezia erosa*

COMMON NAME: Macaw palm.

SIZE: Solitary trunk, 6 m (20 ft) tall or more.

HABITAT: Tropical rainforest.

DISTRIBUTION: Barbados (West Indies).

CONSERVATION STATUS: Unknown.

DESCRIPTION: Trunk is densely spined. Leaves have long, narrow, wedge-shaped leaflets regularly arranged along the midrib. Has scattered spines on upper and lower leaf surfaces and on the petiole. Fruit are round, about 1.6 cm (0.6 in) in diameter and bright red when ripe.

CULTIVATION: Seed germinates readily. Needs a tropical climate.

ALLAGOPTERA

ăl-ăg-'ŏp-tĕr-à

Allagoptera (syn. *Diplothemium*) is a genus of five species of usually clustering palms that grow low to the ground with a very short or subterranean stem and pinnate leaves. Occurring naturally in Brazil and Uruguay, they form thickets along sandy foreshores and sand dunes close to the sea. They are also found in open woodland areas and dry, scrubby and grassy zones. *Allagoptera* palms are potentially good seaside garden palms, especially where sandy areas require stabilising against erosion. They have not, however, been planted to any extent to date. They should be suitable for tropical to warm temperate climatic zones and will tolerate poor, sandy soils.

Long, narrow, tapering leaflets radiate in groups or are regularly arranged along the rachis, forming an attractive leaf shape. The inflorescence arises from among the leaf bases and is a spike of closely arranged male and female flowers on the end of a long erect peduncle. The spike is enclosed in the bud stage by a woody bract which splits open down one side to reveal the inflorescence that is characteristic of the genus. The small egg-shaped fruit are closely appressed on the spike.

Allagoptera arenaria

Allagoptera arenaria

COMMON NAME: None known.
SIZE: Small clustering palm, usually 1–2 m (3–6.5 ft) tall.
HABITAT: Sand dunes along the seaside.
DISTRIBUTION: East coast of Brazil.
CONSERVATION STATUS: Vulnerable.
DESCRIPTION: Branching subterranean stem. Pinnate arching leaves have groups of 2 or 3 long tapering leaflets arranged in groups and arising in various planes along the rachis, giving a plumose effect to the leaf. The spicate inflorescence is about 60 cm (2 ft) long, flowers are yellow, and fruit are egg-shaped, yellowish and about 1.2 cm (0.5 in) long.
CULTIVATION: Tolerates sandy soils and coastal conditions. Likes open sunlight. Propagated from seed, which will germinate readily in a few months.

Allagoptera arenaria

ARCHONTOPHOENIX
'ăr-kŏn-tŏ-'fē-nix

*A*rchontophoenix has two described and named species, both endemic to Australia. Several new species may need to be described. Distribution of the genus extends from Queensland's tropical Cape York Peninsula to temperate southern New South Wales. Semi-emergent to emergent plants of coastal and hinterland rainforests, they inhabit river and stream valleys, often in wet gullies and close to swampy areas where they can form dense colonies.

Moderate to tall in size, *Archontophoenix* palms have solitary, ringed trunks, which are usually enlarged at the base. Arching, twisting, pinnate leaves form a spreading crown of about 9–12 leaves. Leaf bases are sheathing and tubular, forming a prominent green (or sometimes purple or rusty red) crownshaft. Petioles are short and the rachis is approximately 2–3 m (6.5–10 ft) long. Leaflets are numerous, closely spaced, usually gently drooping, and taper to a point. Young leaves may be a pinkish or bronze colour. Inflorescences arise below the crownshaft and are well-branching panicles. In the bud stage, they are held erect and enclosed in two papery bracts, which split and fall as the inflorescence opens. Flowers are lavender to creamy yellow or white in colour, and are borne in triads of two male and one female flower. A few male flowers are borne on the distal ends of the rachillae. Fruit are small, globose to ellipsoidal, red, smooth-skinned and single-seeded.

Widely grown as ornamental palms, the Alexander palm is more suitable for tropical and subtropical areas, the bangalow palm for subtropical to warm temperate areas. Fresh seed germinates in 1–3 months, and growth is rapid if water is plentiful and temperatures warm. Young plants require shade and protection from drying winds. When several palms are planted together they make an attractive group, whether planted directly in the garden or as pot plants. Indoor light and humidity conditions are usually insufficient for these palms to survive as indoor plants.

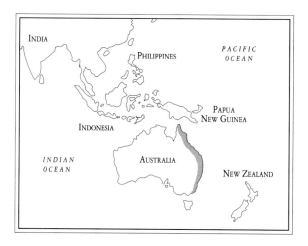

Archontophoenix cunninghamiana

Archontophoenix alexandrae

COMMON NAME:: Alexander palm, king palm.
SIZE: Solitary trunk, up to 20 m (65 ft) tall, tapering, 20–30 cm (8–12 in) in diameter, but wider at the swollen base.
HABITAT: Rainforest from sea level to approximately 1000 m (3300 ft).
DISTRIBUTION: Northeastern to central eastern Queensland (Australia).
CONSERVATION STATUS: Not threatened.
DESCRIPTION: Arching pinnate leaves have leaflets which are silvery grèen on the undersurface. Crownshaft is green, but purplish or reddish-brown in some north Queensland variants. Flowers white to cream. Fruit are ovoid, 1–1.5 cm (0.4–0.6 in) long, but larger in some variants.
CULTIVATION: Needs a tropical to subtropical climate. Sensitive to cold. Several variations of Alexander have been located in north Queensland. After more taxonomic work there may be several new species, subspecies or varieties described. One, currently described as *Archontophoenix* sp. 'Mount Lewis' is widely in cultivation.

Archontophoenix cunninghamiana

Archontophoenix cunninghamiana

COMMON NAME: Piccabean palm, bangalow palm.
SIZE: Solitary trunk, 20–25 m (66–82 ft) tall, 15–20 cm (6–8 in) in diameter, enlarged at the base, but usually not to the same dimensions as *A. alexandrae*.
HABITAT: Coastal and near-coastal rainforest.
DISTRIBUTION: Central eastern Queensland to southeastern New South Wales, Australia.
CONSERVATION STATUS: Not threatened.
DESCRIPTION: Arching pinnate leaves have leaflets which are green on both surfaces. Crownshaft is green to purplish-brown. Flowers pink to lilac. Fruit are ovoid, 1–1.5 cm (0.4–0.6 in) long.
CULTIVATION: Subtropical to warm temperate climate is required. Exhibits some frost tolerance.

Archontophoenix alexandrae

Archontophoenix sp. 'Mt Lewis': showing the purple crownshaft.

ARECA

'ăr-ĕk-à

*A*reca is a genus made up of about 60 species, varying in size from small undergrowth palms to moderately tall trees. They are distributed from India and Sri Lanka, through South China, Myanmar (Burma), Thailand, Malaysia, Vietnam, Laos and Cambodia, to Indonesia, Borneo, the Philippines, New Guinea and the Solomon Islands. In Borneo, in particular, there is a great number of species. Natural habitat for the *Areca* palms is the moist, sheltered tropical rainforest, but some reach for fuller sunlight.

Their slender stems are normally ringed and there is a smooth, distinctive crownshaft in most species. In some species the stems are supported by stilt roots. The crown of leaves gives a relatively open rather than dense appearance, with the individual pinnate leaves varying in segment number and shape, but usually with the terminal leaflet pair united and fishtail-shaped. In some species, the leaves are entire with a terminal notch and the lamina is pinnately ribbed.

The inflorescence, usually branched, sometimes spicate, arises below the crownshaft and has a single protective bract, which falls cleanly once the inflorescence begins to open up. This is rare in acaulescent species, in which the inflorescence arises from between the lower senescent leaves. Flowers are arranged in triads — a female flower surrounded by two male flowers, with male flowers alone on the distal parts of inflorescence branches. Fruit are round, ovoid or spindle-shaped, and are often brightly coloured when ripe. The most important species is *Areca catechu*, which supplies the betel nut, the endosperm of which is chewed with pepper leaves and lime for its mildly narcotic effect. There is widespread use of the betel nut in Asia and Melanesia. Some other *Areca* palm nuts are also used in this way.

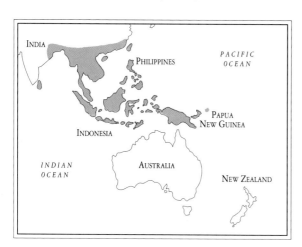

Areca vestiara

Areca catechu

COMMON NAME: Betel nut palm, bunga, pinang, jambe.
SIZE: Solitary tall palm, often over 10 m (33 ft) tall, sometimes
up to 25 m (80 ft).
HABITAT: Wild origin unknown.
DISTRIBUTION: Probably originated in Malaysia or the Philippines but is
now widespread in tropical regions of the world.
CONSERVATION STATUS: Not threatened.
DESCRIPTION: Slender green ringed trunk is 15–20 cm (6–8 in) in
diameter. Grey-green crownshaft. Pinnate arching leaves have broad
leaflets with truncate toothed tips. Branched inflorescence. Fruit are
ovoid, 4–5 cm (1.5–2 in) long and yellow to red when ripe. The species
shows considerable variation in form from one area to another.
CULTIVATION: Grown widely, sometimes on a plantation scale, but also as
an ornamental. Seeds germinate within 2 months and grow rapidly.
Seedlings need protection from open sun and shelter from wind. Partial
shade, regular watering and a tropical to subtropical climate are
required. Sensitive to cold.

Areca ipot

COMMON NAME: Bungang-ipot (Philippines).
SIZE: Solitary stem, up to about 3.5 m (11 ft) tall.
HABITAT: Close to streams in rainforests at low to medium altitudes.
DISTRIBUTION: Philippines.
CONSERVATION STATUS: Indeterminate.
DESCRIPTION: Looks like a small version of *A. catechu*. Has a slender
close-ringed trunk about 8 cm (3 in) in diameter. Branched
inflorescence. Fruit are ovoid, about 5 cm (2 in) long and red
when ripe.
CULTIVATION: This ornamental is suitable for sheltered tropical gardens.
Seed is used as a substitute betel nut for chewing.

Areca catechu

Areca kinabaluensis

COMMON NAME: None known.
SIZE: Solitary stem, usually up to 3 m (10 ft)
tall, but sometimes more.
HABITAT: Occurs in large colonies or as
solitary individual plants in montane
rainforest up to 2000 m (6500 ft) altitude.
DISTRIBUTION: Widespread in Borneo, not just
on Mt Kinabalu.
CONSERVATION STATUS: Vulnerable in Sarawak.
Status unknown elsewhere in Borneo.
DESCRIPTION: Has a slender stem, often with
stilt roots, a narrow crownshaft and fine dark
green pinnate leaves, usually 50 cm (20 in)
long or more. Terminal leaflets are broad and
united to a V-shape. Inflorescences are simply
branched, fruit are about 3 cm (1.2 in) long
and bright red when ripe.
CULTIVATION: Has been difficult to cultivate in
the garden at Mt Kinabalu.

Areca ipot

Areca kinabaluensis: showing the simple-
branched infructescence with ripe red fruit.

Areca minuta

Areca minuta

COMMON NAME: None known.
SIZE: Usually very short, not more than 1 m (3 ft) tall.
HABITAT: Rainforest floor. Often in large colonies.
DISTRIBUTION: Widespread in Borneo.
CONSERVATION STATUS: Unknown.
DESCRIPTION: Leaves dark green and shiny. Leaf is bifid, the lobes short and divergent with serrated truncate tips. New leaves are often red. Inflorescence is very short with usually only 3 rachillae.

Areca vestiaria: showing bright orange crownshafts and inflorescence bracts.

Areca triandra

COMMON NAME: None known.
SIZE: Solitary stem or multi-stemmed, 3–7 m (10–23 ft) tall.
HABITAT: Montane rainforest undergrowth at various elevations from 300–1200 m (1000–4000 ft).
DISTRIBUTION: India, Vietnam, Laos, Cambodia, Sumatra, Borneo, Philippines.
CONSERVATION STATUS: Vulnerable in Peninsular Malaysia. Status unknown elsewhere.
DESCRIPTION: This species exhibits a wide range of morphological variation. Can be solitary or clumping, with slender, grey to green ringed, trunks, sometimes with stilt roots. Green crownshaft. Arching leaves have crowded broad pointed leaflets, the terminal 2 or 4 leaflets being truncated at the ends. Inflorescence is small and simple-branched, arising below the crownshaft. Fruit are ovoid, 2–2.5 cm (0.8–1 in) long, orange-red when ripe.
CULTIVATION: Cultivated from seed or suckers. Needs a tropical to subtropical climate and a sheltered, semi-shaded position.

Areca triandra

Areca vestiaria

syn. *Areca langloisiana*
COMMON NAME: Pinang merah (Indonesia).
SIZE: Solitary or clumping, 5–10 m (16–33 ft) tall.
HABITAT: On well-drained volcanic soils up to 1200 m (4000 ft) altitude.
DISTRIBUTION: North Sulawesi and other Molucca Islands.
CONSERVATION STATUS: Not threatened.
DESCRIPTION: There is a wide variation in morphology — from having profusely-stilted roots to no above-ground roots, from densely clustering to solitary-stemmed. Green to brown ringed trunks. Petioles are short, leaflets broad and truncate at the tips. Petioles and rachis are yellow-orange. Crownshaft and bract protecting the inflorescence are usually bright orange but may be red or brown. Colours are usually brighter at higher altitudes, from 600–1200 m (2000–4000 ft) in natural habitat. Fruit are small, ovoid, about 2 cm (0.8 in) long.
CULTIVATION: Fresh seeds lose their viability quickly, but cultivation is also possible by suckers. Suitable for tropical and subtropical gardens.

ARENGA

ăr-'ĕn-gá

Arenga is a genus with 17 known species, distributed in India, South China, Ryukyu Islands, Taiwan, Southeast Asia, Indonesia, the Philippines, New Guinea and northern Australia. The species vary in size from huge single-stemmed trees which emerge from the rainforest canopy, to small clumping undergrowth palms. *Arenga* palms are found in moist lowland and mountain rainforests. They are usually monoecious (rarely dioecious), and hapaxanthic, but some are pleonanthic. Stems are usually hidden by persistent fibrous leaf bases and sheaths, but older stems may be bare and show the rings left by fallen leaf bases. Leaves are pinnate, sometimes entire, and vary in size and shape. The sheathing leaf bases are usually covered with a mass of spine-like fibres and matted hairs. Leaflets are shallowly induplicate, and range from fine and linear to broad fishtail-shaped wedges with toothed or notched margins. They are regularly arranged or in groups held in several planes along the rachis. The terminal leaflet is usually fan-shaped. The leaf undersurface is often paler than the upper surface.

The inflorescence usually arises from among the leaves, sometimes from below. In hapaxanthic species, the first inflorescence arises in the apical leaf axil, the second and succeeding ones from axils progressing down the stem (i.e. basipetal flowering). The trunk dies when the final and lowest inflorescence is finished.

In pleonanthic species flowering starts from the base of the trunk and goes upward to the apex (i.e. acropetal flowering). The inflorescences are usually simple-branched, but in some species the inflorescence is reduced to a spike. Flowers are separate male and female, sometimes occurring as a triad or female flowers grouped away from the male flowers, or even on separate plants (dioecious). Fruits are globose to oblong and the juice contains calcium oxalate crystals that can be very irritating to the skin.

Arenga palms are popular garden ornamentals. Seed germination is usually within two or three months, but may take longer. Tropical climates are required for most species. A few species are of great economic importance in Southeast Asia, Indonesia and New Guinea. *A. pinnata*, the sugar palm, has many uses, the most important relating to the sugar extracted from the sap.

Arenga australasica

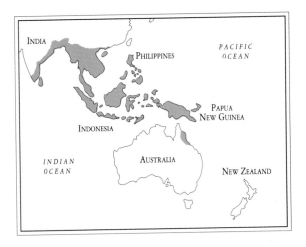

Arenga engleri

Arenga caudata

syn. *Didymosperma caudata*
COMMON NAME: None known.
SIZE: Densely clumping palm, up to 2 m (6.5 ft) tall.
HABITAT: Rainforest understorey.
DISTRIBUTION: Southern Thailand, South Myanmar (Burma), Vietnam, Cambodia.
CONSERVATION STATUS: Unknown.
DESCRIPTION: Slender stems. Pinnate leaves have wedge-shaped leaflets, toothed and lobed at the margins and pointed at the tip. The terminal leaflet is not pointed, but has a truncate toothed end. Leaflets are green on the upper surface and silver white on the undersurface. Flowering is basipetal.
CULTIVATION: This tropical to subtropical palm is fairly easy to grow.

Arenga caudata

Arenga australasica

COMMON NAME: None known.
SIZE: Clumping, up to 10 m (33 ft) tall, up to 30 cm (1 ft) in diameter.
HABITAT: Coastal forests, coral cays and continental islands from sea level to 300 m (1000 ft), dryish areas (or well-drained soil) in areas with high rainfall.
DISTRIBUTION: Coastal Cape York Peninsula and Northern Territory (Australia).
CONSERVATION STATUS: Not threatened. Widespread but uncommon.
DESCRIPTION: Crown has 5–15 rather stiffly-held pinnate leaves about 2–3 m (6.5–10 ft) long. Leaf bases have persistent black fibres. Leaflets are long, fairly narrow, pleated, with truncate ends. Dull green on the underside and dark green on the upper. Inflorescence is a panicle about 1 m (3 ft) long. Flowering is hapaxanthic. Fruit are globose, up to 2 cm (0.8 in) in diameter and brown to purple or red when ripe.
CULTIVATION: Seed may be slow to germinate. Shady conditions are best when the plant is young, but they are more tolerant to sun as they get larger. It is slow growing, adaptable and tolerates a range of climates from the tropics to warm temperate, but does not tolerate cold.

Arenga australasica

Arenga engleri

COMMON NAME: None known.
SIZE: Clumping, up to about 5 m (16 ft) tall, but usually much less.
HABITAT: Slopes of dense forests.
DISTRIBUTION: Taiwan, Ryukyu Islands, India.
CONSERVATION STATUS: Unknown.
DESCRIPTION: Has long pinnate leaves with narrow wedge-shaped leaflets, ragged-toothed at the apex. The leaf has a silvery undersurface and is dark green above. Fruit are globose, around 2 cm (0.8 in) in diameter, and red when ripe.
CULTIVATION: A popular large clumping garden palm for anywhere from the tropics to temperate areas. Tolerates frost well. Germination is slow but plants respond well to fertile, well-drained soil and watering in warm months.

Arenga hastata

Arenga hastata

syn. *Arenga borneensis, Didymosperma borneense*
COMMON NAME: None known.
SIZE: Small, clustering, up to about 1.5 m (5 ft) tall.
HABITAT: Lowland forest.
DISTRIBUTION: Borneo, Peninsular Malaysia.
CONSERVATION STATUS: Vulnerable in Peninsular Malaysia. Status unknown in Borneo.
DESCRIPTION: Leaves are pinnate with several stalked fishtail leaflets and 2 divergent terminal leaflets. Flowering is acropetal with several pendulous spicate inflorescences at each node. Fruits are globose, 0.5 cm (0.2 in) in diameter, dull red when ripe.
CULTIVATION: Makes a good pot plant.

Arenga hookeriana

syn. *Didymosperma hookerianum*
COMMON NAME: None known.
SIZE: Very small clustering palm, up to 0.5 m (1.5 ft) tall.
HABITAT: Lowland rainforest, sometimes on limestone.
DISTRIBUTION: Southern Thailand, Peninsular Malaysia.
CONSERVATION STATUS: Vulnerable.
DESCRIPTION: Clumping habit, with very short slender stems. Leaves are often simple, with a beautifully-shaped broad blade with lobed and toothed margins. Sometimes has pinnate leaves with a few leaflets. Leaves have a silvery undersurface. Inflorescences are spicate, with several at each node, and are held erect. Fruits are crowded, small, globose and green when ripe.
CULTIVATION: Tropical climate is required.

Arenga microcarpa

COMMON NAME: None known.
SIZE: Clumping, up to 7 m (23 ft) tall.
HABITAT: Up to 200 m (650 ft) altitude along river edges. Common in the lowlands where there are gaps in the forest canopy and secondary regrowth.
DISTRIBUTION: Papua New Guinea, Irian Jaya, Moluccas.
CONSERVATION STATUS: Unknown.
DESCRIPTION: Densely clumping. Older trunks are prominently ringed. Large pinnate leaves have a long petiole and a blade up to 3 m (10 ft) long. Linear leaflets are up to 75 cm (30 in) long and 3 cm (1.2 in) wide. Lower leaflets are in 2 ranks and sometimes clustered in groups, the terminal leaflet fishtail shaped. Has a branched infloresence, usually only the terminal part bearing fruit. Fruit are globose and red, up to 1.7 cm (0.7 in) in diameter.
CULTIVATION: This tropical clumping palm is not commonly grown. It is used as a source of sago in Sangihe and the Talaud Islands of Indonesia. Propagated from suckers or seed.

Arenga hookeriana

Arenga microcarpa

Arenga pinnata

Arenga undulatifolia has undulating margins to the leaflets.

Arenga undulatifolia

COMMON NAME: None known.
SIZE: Solitary clump, up to 10 m (33 ft) tall.
HABITAT: Moist rainforest up to 800 m
(2600 ft) on limestone hills. Usually in light
gaps and along river banks.
DISTRIBUTION: Borneo, Indonesia, Philippines.
CONSERVATION STATUS: Not threatened.
DESCRIPTION: Dense clumps, with trunks
covered in persistent leaf bases and dark
fibres. Large pinnate leaves have a short
petiole and many broad leaflets with wavy
margins, giving a distinctive rippled
appearance. Fruit are oblong-ellipsoid, up to
5 cm (2 in) long.
CULTIVATION: Suitable for tropical to
subtropical climates. The stems are a source
of sago starch for the nomadic Penans of
Sarawak. The palm 'cabbage' is also edible.

Arenga pinnata

syn. *Arenga saccharifera*
COMMON NAME: Sugar palm, gomuti palm.
SIZE: Massive solitary trunk, up to about 25 m (82 ft) tall
HABITAT: Original habitat uncertain since it is now widely grown.
DISTRIBUTION: India, Southeast Asia, Malaysia, Indonesia.
CONSERVATION STATUS: Not threatened.
DESCRIPTION: Has a dense crown of very dark green erectly-held
leaves, each up to 12 m (40 ft) long. Leaflets are narrow, wedge-
shaped, in groups, and held at different angles to the leaf rachis.
Trunk is usually covered in persistent leaf bases with coarse black
spine-like fibres. Monocarpic, the inflorescence is a large panicle
with strongly-perfumed flowers. Fruit are oblong to globose, about
5 cm (2 in) long.
CULTIVATION: Of great economic importance in Asia. Flowering
begins at 8–12 years and continues for several years. The
inflorescence is bruised and then cut to collect the sugary juice.
Fibre is collected from the trunk for rope making. Leaves are used for
thatch and new shoots are edible. It also has many other uses.

Arenga tremula

Arenga tremula

syn. *Arenga mindorensis*
COMMON NAME: None known.
SIZE: Clumping, 3–4 m (10–13 ft) tall.
HABITAT: Forms thickets in areas previously
cleared.
DISTRIBUTION: Endemic to the Philippines.
CONSERVATION STATUS: Not threatened.
DESCRIPTION: Has slender green trunks with
prominent rings. Large spreading pinnate
leaves have narrow leaflets with a toothed
truncate tip. Has a spicate pendulous
inflorescence. Fruits are globose, up to 1.7 cm
(0.7 in) in diameter and red when ripe.
CULTIVATION: Adaptable to tropical and
temperate climates.

Arenga westerhoutii

Arenga westerhoutii

COMMON NAME: Kerjim (Peninsular Malaysia).
SIZE: Clumping, up to 10 m (33 ft) tall.
HABITAT: Primary and secondary rainforest
and old landslips, sometimes in colonies in
the gullies of hilly rainforest up to 1200 m
(3900 ft).
DISTRIBUTION: Peninsular Malaysia, India,
Thailand, China, Myanmar (Burma).
CONSERVATION STATUS: Not threatened.
DESCRIPTION: Trunks are covered with
persistent leaf bases. Pinnate leaves are large
and flat, leaflets held in 1 plane and with a
truncate, toothed tip. Leaves are very dark
green on upper surface, grey to grey-brown
on underside. Fruits are rounded.
CULTIVATION: This handsome tropical palm has
very little cold tolerance.

ASTEROGYNE

,ăs-tĕr-ō-'gȳ-nē

*A*sterogyne has five species described, from Central and northern South America. Small, understorey palms, they have attractive, usually simple leaves of great ornamental potential. They are found in wet forest, sometimes on slopes and sometimes in swampy soil. Habitat locations vary from 150–1400 m (500–4600 ft).

Solitary or clumping palms, they have short, closely-ringed stems that, in two species, have small vegetative branches. The leaf sheath is short and eventually splits opposite the petiole. The petiole is short and rounded. The blade is undivided, with a bifid apex, and is a paler green on the undersurface. It is pinnately ribbed and sometimes is split irregularly. Inflorescences are solitary, arise among the leaves, and are spicate or simple-branched, the number of rachillae varying according to the species. Flowers are borne in triads of one female and two male flowers, each triad within a pit that is covered by a 'lipped' bract when the flowers are in bud. Fruit are ellipsoidal to ovoid, smooth-skinned and one-seeded.

Asterogyne martiana

Asterogyne martiana

Asterogyne martiana

COMMON NAME: None known.

SIZE: Single stemmed, usually less than 1.2 m (4 ft) tall, but up to 2 m (6.5 ft). Sometimes forms suckers.

HABITAT: Understorey palm of wet dense forests at low altitudes up to 500 m (1650 ft). Found in wet and well-drained locations.

DISTRIBUTION: Southern Mexico, Central America, Colombia.

CONSERVATION STATUS: Not threatened.

DESCRIPTION: Leaf blade is simple and deeply bifid at the apex, 70–100 cm (28–40 in) long and 15–25 cm (5–10 in) wide, with prominent veins on both sides. Petiole 10–30 cm (4–12 in) long. Inflorescence is simple-branched, with 1–8 (usually 5) rachillae. Inflorescence is enclosed in 2 or 3 tubular bracts in bud. Fruit are ellipsoid, purplish-black, 1.2 cm (0.5 in) long.

CULTIVATION: Needs a tropical to subtropical climate and well-drained soil. Susceptible to root fungal infections. Requires moderate to heavy shade when young and a humid environment. Capable of rapid growth. Reported to form suckers when the growing tip is damaged.

ASTROCARYUM

ˌăs-trŏ-ˈkär-ė-ŭm

Astrocaryum are spiny feather-leaved palms from Mexico, Trinidad, Central America and South America (to Brazil and Bolivia). There are about 47 described species, which vary from tall solitary palms to multi-stemmed palms. Some species are acaulescent. Natural habitats are varied — some are found in primary rainforest undergrowth, others in secondary forest areas where they receive more light. Trunks are often armed with long sharp spines pointing in several directions. Leaves are usually pinnate, sometimes persistent so that they obscure the trunk. Leaflets are regularly arranged or grouped, and fanned within the group. They are whitish on the underside and the leaflet surfaces and margins are usually armed with short spines or bristles. The leaf sheath is split opposite the petiole. Both petioles and leaf sheaths are usually fiercely spined and very hairy. The inflorescence arises among the leaves, is simply branched, protected by two persistent bracts, one of which is spindle shaped and covered with spines. Male and female flowers are on the same inflorescence, with the male flowers closely covering catkin-like branchlets,

the female flowers (a few or even only one) at the base of the branchlet. Fruits are of variable shape with a distinct beak at the apex. *Astrocaryum* palms are grown mainly in botanical garden collections rather than private collections, because of their spininess. Some species are very ornamental and worth the effort of cultivation. The seeds are not difficult to germinate if fresh. In tropical to subtropical areas, with selection of a sheltered sunny position, fertile soil and abundant water, *Astrocaryum* palms can have a rapid growth rate.

Astrocaryum mexicanum

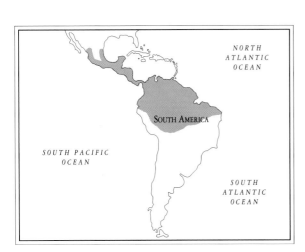

Astrocaryum mexicanum

Astrocaryum aculeatum

COMMON NAME: Star-nut.

SIZE: Single stem, up to about 25 m (82 ft) tall, 20–30 cm (8–12 in) in diameter, or (occasionally) clumping, with several stems up to about 8 m (26 ft).

HABITAT: Primary and secondary rainforest.

DISTRIBUTION: Trinidad, northern South America.

CONSERVATION STATUS: Unknown.

DESCRIPTION: Slender trunk is covered in black spines. Has a dense crown of dark green pinnate leaves which have many narrow leaflets arising at different angles and giving a plumose appearance to the leaf. The leaf petiole and rachis are spiny. Fruit are 4–5 cm (1.8–2 in) in diameter and orange when ripe. Star-like marking on the endocarp.

CULTIVATION: A tropical palm. If seed is not fresh it may be difficult to germinate and will need soaking in water. The palm is useful because of its edible fruit, hard wood, and the oil extracted from the fleshy mesocarp.

Astrocaryum mexicanum

COMMON NAME: 'Chocho'.

SIZE: Single stem, up to about 2.5–6 m (8–20 ft) tall.

HABITAT: Tropical dry, dense forest.

DISTRIBUTION: Mexico to Guatemala.

CONSERVATION STATUS: Not threatened.

DESCRIPTION: Juvenile leaves are large and simple or have a few divisions. Has very spiny stems, leaf bases, petioles and leaf rachises. Older leaves become pinnate although leaflets can be broad and uneven in width. The terminal pair has a united fishtail shape. The bract covering the inflorescences is large, rounded and very spiny. Fruit are also spiny and up to 5 cm (2 in) long.

CULTIVATION: Can grow in tropical to subtropical areas.

Astrocaryum aculeatum

ATTALEA

ăt-'tăl-ē-à

Attalea has about 70 species in number, including *Orbignya*, *Scheelea* and *Maximiliana*. They are found in Central and South America, and are most useful palms. Taxonomic work in 1965 by Wessels Boer recognised the affinities of five genera — *Attalea*, *Scheelea*, *Parascheelea*, *Maximiliana* and *Orbignya* — and placed them all under the one genus *Attalea*. The work has been controversial, but was recently recognised as valid. *Parascheelea* has since been included in *Orbignya*, and the four genera which remain — *Attalea*, *Scheelea*, *Maximiliana* and *Orbignya* — are now reduced to one, *Attalea*.

Some species inhabit humid tropical rainforests while others are found in the drier climates of the savanna. One, *Attalea maripa*, is found in lowland and coastal swamps. The babaçu or babassu palms (*Attalea phalerata* and *A. oleifera*) are among the most important edible oil sources in South America and account for the majority of oil production in Brazil. This is all the more remarkable when one considers that the industry depends upon fruit collected from wild palms. Other *Attalea* palms are useful for the wood derived from their petioles, and the leaves are variously used for thatch or making hats and umbrellas. The woody inflorescence bracts are useful scoops and containers. The terminal buds are also tapped for their sugary sap, used in making wine.

Most *Attalea* are tall to massive trees, eventually with bare trunks showing irregular leaf scars. A few are small and lacking a visible trunk. The crown of leaves is dense and leaves usually persist after dying. There is no crownshaft. Leaves are very long, the leaf sheath very large and thick, with fibrous margins. The petioles may be lacking, short or long. Leaflets are long, regularly arranged or in groups of about two to five, each tapering to an asymmetrical tip or, occasionally, with a short split at the tip. The inflorescence is borne among the leaves and is enclosed by a large, woody, peduncular bract which persists after it has split open and revealed the flowers. The flowering branches sometimes bear entirely male flowers or entirely female flowers, or sometimes flowers of both sexes together. Fruit is large and one- to several-seeded, ovoid, often asymmetrical, and with an apical beak.

Attalea cohune

Attalea cohune

Attalea cohune

syn. *Orbignya cohune*

COMMON NAME: Cohune palm.

SIZE: Single trunk, up to 15 m (50 ft) or more tall and 30–40 cm (12–16 in) in diameter.

HABITAT: Humid tropical rainforest.

DISTRIBUTION: Belize, El Salvador, Honduras, Guatemala, Costa Rica, southern Mexico.

CONSERVATION STATUS: Rare in southern Mexico, not threatened elsewhere.

DESCRIPTION: Dense crown of huge, erect, stiffly-held pinnate leaves. Leaves are up to 10 m (33 ft) long, leaflets up to 1 m (3.3 ft), arising in various planes along the rachis. Fruit are ovoid and large, 7–8 cm (2.8–3.2 in) long, single seeded, and are produced abundantly.

CULTIVATION: Slow-growing. Needs a tropical climate, tolerates open sun. Fresh seed germinates readily within a few months.

Attalea cohune infructescence

Attalea cohune inflorescence

BACTRIS

'băk-tris

$Bactris$ is a genus with about 240 species distributed from Mexico to the West Indies and into South America (to Paraguay). The greatest diversity is found in Brazil. They range from very small to large, are clumping or solitary feather-leaved palms, usually armed with spines on all parts except (usually) the fruit. Their natural habitats vary from one species to another but they are not found at high elevations. Most are tropical undergrowth rainforest palms but some are found on the landward edge of mangroves, others in freshwater swamps, and some on open white sand savanna.

Stems in some species are very short and underground, but most are erect and usually slender, with conspicuous rings from which arise rows of black spines. There are no crownshafts and the sheathing leaf bases are split opposite the petiole and usually covered with black needle-like spines, bristles or scales. Leaves are entire with pinnate ribs and an apical V-shaped notch, or pinnately divided with leaflets of various shapes according to the species, sometimes grouped and held in different planes, giving a plumose appearance to the leaf. Inflorescences, usually simply branched, rise from amongst the leaves and are protected by two bracts. The larger bract is leathery or woody, usually covered with hairs and spines on the outside but smooth inside. It splits lengthwise as the inflorescence develops and expands but usually persists and hangs down. Flowers are in triads (two male flowers surrounding a female) and there are usually more scattered or grouped male flowers, particularly towards the distal part of the inflorescence. Fruit are usually one-seeded and are variously shaped, from ovoid to a flattened sphere, top-shaped or pear-shaped. The endocarp has three pores situated above the midline.

Some $Bactris$ species have edible fruits. $Bactris$ $gasipaes$, the peach palm, is cultivated for its fruit and edible 'cabbage'. Some species are used as a source of walking sticks and thatch.

Bactris gasipaes

NORTH
ATLANTIC
OCEAN

SOUTH AMERICA

SOUTH PACIFIC
OCEAN

SOUTH
ATLANTIC
OCEAN

Bactris gasipaes

COMMON NAME: Peach palm, pejibaye, chonta, pupunha.
SIZE: Clumping, 8–10 m (26–33 ft) tall or more.
HABITAT: Original habitat not known.
DISTRIBUTION: Widely and plentifully cultivated in Amazonian parts of Brazil, Colombia, Peru, Central America.
CONSERVATION STATUS: Status in the wild unknown. Abundant in cultivation.
DESCRIPTION: Slender, ringed, trunks in clumps, sometimes solitary. Spines on trunks are arranged in rings. Crown has 10 or more pinnate leaves, each about 3 m (10 ft) long. Has a spiny petiole and leaf rachis. Long drooping leaflets are arranged in groups in several planes, giving a soft, plumose appearance to the leaf. Fruit are 5 cm (2 in) in diameter or more, red, orange or yellow in colour. There is also a spineless form of *B. gasipaes*.
CULTIVATION: Economically important for its fleshy mesocarp, which is cooked and eaten. The tree can produce 3–5 infructescences in 1 year, each with a yield of 50–70 fruit. The 'cabbage' is also harvested for food. Seeds germinate readily, but the palm can be propagated from suckers. The peach palm exhibits some cold tolerance, but needs a tropical to subtropical climate and plenty of water to grow rapidly.

Bactris guineensis

syn. *Bactris horrida, B. minor*
COMMON NAME: Tobago cane, prickly-pole.
SIZE: Clumping, 3–5 m (10–16 ft) tall.
HABITAT: Semi-dry plains.
DISTRIBUTION: South America, Central America.
CONSERVATION STATUS: Not threatened.
DESCRIPTION: Has several to many stems in a clump, each about 3 cm (1.2 in) in diameter and covered in spiny leaf sheaths. Pinnate leaves are up to 1 m (3.3 ft) long or more, light green, and have vicious spines up to 6 cm (2.5 in) long on the petiole. Leaflets are regularly arranged, short and narrow. Fruit are flattened, globose, purple–black when ripe, up to 1.5 cm (0.6 in) long.
CULTIVATION: Fruit are edible. Propagated from seed.

Bactris gasipaes

Bactris guineensis

Bactris major

Bactris major

syn. *Bactris balanoidea*
COMMON NAME: Cubaro, prickly palm.
SIZE: Large and clumping, 6–8 m (20–26 ft) tall.
HABITAT: Woodland and open land liable to temporary flooding.
DISTRIBUTION: Trinidad, Tobago, Panama, Colombia, Venezuela.
CONSERVATION STATUS: Not threatened.
DESCRIPTION: Has multiple spiny trunks densely clumping, each about 5 cm (2 in) in diameter. Trunks become smooth of spines and show white rings. Finely pinnate leaves are 2–2.5 m (6.5–8 ft) long. Petiole is 40–50 cm (16–20 in) and heavily armed with spines of various lengths. Rachis also has long, slender spines. Fruit are elliptic-ovoid, 4–5 cm (1.6–2 in) and purplish when ripe.
CULTIVATION: Grown from seed that germinates after about 5 months. A tropical garden ornamental, but very spiny.

BALAKA

'băl-à-kà

Balaka has about seven species and is related to *Ptychosperma* and *Veitchia*. Some are endemic to Fiji and others to Samoa. Growing in moist rainforest areas at various altitudes, they are mostly understorey palms, occasionally semi-emergent through the forest canopy. All are solitary, small to moderate-sized, pinnate-leaved palms. Leaf bases are sheathing, forming a prominent crownshaft which is covered in brown scales. Leaf segments are either elongate and tapering to a pointed tip, or wedge-shaped with a broad tip. The inflorescences are branched, bearing male and female flowers. Fruit varies in shape, usually more or less ovoid, often beaked, and is reddish-brown to crimson when ripe.

The straight stems have been used in the past for making walking sticks and spears. The immature fruit is reported to be edible. *Balaka* palms are tropical palms and are little known as yet in cultivation. They require shade and very humid conditions and are potentially good pot plants given these conditions.

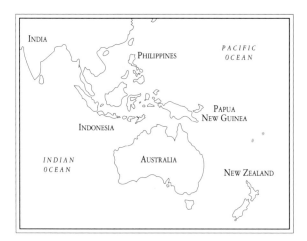

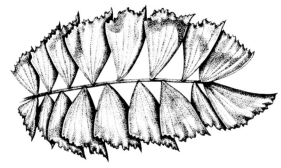

Balaka seemannii: leaf.

Balaka seemanii

COMMON NAME: Mbalaka (Fiji).
SIZE: Solitary narrow trunk, up to 8 m (26 ft) tall.
HABITAT: Rainforest, from near sea level to 1000 m (3300 ft).
DISTRIBUTION: Endemic to Fiji.
CONSERVATION STATUS: Vulnerable.
DESCRIPTION: Dark green trunk is around 5 cm (2 in) in diameter, marked with prominent leaf scars. Leaves are about 2 m (6.5 ft) long, with about 7 leaves in a crown. Leaflets are wedge-shaped, each with a toothed apex. There are about 12 pairs of leaflets on each leaf, the terminal pair united. The inflorescence is below the modest crownshaft. Fruit is a curved ellipsoid shape with a longish pointed apex, bright red when ripe.

Balaka seemannii

BASSELINIA

'băs-ė-lĭn-ī-à

Basselinia has 11 species, all endemic to the southwest Pacific island of New Caledonia. The genus is divided into two sections. One section has seven species, all tall solitary palms with green crownshafts and fruit larger than 1 cm (0.4 in). The other section contains four species, all but one of which are small clustering palms with colourful crownshafts and fruit smaller than 1 cm (0.4 in). Most species are found in moist rainforests at moderate elevations, around 1000 m (3300 ft). Some grow on serpentine soils and others on schistose soils, while *Basselinia gracilis*, the most widely-distributed species, grows on both soil types.

Leaf shape varies from regular pinnate to entire with pinnate ribs. There are scales on the undersides of the leaves. The crownshaft may be covered with tomentum. The inflorescence arises below the crownshaft, is covered by two bracts in the bud stage, and is simply to moderately branched. Male and female flowers are borne in triads with mostly male flowers towards the distal parts of the branches. Fruit varies in size and is usually round to ellipsoid and red or black when ripe. These handsome palms are most promising in their potential for cultivation in subtropical and temperate regions as they appear to exhibit some cold hardiness. So far, *B. gracilis* and *B. pancheri* have succeeded in cultivation outside New Caledonia.

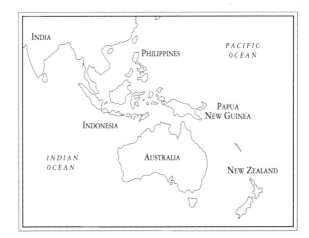

Basselinia gracilis

Basselinia gracilis

syn. *Basselinia eriostachys*

COMMON NAME: None known.

SIZE: Usually clustering, up to 8 m (26 ft) tall.

HABITAT: Understorey of moist forests on schistose or serpentine soils up to 1600 m (5200 ft), but most populous at about 900 m (3000 ft).

DISTRIBUTION: New Caledonia.

CONSERVATION STATUS: Indeterminate.

DESCRIPTION: Stem is prominently ringed, the crownshaft red with black tinging the upper part and extending onto the petioles. Leaves are pinnate and over 1 m (3.3 ft) long on mature plants. Leaflets are regularly or irregularly placed and taper to a point. The terminal pair is joined, making a V shape at the leaf end. The inflorescence branches are covered with a tomentum of dark red to brown fine hairs. Fruit are globòse, about 0.6 cm (0.25 in) in diameter and black when ripe.

CULTIVATION: Seed germinates readily. Plants apparently require a well-drained soil medium but otherwise are fairly easily grown. Adaptable to subtropical to temperate climates.

Basselinia gracilis

Basselinia pancheri

COMMON NAME: None known.

SIZE: Solitary trunk, up to 10 m (33 ft) tall and 10 cm (4 in) in diameter.

HABITAT: Generally semi-emergent in moist to dryish forests on serpentine soils from 200–1200 m (650–4000 ft), most populous from 800–1000 m (2600–3300 ft).

DISTRIBUTION: New Caledonia.

CONSERVATION STATUS: Rare.

DESCRIPTION: Bright green to grey ringed trunk. Has a slightly bulging scaly crownshaft, about 55 cm (22 in) long, which may be coloured red, orange, purple-black, or slate grey to brown. Has about 7 erectly-held pinnate leaves, up to about 1.5 m (5 ft) long. Leaflets are of irregular width, irregularly placed on the rachis. Inflorescence is well-branched. Fruits are kidney-shaped to bilobed, black when ripe.

Basselinia pancheri

Basselinia pancheri: inflorescence.

BENTINCKIA

běn-'tĭng-kē-à

Bentinckia is a genus with only two described species. *Bentinckia nicobarica* is endemic to the Nicobar Islands just north of Sumatra in the Indian Ocean, and grows in the moist forest areas which are rapidly being destroyed, unfortunately. *B. condapanna* is now rare because its succulent 'cabbage' has been prey to both elephants and humans. It grows in a few sheltered, inaccessible pockets of the Western Ghats of southern India, from 1000–1500 m (3300–5000 ft) elevation, and in the central mountains (Palni Hills).

Bentinckia are handsome, moderate to tall, solitary, slender palms with brown ringed trunks, a conspicuous crownshaft and arching pinnate leaves. Leaflets are long, tapering and alternate, with bifid tips. Superficially they resemble *Archontophoenix* palms, but with longer crownshafts and the leaves having a more drooped habit. The inflorescence arises below the crownshaft, is enclosed by two bracts in bud, is well-branched, and bears both male and female flowers in triads. Fruit is round to egg-shaped, and black or purplish when ripe. *B. nicobarica* is cultivated from seed and has found its way into many tropical botanical collections.

Bentinckia nicobarica

Bentinckia nicobarica

Bentinckia nicobarica

COMMON NAME: Bentinckia palm.
SIZE: Solitary slender trunk, up to 15 m (50 ft) tall.
HABITAT: Moist forest at low elevations, in association with *Areca catechu*, *Pinanga manii* and *Rhopaloblaste augusta*.
DISTRIBUTION: Nicobar Islands.
CONSERVATION STATUS: Vulnerable.
DESCRIPTION: Long arching pinnate leaves have a short petiole. Long green crownshaft. Leaflets are often unequal in width and irregularly placed, the basal leaflets sometimes fused. Leaflet tips are bifid. Fruit are about 1.3 cm (0.5 in), almost round and purplish-black when ripe.
CULTIVATION: Seed germinates rapidly. This palm grows rapidly in a tropical moist climate. Sensitive to cold.

BISMARCKIA

bĭs-'măr-kē-à

Bismarckia is represented by one species, the giant Bismarck palm, *Bismarckia nobilis.* It is endemic to Madagascar where it is found in the savanna areas of the western part of the island. It is a large, fast-growing, solitary palm with huge, stiffly-hanging costapalmate leaves, up to 3 m (10 ft) across, which are a silvery blue-green in colour. The leaf is divided to about one-third down the blade and there are conspicuous filaments between the segments. There is a large distinctive hastula on the upper surface of the petiole, but none on the undersurface. The petiole is robust and covered with white wax and patches of reddish scales. The leaf sheath is split just below the petiole. Leaves drop cleanly from the irregularly ringed clean trunk and the crown is dense, wide and heavy in appearance. The Bismarck palm, as it is sometimes named, is a dioecious palm, the male and female flowers being on different plants and borne on long, simple-branched inflorescences in which the terminal rachillae are like catkins. Fruit are more or less globose, approximately 4 cm (1.6 in) in diameter and speckled brown in colour.

In the wild, *B. nobilis* is said to grow to 30 m (100 ft) or more, but specimens growing outside Madagascar are, to date, much shorter. The Bismarck palm is gaining popularity as an open landscape palm because of its majestic-sized leaves and its tolerance to drought and frost. Its seeds are easily germinated if the hard woody epicarp is cut back from the lipped end of the seeds to expose the endocarp. The extensive root system of the seedling requires a deep pot. The preferred alternative is to choose the final location for the plant first, and place the germinated seed directly into that spot. Seedlings require full sun to grow rapidly, and plenty of water in the warmer months. *Bismarckia* is hardy in a range of climates — from dry tropical to subtropical conditions — and in a range of soil types.

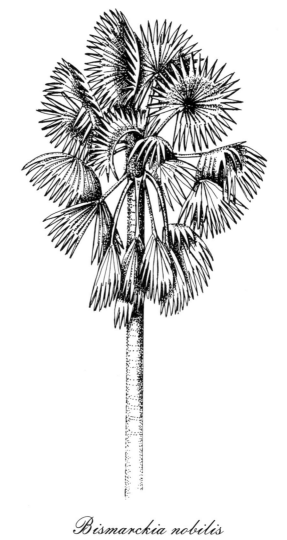

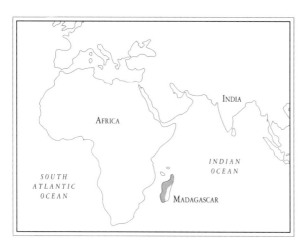

Bismarckia nobilis

Bismarckia nobilis

Bismarckia nobilis

COMMON NAME: Bismarck palm.
SIZE: Solitary trunk, up to 30 m (100 ft) tall (or more) in habitat, but shorter in cultivation.
HABITAT: Savanna woodland.
DISTRIBUTION: Madagascar.
CONSERVATION STATUS: Not threatened.
DESCRIPTION: Huge, silvery blue-green, costapalmate leaves up to 3 m (10 ft) across. The blade is divided to about one third and there are filaments between the segments. Has a large hastula on the upper surface. Leaf sheath is split just below the petiole. Has simple-branched inflorescences in which the terminal rachillae are like catkins. Fruit are more or less globose, speckled brown, around 4 cm (1.6 in) in diameter.
CULTIVATION: Tolerates drought and frost. Is adaptable to a wide range of climates.

BORASSODENDRON

bŏ-ˌrăss-ŏ-'dĕn-drŏn

*B*orassodendron, a genus comprising two species, has close affinities to *Borassus* and may be included in that genus after more taxonomic work. *Borassodendron machadonis* is the species from the Malay Peninsula, while *B. borneensis* is found in Borneo. Both are tall, solitary, dioecious fan palms with massive leaves. *B. machadonis* is a relatively rare palm found in northern Malaysia and southern Thailand in deep soil on limestone hills. In contrast, *B. borneensis* can be abundant in small local areas of lowland dipterocarp forest, but does not have wider distribution in apparently suitable forest. It is collected for its edible 'cabbage' and may be under threat for this reason.

Grown in tropical botanical garden collections, these palms are not yet widely cultivated.

Borassodendron borneensis

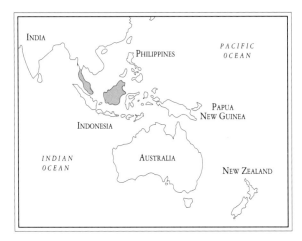

Borassodendron machadonis

COMMON NAME: None known.
SIZE: Solitary trunk, up to 20 m (65 ft) tall.
HABITAT: Pockets of deep soil in montane rainforest.
DISTRIBUTION: Northern Peninsular Malaysia, southern Thailand.
CONSERVATION STATUS: Rare.
DESCRIPTION: Trunk is usually bare when mature, around 30 cm (1 ft) in diameter and marked with rings. Leaves are massive, palmate to slightly costapalmate, deeply split and loosely hanging in an untidy crown. Petiole is about 4 m (13 ft) long, the leaf blade up to 3.5 m (11.5 ft) in diameter. Dioecious. Male inflorescence catkin-like and female simple and up to four branches. Infructescence club-like. Fruit in three segments, roundish, 9 cm (3.5 in) long and purple-green in colour.
CULTIVATION: A hot humid climate with plentiful water supply is required for successful cultivation.

Borassodendron machadonis

BORASSUS

bŏ-'răss-ŭs

Borassus has seven species described, but probably only three or four will be recognised after more taxonomic work. They are widely distributed from Africa, Madagascar and northern Arabia through to India, Southeast Asia and New Guinea. The most important is *Borassus flabellifer*, which is reported as having over 50 different uses to humans and being the source of over 800 products. Its fruit and 'cabbage' (apical leaf bud of the crown) are edible and the sap is a source of sugar and and also used to make wine. Leaves are useful at all stages for weaving and the trunk yields a durable wood.

Borassus palms are large solitary palms with broad costapalmate leaves, which have a well-developed hastula on both sides. In young trees the trunk is covered with a lattice of overlapping leaf bases edged with irregular teeth. In older trees these bases fall away revealing a broadly-ringed clean trunk. The petiole also has large irregular teeth on the margins, and is split or cleft (except in young plants) where it joins the sheathing base. The leaf blade ranges from almost round to fan-shaped, divided (to about halfway) into regular pointed segments, which are split at the tips. These are dioecious palms, carrying male flowers on one plant and female flowers on another. Inflorescences arise among the leaves and do not protrude beyond the crown. Male inflorescences are moderately branched with the rachillae resembling catkins. Female inflorescences are unbranched or with a single simple branch which bears very large flowers. Fruit are also large, round, sometimes wider than long, with a thick fibrous mesocarp and bearing one to three seeds.

Preferring drier tropical climates, they are well suited as landscape plants in large open areas. Germinating seeds grow a long sinker root, which means that they are best sown *in situ* or given a deep pot for development.

Borassus flabellifer

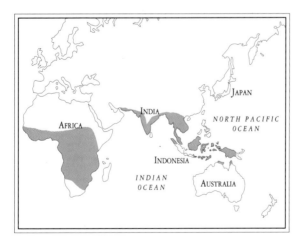

Borassus flabellifer

Borassus flabellifer

COMMON NAME: Palmyra palm, toddy or wine palm, siwalan, rontal, lontar.

SIZE: Solitary trunk, up to 20 m (65 ft) tall or more, 60 cm (2 ft) in diameter, often swollen at the base.

HABITAT: Various monsoonal tropical habitats from low sandy plains near sea level to dry forest areas at 500–750 m (1600–2500 ft) altitude.

DISTRIBUTION: India, Sri Lanka, Southeast Asia, New Guinea.

CONSERVATION STATUS: Not threatened.

DESCRIPTION: A lattice of old leaf bases often persists on the trunk. Has a large dense crown of blue-green costapalmate leaves, each blade 2.5–3 m (8–10 ft) wide. Petioles are about 1 m (3.3 ft) long with spines on the margins. Fruit are round, yellow-brown, 15–20 cm (6–8 in) in diameter.

CULTIVATION: Informally cultivated throughout Southeast Asia (especially Indonesia) and India, for the food and useful resources it provides

BRAHEA

'*bră-hē-à*

Brahea (syn. *Erythea*) is a genus that contains about 16 species of the hardy fan-leaved palms known as hesper palms. They are found throughout Mexico and Guatemala. They grow in dry gullies, on open grassy hills, on limestone slopes and in other dry inhospitable areas.

Brahea are short to tall, robust, solitary palms, their leaves often persisting in a petticoat of dead material surrounding the trunk. Leaves are deeply divided, rigid, palmate to costapalmate, with each segment deeply bifid at the apex. Leaves have a conspicuous hastula on the upper surface. Long inflorescences arise from among the leaves and often hang in drooping well-branched panicles well beyond the leaf crown. They carry bisexual flowers spirally arranged as single flowers or in clusters of twos or threes. Fruit are roundish, dark blue to black when ripe, and are usually carried in heavy, drooping clusters.

These slow-growing palms are useful ornamentals in harsh dry climates. Once established, they are tolerant of poor dry soils and frosts. They will often fail in wet tropical climates. Fresh seed generally germinates in two to four months, but may take longer if the seed has been allowed to dry out. The hesper palms are used by Mexican Indians for thatch and fibre.

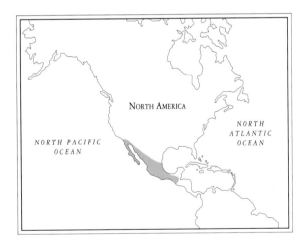

Brahea armata

Brahea aculeata

syn. *Erythea aculeata*
COMMON NAME: None known.
SIZE: Small slender trunk, up to about 3 m
(10 ft) tall.
HABITAT: Dry rocky ground and grassy hills to
about 600 m (2000 ft) above sea level.
DISTRIBUTION: Sonora (Mexico).
CONSERVATION STATUS: Vulnerable. Numbers
are dwindling in natural habitat.
DESCRIPTION: Slender ringed trunk. Has
relatively few leaves, and they tend to fall off
after dying. Leaf blades are deeply divided
(to more than halfway), uniformly green on
both surfaces. Petiole is slender with small
teeth on the margin. Inflorescence is shorter
than the leaves. Fruit are small, almost round
and black.
CULTIVATION: Not cultivated much, but suitable
for temperate to drier tropical areas.

Brahea armata

Brahea brandegeei

syn. *Erythea brandegeei*
COMMON NAME: San José hesper palm.
SIZE: Slender single trunk, 10–24 m
(33–80 ft) tall.
HABITAT: Mountains and canyons.
DISTRIBUTION: Baja California (northwest
Mexico).
CONSERVATION STATUS: Not threatened.
DESCRIPTION: Trunk is usually covered in
persistent dead leaves. Dull green leaf blades
are segmented about halfway, the blade
having a distinctive white waxy bloom on the
underside. Spiny slender petioles are about
1 m (3.3 ft) long. Inflorescence is shorter than
the leaves. Fruit are small, oblong to round,
1.5–2.2 cm (0.6–0.9 in) long, and shiny brown
when ripe.
CULTIVATION: A widely-grown ornamental,
suitable for subtropical to temperate areas.

Brahea edulis

syn. *Erythea edulis*
COMMON NAME: Guadalupe palm.
SIZE: Solitary trunk, 10–12 m (33–40 ft) tall.
HABITAT: Deep warm ravines.
DISTRIBUTION: Guadalupe (Mexican island).
CONSERVATION STATUS: Rare. Remnant
populations only. It covered the entire island
before the arrival of goats and sheep.
DESCRIPTION: Trunk is about 40 cm (10 in) in
diameter and has many irregular rings. Has
12 or more heavy, deep green leaves with
long, stout-armed petioles. Leaf blade is
1–2 m (3.3–6.5 ft) across, divided into many
segments (to about halfway). Inflorescence is
shorter than the leaves. Heavy clusters of
fruit. Fruit are black when ripe, 2.5–3.5 cm
(1–1.4 in) in diameter.
CULTIVATION: Suitable for dry tropical to
temperate climates. Very hardy.

Brahea edulis

Brahea aculeata

Brahea armata

syn. *Erythea armata, E. glauca, E. roezlii*
COMMON NAME: Blue hesper palm.
SIZE: Solitary trunk, up to 12 m (40 ft) tall.
HABITAT: Canyons.
DISTRIBUTION: Baja California (northwest Mexico).
CONSERVATION STATUS: Insufficiently known.
DESCRIPTION: Leaves persist, and form a petticoat around the thick
trunk. Leaf blades are bluish, stiffly held and deeply divided to about
halfway. Petiole is about 1 m (3.3 ft) long, very spiny on the margins.
Inflorescence extends beyond the leaves. Has drooping panicles of
fruit. Fruit are small, round to ovoid, around 2 cm (0.8 in) long, with a
thin mesocarp.
CULTIVATION: Suitable for temperate to subtropical areas. Tolerates frost
and is hardy in dry conditions once established.

Brahea brandegeei

BUTIA
'bōo-tī-à

Butia has eight described species, one of which, *Butia capitata*, is very widely grown in tropical to temperate regions of the world. All eight are from the cooler, drier areas of southern Brazil, Paraguay, Uruguay and Argentina. Often referred to as *Butia* palms, yatay palms or jelly palms, they are very hardy, their natural habitat being open grassland, woodlands and campos. Taxonomists have had difficulties deciding to which genus many of these palms best belong — *Cocos*, *Syagrus* or *Butia*. A re-evaluation of the genus *Butia* by Glassman in 1979 is the most recent reference on the subject.

Some species are without an above-ground trunk, while others have tall trunks covered with the remains of leaf bases, eventually becoming bare and showing scars where the bases have come away. A distinctive character of the pinnate leaves is that they are strongly and stiffly arched. Leaf sheaths encircle the trunk and disintegrate into a fibrous network. The petiole is usually armed with spines or teeth and the leaf segments are regularly arranged, narrow, stiffly held, and green to blue-green in colour. Inflorescences arise among the leaves, are branched to only one order, and are held in a protective bract that persists after the inflorescence has been released. *Butia* palms are monoecious, producing both male and female flowers in groups of three (triads) on the same inflorescence. The outer branches of the inflorescence often have only male flowers. Fruit are small to moderate in size, round to ovoid, and yellow, brown or purple when ripe.

Butia palms are generally cold-tolerant, resistant to dry periods and to harsh, hot sun. They are fast growing in warm climates when well supplied with water. Hybridisation occurs spontaneously between species of *Butia* and *Syagrus*. Seed of *Butia* are often slow and difficult to germinate and you may need to soak or even crack them to assist the process.

Butia capitata

NORTH
ATLANTIC
OCEAN

SOUTH AMERICA

SOUTH PACIFIC
OCEAN

SOUTH
ATLANTIC
OCEAN

Butia arenicola

syn. *Cocos arenicola, Syagrus arenicola*
COMMON NAME: None known.
SIZE: Less than 1 m (3.3 ft) tall.
HABITAT: Campos and pastures.
DISTRIBUTION: Paraguay, Brazil.
CONSERVATION STATUS: Unknown.
DESCRIPTION: Closely related to *B. capitata*, but smaller and acaulescent. Below the ground, the trunk may be 5 cm (2 in) long and 8 cm (3 in) in diameter. The petiole is short and with spines, the leaf about 1 m (3.3 ft) long with regularly-arranged pointed leaflets. Fruit are ovoid and about 2 cm (0.8 in) long.

Butia arenicola

Butia capitata

Butia yatay

Butia eriospatha: the inflorescence bract is covered with a brown woolly tomentum.

Butia capitata

syn. *Cocos capitata, Syagrus capitata*
COMMON NAME: Wine palm, jelly palm.
SIZE: Solitary trunk, 3–5 m (10–16 ft) tall.
HABITAT: Woodlands and campos.
DISTRIBUTION: Brazil, Uruguay.
CONSERVATION STATUS: Not threatened.
DESCRIPTION: Grey clean trunk has a rough surface after the leaf bases have fallen away. Crown of blue-green arching leaves have petioles about 70–90 cm (28–36 in) long, edged with spines near the base and teeth further down the petiole. Mature fruit are ovoid, 1.8–2.6 cm (0.7–1 in) long and orange.
CULTIVATION: Widely cultivated. About 10 varieties have been described. Very tolerant of dry heat and cold. Seeds are difficult to germinate and may need presoaking. The fleshy mesocarp of the fruit is edible and can be boiled into jam.

Butia eriospatha

syn. *Cocos eriospatha, Syagrus eriospatha*
COMMON NAME: None known.
SIZE: Solitary trunk, 3–6 m (10–20 ft) tall.
HABITAT: Woodlands and campos.
DISTRIBUTION: Brazil.
CONSERVATION STATUS: Unknown.
DESCRIPTION: Leaf bases are partially covered with a brownish tomentum. Petiole is nearly 1 m (3.3 ft) long and armed with short teeth or spines. Leaf is over 3 m (10 ft) long with regularly-arranged pointed leaflets. Bract protecting the inflorescence is covered in a dense brownish tomentum. Fruit are roundish, 1.8–2.0 cm (0.7–0.8 in) long, yellow when ripe.
CULTIVATION: These hardy palms are uncommon in cultivation.

Butia yatay

syn. *Cocos yatay, Syagrus yatay*
COMMON NAME: Yatay palm.
SIZE: Solitary trunk, 8–12 m (26–40 ft) tall.
HABITAT: Large stands in sandy areas. Grows sympatrically with *B. paraguayensis* in some areas.
DISTRIBUTION: Argentina, Paraguay, Uruguay.
CONSERVATION STATUS: Not threatened.
DESCRIPTION: Old petiole bases persist on the young trunks. Petiole is edged with coarse teeth. Leaf is about 2 m (6.5 ft) long with numerous, regularly-arranged, narrow leaflets with asymmetrical pointed tips. Bract protecting the inflorescence is glaucous. Fruit are ovoid, 3.0–4.2 cm (1.2–1.7 in) long, with a prominent conical beak.
CULTIVATION: Little is known about cultivation.

CALAMUS

'kă-lăm-ŭs

Calamus is the largest genus of palms, having approximately 400 species. Most are spiny climbing palms known as rattans, although rattans are not exclusively from this genus. Not only does *Calamus* have a huge number of species, but the genus is widely distributed. The Malay Peninsula, Borneo and New Guinea have the greatest diversity, but *Calamus* palms are also found in Africa (perhaps just one variable species), Nepal, Sikkim, south China, India, Sri Lanka, the countries of Southeast Asia, Taiwan, across the Pacific to the Solomon Islands, Vanuatu, Fiji and northeastern and eastern Australia. Habitats also show a great diversity — from sea level to 3000 m (10 000 ft) altitude, from seasonally-dry forests which are subject to monsoonal rains, to swampy mangroves. They are most plentiful in humid tropical rainforests and can form dense stands where there is a break in the canopy created, perhaps, by a fallen tree or selective logging. They are often along trails or roadways where the pedestrian would soon learn about the spiny whip-like extensions of *Calamus*, which can tear at the skin and clothing.

Calamus palms can be solitary or clustering, with new stems arising from axillary shoots near the base. They may be high climbing with very long stems, non-climbing with short stems, or occasionally acaulescent. Stems eventually become bare and reveal short or long internodes. Leaves are pinnate or (rarely) bifid.

Sometimes the tip of the leaf develops into a whip-like extension called a cirrus, which is armed with reflexed spines that act like grapnel hooks. The leaf rachis is often spined. Leaflets vary in number, arrangement and shape, but are most often lanceolate to linear and covered in hairs, bristles, spines or scales. In most species, the leaf sheath is armed with a dense covering of spines, which are scattered or in whorls; in *Calamus polystachys*, they are arranged in interlocking rows forming galleries, which are havens for ant colonies. The leaf sheath may possess a bump, termed a knee, below the point where it joins the petiole. The knee often extends along the stem forming an organ called an ocrea. From the leaf sheath may also arise another type of spiny whip-like structure called a flagellum. It is derived from a sterile inflorescence and is often present in species which lack cirri (plural of cirrus). These leaf sheath characteristics are important in the determination of species.

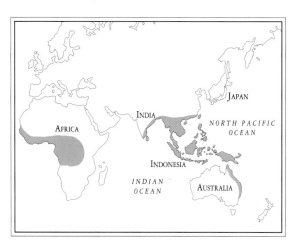

Calamus australis

Calamus palms are dioecious. The inflorescences (the male and female are superficially similar) arise from leaf axils and are usually long-branched structures, each branch subtended by a tubular bract. Male flowers are arranged singly along each side of the rachilla, while female flowers, usually larger, are in dyads of one female and one sterile male flower. Fruits are usually one-seeded, variously shaped, but are always covered in neat rows of scales.

Calamus canes are collected from the wild. In many areas the supply is rapidly dwindling, and in some places it is exhausted. In recent years, they have been planted and cultivated, often among other long-term plantation trees, such as rubber trees. The international rattan trade uses many different species, mostly for furniture making, the most valuable being *C. manan*, *C. caesius*, *C. trachycoleus* and *C. scipionum*. *Calamus* canes, leaves and whip-like extensions all have uses among rural communities and indigenous peoples for building, weaving baskets and mats and making other goods to use and sell. The fruit and young emergent leaves are often edible and so are collected. *Calamus* palms make attractive small pot plants, and can be kept under control by cutting the long stems and stimulating sucker growth.

Calamus australis

COMMON NAME: Lawyer vine, lawyer cane, wait-a-while.

SIZE: Climbing and clumping, with stems up to about 25 m (82 ft) long, 1.5 cm (0.6 in) in diameter.

HABITAT: Swampforest, monsoon forests, mangroves, but primarily rainforests from the coast to 2500 m (8200 ft) altitude.

DISTRIBUTION: Endemic to northeastern Australia.

CONSERVATION STATUS: Not threatened.

DESCRIPTION: Leaf sheath is armed with many brown to maroon, needle-like spines about 2 cm (0.8 in) long. Pinnate leaves are up to 2 m (6.5 ft) long, with regularly-placed (usually) pointed leaflets about 30 cm (1 ft) long. Leaf rachis has needle-like spines above and short hook-like spines below. Inflorescences are up to 4 m (13 ft) long with a long flagellum. Fruit are scaled, round and have a slightly pointed apex. They are up to 1.5 cm (0.6 in) in diameter, and cream to pale brown.

CULTIVATION: An adaptable palm for growing in a container or in the garden, under conditions from tropical to subtropical. Fastest growth is obtained in full sunlight, but partial or light shade is suitable. Cut the palm back to promote sucker growth.

Calamus australis

Calamus caryotoides

Calamus caryotoides

COMMON NAME: Fishtail lawyer vine, wait-a-while.

SIZE: Small climbing and clumping rattan with stems up to about 15 m (50 ft) long, and approximately 1–2 cm (0.4–0.8 in) in diameter. Can form dense thickets.

HABITAT: Rainforests, monsoon forests, often in dry locations where other rattans are absent. Range of altitudes from coastal to 1000 m (3300 ft).

DISTRIBUTION: Endemic to northeastern Australia.

CONSERVATION STATUS: Not threatened.

DESCRIPTION: One of the smaller *Calamus* species. New shoots arise from short stolons. Leaf sheaths are covered with scattered needle-like spines up to 1 cm (0.4 in) long. Has pinnate leaves up to 30 cm (1 ft) long, with the truncate fishtail leaflets regularly or irregularly placed on the rachis. Inflorescences are up to 120 cm (4 ft), but are usually much shorter, often with a terminal spined flagellum. Fruit are pale brown, scaled, round and about 1–2 cm (0.4–0.8 in) in diameter.

CULTIVATION: Makes a good pot plant or garden plant, growing well in full sun or partial shade. Tolerates dry conditions. Stems can be cut back and new suckers readily form, giving a clumping plant.

Calamus hollrungii

COMMON NAME: Mission Beach wait-a-while, Daintree lawyer vine.
SIZE: Medium-sized climbing rattan with a solitary stem, up to 25 m (82 ft) long and 2.5 cm (1 in) in diameter.
HABITAT: Lowland rainforest and swamp forest, up to 200 m (650 ft).
DISTRIBUTION: New Guinea, northeastern Queensland (Australia), Solomon Islands.
CONSERVATION STATUS: Not threatened.
DESCRIPTION: Single stem has leaf sheaths covered with dense needle-like brown spines up to 2 cm (0.8 in) long. Leaves are up to about 2.5 m (8 ft), pinnate, with groups of 2 to 5 leaflets clustered together along the rachis. Has a terminal spiny cirrus. Infloresence is up to 3 m (10 ft) long, with flowers borne on lateral branches. Fruit are round, scaled, pale green to white, about 1 cm (0.4 in) in diameter.
CULTIVATION: Makes a good indoor pot plant as it is adaptable to low light intensities. Grows very rapidly in tropical and subtropical conditions. Older stems can be layered since they will take root when touching the ground or partially buried.

Calamus javensis

COMMON NAME: Batu (Sarawak), rotan lilin (Peninsular Malaysia).
SIZE: Very slender, clustering, forming low thickets or climbing to 10 m (33 ft) or more, stems 2–6 mm (0.1–0.25 in) in diameter (measured without the sheath).
HABITAT: Forests from sea level to 2000 m (6500 ft) altitude.
DISTRIBUTION: Borneo, west Java, Sumatra, Peninsular Malaysia, southern Thailand.
CONSERVATION STATUS: Vulnerable in Peninsular Malaysia, not threatened in Sarawak, status unknown elsewhere.
DESCRIPTION: An extremely variable species. Leaf sheaths are bright green, often with a reddish tinge, with a knee. They may be spined or not. Ocrea is up to 1 cm (0.4 in) long, moderately conspicuous, crimson when young. Flagellum up to 1 m (3.3 ft) long. Leaves are irregularly pinnate with wide leaflets, the terminal pair united and often with several other leaflets forming a fan-shaped arrangement at the end of the leaf. Inflorescences bear crimson rachillae. Fruit are ovoid, 1.2 cm (0.5 in) long, covered with pale green scales.
CULTIVATION: This strong rattan is used for tying and binding, and split for weaving baskets and mats. Frequently collected.

Calamus hollrungii

Calamus manan

COMMON NAME: Rotan manau.
SIZE: Massive single-stemmed climbing rattan, reaching over 100 m (330 ft) long.
HABITAT: Steep slopes in hill dipterocarp forest from 50–1000 m (160–3300 ft) altitude.
DISTRIBUTION: Peninsular Malaysia, Sumatra, Borneo.
CONSERVATION STATUS: Vulnerable.
DESCRIPTION: Leaf sheaths are dull grey-green and densely armed with black triangular spines, some short and some to 3 cm (1.2 in) long. Knee is conspicuous and armed. Ocrea not well defined. Leaves are massive, up to about 8 m (26 ft) long including the cirrus (up to 3 m (10 ft) long). Has about 45 pale grey-green leaflets (regularly arranged in mature leaves) on each side of rachis, the largest 60 cm (2 ft) long, all with a limp and pendulous appearance. Inflorescences are massive, finely branched and up to 2.5 m (8 ft) long. Fruit are round to ovoid, up to 2.8 cm (1.1 in) long with a short beak, covered with yellowish scales.
CULTIVATION: Gives the best quality large-sized canes used in furniture making. Planted experimentally and commercially since wild sources are almost depleted.

Calamus manan

Calamus moti

COMMON NAME: Yellow lawyer cane, wait-a-while, moti (Aboriginal name from Barron River area of Australia).
SIZE: Large climbing and clumping palm, stems up to 20 m (65 ft) or more and 2.5 cm (1 in) in diameter.
HABITAT: Rainforests at low to mid-altitudes, up to 1000 m (3300 ft).
DISTRIBUTION: Endemic to northeastern Australia.
CONSERVATION STATUS: Not threatened.
DESCRIPTION: Many stems per clump. Pinnate leaves are 2–3 m (6.5–10 ft) long with up to 100 long, narrow, crowded leaflets. Leaf sheaths are distinctively armed with rows of long yellow thorns up to 2 cm (0.8 in) long. Underside of leaf rachis has groups of yellow hook-like spines. Flagella are 3–4 m (10–13 ft) long. Fruit are round, 0.8–1.3 cm (0.3–0.5 in) in diameter, scaled, cream in colour.
CULTIVATION: Seeds germinate readily. Tolerates tropical to temperate climates.

Calamus javensis

Calamus moti: the leaf sheath is armed with rows of spines

Calamus muelleri

Calamus muelleri

COMMON NAME: Southern lawyer cane, wait-a-while.
SIZE: Slender climbing and clumping palm, stems up to about 25 m (82 ft) or more, 1.5 cm (0.6 in) in diameter.
HABITAT: Rainforests and moist scrubs.
DISTRIBUTION: Endemic to eastern Australia.
CONSERVATION STATUS: Not threatened.
DESCRIPTION: Up to 12 stems per clump. Pinnate leaves are up to 1 m (3.3 ft) long, with 15–20 lanceolate leaflets per leaf. Margins and veins are spiny, leaf rachis has hook-like spines. Leaf sheath is armed with dense brownish spines. Flagella 1–2 m (3.3–6.5 ft). Inflorescence is usually less than 1 m (3.3 ft) long, sparsely branched. Fruit are round, 0.9 cm (0.4 in) in diameter, scaled, cream in colour.
CULTIVATION: Seed germinates readily. Tolerates cool temperate climates.

Calamus scipionum

Calamus scipionum

COMMON NAME: Rotan semambu (Malaysia).
SIZE: Robust clustering rattan, climbing to 50 m (160 ft) or more. Stems 2.5–3.5 cm (1–1.4 in) in diameter without the sheath.
HABITAT: Lowlands and up to 500 m (1600 ft) altitudes in primary and secondary forests.
DISTRIBUTION: Borneo, Sumatra, southern Thailand, Palawan.
CONSERVATION STATUS: Vulnerable.
DESCRIPTION: Internodes are very long, sometimes over 100 cm (40 in). Leaf sheaths are green and armed with large flattened triangular spines scattered or in groups of two or three. Knee conspicuous. Ocrea is short and tattering. Stem dries to a brown–black. Long robust flagella are up to 7 m (23 ft) long. Leaves are about 2 m (6.5 ft) long, without a cirrus. Has about 25 dull green leaflets regularly arranged each side of rachis, bristly at the tips. Inflorescences are up to 6 m (20 ft) or more, male and female similar. Fruit are ovoid, up to 1.4 cm (0.6 in) long with a short beak, covered with green scales.
CULTIVATION: Canes are used for making furniture, walking sticks and umbrella handles.

Calamus usitatus var. *palawanensis*

Calamus usitatus

syn. *Calamus blancoi, C. mollis*
COMMON NAME: Talola (Philippines).
SIZE: Slender to moderate, clustering, stems to 10 m (33 ft) long, stems 1–2.3 cm (0.4–0.9 in) in diameter.
HABITAT: Low altitude forests.
DISTRIBUTION: Coastal Sabah (Malaysian Borneo), Philippines.
CONSERVATION STATUS: Indeterminate.
DESCRIPTION: Leaf sheaths are green, densely covered with brown spines up to 4.5 cm (1.8 in) long, but 2 to 3 times longer around the mouth of the sheath where they are close together and often erect. Knee conspicuous. Short ocrea with very fine, minute spines. Flagella are up to 1.5 m (5 ft) long. Pinnate leaves are up to 90 cm (3 ft) long, without cirri. Has about 30 pairs of leaflets, either regularly placed or in groups (Philippines). Male and female inflorescences are similar, about 2 m (6.5 ft), with tubular bracts on the main axis. Fruit are ovoid with a short beak, 0.8 cm (0.3 in) long, covered in rows of small straw-coloured scales.
CULTIVATION: A rattan collected for tying purposes.

CALYPTROCALYX

kă-,lĭp-trō-'kā-lĭx

Calyptrocalyx is a genus of about 38 species of rainforest understorey palms found in New Guinea, with one species, *C. spicatus*, found in the Moluccas. The genus now includes *Paralinospadix*. Found in primary rainforest, usually on mountain slopes up to approximately 1000 m (3300 ft), they are sometimes found at low levels near streams and in swampy areas.

Calyptrocalyx palms may be solitary or clustering, sometimes forming dense clumps. Stems eventually become bare and show conspicuous rings. Leaf blades are entire and bifid, or are pinnately divided into segments with one or more ribs. Leaflets may be tapering and pointed, or sometimes toothed. Petioles may be short to long. Leaf sheaths soon split opposite the petiole and although the sheaths wrap around the stem there is no well-developed crownshaft. Inflorescences are unbranched, pendulous spikes arising among the leaves, and may be solitary or several. Flowers are arranged spirally in triads. Fruit are small to large, variously shaped from globose to elliptical or sickle-shaped, single-seeded, and usually red when ripe.

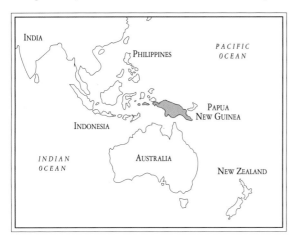

Calyptrocalyx spicatus

Calyptrocalyx spicatus

syn. *Areca spicata*

COMMON NAME: None known.

SIZE: Solitary, slender trunk, up to 12 m (40 ft) tall.

HABITAT: Lowland rainforest, where it is an understorey to semi-emergent plant.

DISTRIBUTION: Moluccas.

CONSERVATION STATUS: Unknown.

DESCRIPTION: Prominently ringed, slender trunk. Green sheathing leaf bases form a poorly-developed crownshaft. Has numerous narrow, pointed leaflets regularly arranged. Spicate inflorescence is up to 2 m (6.5 ft) long. Fruit are ovoid, and orange.

CULTIVATION: In the Moluccas, the fruit is chewed as a substitute for betel nut. Has tropical to subtropical requirements. A shaded and wind-protected location in a well-drained soil rich in organic matter is suggested, with extra mulching and a good water supply.

Calyptrocalyx spicatus

CARPENTARIA

kăr-pĕn-'tăr-ē-à

*C*arpentaria is a monotypic genus. *Carpentaria acuminata*, the Carpentaria palm, is endemic to the northern areas of the Northern Territory, Australia. Its habitat is the small scattered areas of monsoon forest near the coast, and sandstone ravines further from the coast. The Carpentaria palm is planted frequently as a street and garden tree in Australia's tropical north and in southern Florida.

Closely related to *Veitchia*, the Carpentaria is a slender palm with a smooth, grey, ringed trunk. The fast-growing Carpentaria enjoys fertile, well-drained soil with an abundant supply of water. It is best suited to tropical climates and is unsuitable for most indoor situations. Fresh seed germinates within three or four months, and young plants require shade and protection from wind.

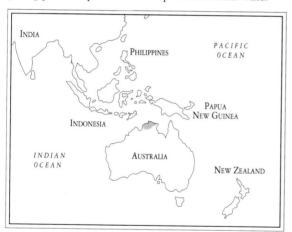

Carpentaria acuminata

Carpentaria acuminata

Carpentaria acuminata

COMMON NAME: Carpentaria palm.
SIZE: Slender trunk, up to 20 m (65 ft) tall.
HABITAT: Monsoon forest near the coast, and sandstone ravines further from the coast.
DISTRIBUTION: Northern Territory (Australia).
CONSERVATION STATUS: Not threatened.
DESCRIPTION: Slender grey-green crownshaft. The pinnate leaves arch strongly. Leaflets are numerous, narrow, tapering, closely spaced, about 30–40 cm (12–16 in) long, forming an upward V-shape from the rachis and then drooping. The tips are truncate and 2- to 4-lobed. The well-branched inflorescences are covered by 2 bracts when in bud. Fruit are ovoid, red, about 1 cm (0.4 in) long.
CULTIVATION: Needs a tropical to subtropical climate.

CARYOTA

kăr-i-'ō-tă

Caryota palms are commonly known as fishtail palms because of their unmistakable and unique bipinnate (doubly-divided) leaf. Each leaflet is suggestive of a fishtail, as they are wedge-shaped, with the upper margins jaggedly toothed. There are about 12 species distributed over India, Sri Lanka, southern China, Thailand, Malaysia, Myanmar (Burma), Cambodia, Laos, Vietnam, the Philippines, New Guinea, northeastern Australia, the Solomon Islands and Vanuatu. They have a range of habitats, but are generally found in monsoonal forests or very humid rainforests, and sometimes in mountain areas up to 2000 m (6500 ft). They are usually found in primary forest, but are very able to colonise secondary forest.

Some species have tall, stout, solitary trunks that reach for the forest canopy, while others are small to moderate clumping understorey palms. Trunks are often partly obscured by persistent, fibrous, leaf bases and sheaths, but these eventually fall to reveal a fairly smooth, ringed trunk. Leaf sheaths break down opposite the petiole to form a dark fibrous mass. The crown of leaves is elongate, with anything from a few to twelve or more erect to spreading leaves. The inflorescence is enclosed by a number of overlapping, leathery, tomentose bracts in the bud stage. Once open, the inflorescence is usually large, pendulous and simply branched. Flowering occurs in a basipetal sequence and can take a number of years on each stem. Both male and female flowers are produced on each inflorescence in triads. Fruit is round, has one to three seeds, and has a smooth outer skin. It becomes brightly coloured (usually yellow to red or purple) or dark at maturity. The mesocarp is filled with needle-like, calcium oxalate cystals, which are extremely irritating if they penetrate the skin, and render the fruit inedible.

Caryota palms are useful plants to humans; the apical leaf bud is edible, the trunks have a starchy pith used to make sago, the timber is used in construction, the fibrous material of leaf sheaths is used for wadding or tinder, and the inflorescences are tapped for a sugary sap used to make wine or sugar. As ornamentals, the fishtail palms are fast growing and very popular. They are generally able to adapt to a more subtropical climate than their natural habitat would indicate. *Caryota mitis* and *C. urens* are widely grown around the world.

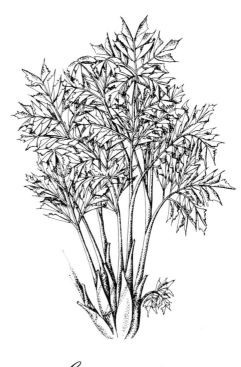

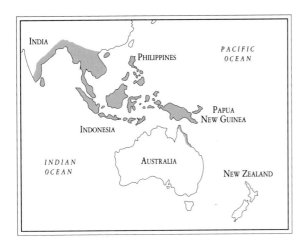

Caryota mitis

Caryota albertii: juvenile plant.

Caryota mitis: juvenile plant.

Caryota no

syn. *Caryota rumphiana* var. *borneensis*
COMMON NAME: None known.
SIZE: Solitary trunk, up to 25 m (82 ft) tall, or more, bulging in the middle to 70 cm (28 in) in diameter or more.
HABITAT: From lowlands up to about 400 m (1300 ft) altitude.
DISTRIBUTION: Borneo.
CONSERVATION STATUS: Vulnerable.
DESCRIPTION: Leaves are up to 4 m (13 ft) long or more. Leaflets have a narrow fishtail shape, are 30 cm (1 ft) long or more. Inflorescence 2 m (6.5 ft) long or more. Fruit are purple to black, round, about 2 cm (0.8 in) in diameter or more, and have 2 seeds.
CULTIVATION: Increasing in popularity as an ornamental palm in the subtropics and tropics.

Caryota albertii

syn. *Caryota rumphiana* var. *australasica*
COMMON NAME: Kulandoi (Aboriginal).
SIZE: Solitary trunk, up to 15 m (50 ft), diameter up to 40 cm (16 in).
HABITAT: Lowland rainforest and in and around mangrove areas.
DISTRIBUTION: Northeastern Cape York Peninsula (Australia), Solomon Islands, Vanuatu.
CONSERVATION STATUS: Not threatened.
DESCRIPTION: Leaves are large, rather flat in appearance, up to 7 m (23 ft) long and 5 m (16 ft) wide. The fishtail leaflets are very broad and up to 30 cm (1 ft) long. Inflorescences are often over 3 m (10 ft) long. Fruits are round, about 2 cm (0.8 in) in diameter, dull red-purple to black when ripe and contain 1–3 seeds.
CULTIVATION: Seeds germinate in 2–4 months and grow rapidly. Do not tolerate frost or cold temperatures.

Caryota mitis

COMMON NAME: Common fishtail palm.
SIZE: Clustering palm suckering freely, trunks up to 13 m (40 ft), but usually under 5 m (16 ft) in cultivation. Stem diameter up to 12.5 cm (5 in).
HABITAT: Lowland primary and secondary rainforest and swamp forest.
DISTRIBUTION: Andaman and Nicobar Islands, Myanmar (Burma), Malay Peninsula, Minahasa Peninsula of the North Celebes, Java, Sumatra.
CONSERVATION STATUS: Not threatened.
DESCRIPTION: Leaves are up to 3 m (10 ft) long. Inflorescences 30–40 cm (12–16 in) long. Fruit are roundish and black, about 1.2 cm (0.5 in) in diameter.
CULTIVATION: Grown as an ornamental, but the starchy pith is used to make sago by some peoples. Adaptable to warm temperate climates.

Caryota no

Caryota urens

Caryota urens

COMMON NAME: Jaggery palm, toddy palm, kitul palm (Sri Lanka).
SIZE: Solitary, robust trunk, up to 20 m (65 ft) tall, 30 cm (12 in) in diameter or more.
HABITAT: Primary and secondary lowland rainforests.
DISTRIBUTION: India, Myanmar (Burma), Sri Lanka.
CONSERVATION STATUS: Not threatened.
DESCRIPTION: Leaf is up to 6 m (20 ft) long. Leaflets are narrow, fishtail-shaped, 20–30 cm (8–12 in) long. Inflorescence 3 m (10 ft) long or more. Fruit are round and red, about 2 cm (0.8 in) in diameter, 1–2 seeded.
CULTIVATION: This palm is a source of sugar, toddy (an alcoholic drink of fermented sugary sap), fibre and wood for people in India and Sri Lanka. It is a popular ornamental in subtropics and temperate frost-free areas, as well as in tropical areas.

CHAMAEDOREA

kăm-ĕ-'dŏr-ē-à

Chamaedorea is a large New World genus, recently revised by Hodel (1992). It now includes about 100 species. Ranging from Mexico through Central America and into South America as far south as Brazil and Bolivia, *Chamaedorea* are generally small understorey palms of rainforests and cloud forests. Forest habitats vary from lowland to montane, and from moist to wet with some of mixed type.

The diversity of morphology and habit within the genus is great. *Chamaedorea* species are usually small, sometimes moderate in size, solitary or clustering, and in a few cases appear to have no visible stem. The smallest is probably *C. tuerckheimii*, which can fruit when less than 20 cm (8 in) tall. *C. costaricana*, on the other hand, has been found with stems to 15 m (50 ft) long. Stems of most species are slender, covered in dried leaf bases, fibrous to papery in texture, or with leaf bases falling to reveal a smooth, green, ringed stem surface. Most species have pinnate leaf blades, and there is a wide variety in leaflet size and shape between and within the species. Some species have bifid leaf blades, and one, *C. tuerckheimii*, has an entire leaf blade as its usual form. Leaf sheaths may be short or long and tubular, or sometimes splitting opposite the petiole and only tubular at the base. Ligules at the top of the sheath on either side of the petiole can be important in helping to distinguish one species from another. Petioles vary in length, but are usually flattened on the upper surface and rounded below. *Chamaedorea* species are dioecious. Inflorescences arise among the leaves or below the leaves, and are usually solitary at a node, but (in a few species) may be several. Inflorescences may be spicate, simply branched or moderately branched, the male inflorescence often having more rachillae than the female. Inflorescences are enclosed in tubular, persistent bracts, usually several. Fruit are small, usually globose to oblong, smooth-skinned, and single-seeded. Hodel (1992) recognises eight subgenera of *Chamaedorea* on the basis of differences in floral anatomy.

Chamaedoreas are particularly suitable as indoor plants as most are very tolerant of low light intensities and cool temperatures. Species such as *C. elegans* and *C. seifrizii* are commercially very significant plants, being produced in large numbers for the retail market. Many species can be grown outdoors in cool temperate zones where frosts occur. Propagation is usually from seed, which should germinate in 30 to 120 days if it is fresh and the temperature is maintained at 22–33°C (75–90°F).

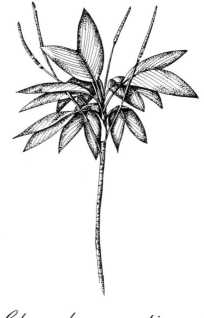

Chamaedorea ernesti-augustii

Chamaedorea amabilis

Chamaedorea amabilis

COMMON NAME: None known.
SIZE: Solitary stems, up to 2 m (6.5 ft) tall,
0.7–1 cm (0.3–0.4 in) in diameter. Sometimes
decumbent.
HABITAT: Wet forest from 500–1000 m
(1600–3300 ft).
DISTRIBUTION: Costa Rica, Panama, Colombia.
CONSERVATION STATUS: Endangered.
DESCRIPTION: Has 4–5 bifid leaves. Blade is
30–50 cm (12–20 in) long, 15–30 cm (6–12 in)
wide, incised to about quarter its length, with
the outer margins serrated to toothed.
Inflorescences are below the leaves, the male
simple-branched with 3–7 rachillae, the
female spicate or sometimes forked, the
rachillae orange in fruit. Fruit are black,
globose to oblong, 1.2 cm (0.5 in) long.
CULTIVATION: Has withstood frosts of 0°C
(32°F) in cultivation without damage.

Chamaedorea brachypoda

Chamaedorea brachypoda

COMMON NAME: None known.
SIZE: Stems clustering and rhizomatous,
forming dense, spreading clumps 1–2 m
(3.3–6.5 ft) tall, stems 0.5–0.7 cm (0.2–0.3 in)
in diameter.
HABITAT: Wet forest up to 150 m (500 ft).
DISTRIBUTION: Guatemala, Honduras.
CONSERVATION STATUS: Endangered.
DESCRIPTION: Has 5–8 bifid leaves. Blade is up
to 30 cm (12 in) long and 22 cm (9 in) wide,
incised to about half its length, margins
toothed. Inflorescences are below the leaves,
simple-branched in both sexes, the rachillae
orange in fruit. Fruit are black, ellipsoid,
0.5–1 cm (0.2–0.4 in) long.
CULTIVATION: Propagated from seed or by
dividing the stems or rhizomes. Best in a
tropical to subtropical climate. Can be grown
in cooler climates, but the leaves develop
brown tips. Makes a good pot plant.

Chamaedorea cataractarum

Chamaedorea costaricana

Chamaedorea cataractarum

syn. *Chamaedorea atrovirens* Hort.
COMMON NAME: Cascade palm.
SIZE: Can form dense clumps up to 2 m
(6.5 ft) by 3 m (10 ft), stems 2–4 cm
(0.8–1.2 in) in diameter. It creeps along the
ground and branches dichotomously.
HABITAT: The banks of rivers and streams,
sometimes wholly or partially submerged in
flooding water.
DISTRIBUTION: Mexico.
CONSERVATION STATUS: Vulnerable.
DESCRIPTION: Has 4–5 pinnate leaves, each to
2 m (6.5 ft) long. Has 13–20 leaflets on each
side of rachis, linear-lanceolate, up to 30 cm
(1 ft) long. Inflorescences are among the
leaves, sometimes below the leaves when in
fruit. Both sexes are simple-branched on a
long peduncle. Rachillae are orange in fruit.
Fruit are dark brown to black, ovoid-oblong,
1 cm (0.4 in) long.
CULTIVATION: A suitable indoor plant which
can be propagated from seed. Can make a
hedge-like clump in partially-shaded to open
sunny location. Suits tropical to warm
temperate climates.

Chamaedorea costaricana

COMMON NAME: None known.
SIZE: Stems are clustering, generally 3–8 m
(10–26 ft) tall, 2–8 cm (0.8–3.2 in) in
diameter. One very large form has stems
over 15 m (45 ft) tall and 6 cm (2.4 in) in
diameter. Clumps can be large, with stems
leaning or decumbent.
HABITAT: Dense, moist to wet forest, from
700–2000 m (2300–6500 ft).
DISTRIBUTION: Costa Rica, Panama, Nicaragua,
Honduras.
CONSERVATION STATUS: Vulnerable.
DESCRIPTION: Has 4–6 leaves, up to 1–2 m
(3.3–6.5 ft) long. Has 20–26 leaflets on each
side of rachis. They are linear-lanceolate, and
25–40 cm (10–16 in) long. Has short
triangular ligules at the apex of the sheath at
each side of the petiole. Inflorescences are
below the leaves, simple-branched in both
sexes, with 10–20 rachillae in the female,
15–30 in the male. Rachillae are red when in
fruit. Fruit are globose, black, 0.6–1 cm
(0.25–0.4 in) in diameter.
CULTIVATION: This variable species is suitable
for a tropical to temperate climate.

Chamaedorea deckeriana

COMMON NAME: None known.

SIZE: Solitary stemmed, 0.3–2 m (1–6.5 ft) tall, 2–3 cm (0.8–1.2 in) in diameter, sometimes decumbent.

HABITAT: Wet forest up to 900 m (3000 ft).

DISTRIBUTION: Costa Rica, Panama.

CONSERVATION STATUS: Vulnerable.

DESCRIPTION: Has 4–5 bifid leaves. Blade is 50–70 cm (20–28 in) long, 25–35 cm (10–14 in) wide, incised to about half its length, with outer margins toothed. Inflorescences are among the leaves (sometimes below the leaves in fruit), spicate on a long peduncle, with several per node in the male, but solitary in the female. Infructescence is club-like, with densely-packed fruit. Fruit are globose to egg-shaped, green ripening to red-orange and ageing to blackish, 1–1.5 cm (0.4–0.6 in) long.

CULTIVATION: Little known in cultivation. Does not tolerate cool temperatures.

Chamaedorea deckeriana: with spicate infructescence.

Chamaedorea elatior

Chamaedorea elegans

Chamaedorea elatior

COMMON NAME: None known.

SIZE: Vine-like, climbing or sprawling along the ground, solitary, or clumping and then branching up to 1 m (3.3 ft) above ground. Stems are 0.8–2 cm (0.3–0.8 in) in diameter, up to 20 m (65 ft) long.

HABITAT: Moist or wet dense forest, 100–1500 m (330–5000 ft).

DISTRIBUTION: Mexico, Guatemala.

CONSERVATION STATUS: Indeterminate.

DESCRIPTION: Has 5–15 leaves, bifid when young, becoming progressively pinnate up the stem. Blade usually 0.5–1.5 m (15 in–5 ft) long, with 10–55 linear-lanceolate leaflets on each side of rachis. In an adaptation for climbing, the leaflets are reflexed and hook-like towards the apex of the leaf. Inflorescences are among the leaves, simple-branched. It sometimes flowers when the leaves are still bifid. Fruit are globose, black, 0.8–1.1 cm (0.3–0.4 in) in diameter.

CULTIVATION: Suitable for tropical to warm temperate climates. Will climb on a trellis or tree.

Chamaedorea elegans

syn. *Neanthe bella, Collinia elegans*

COMMON NAME: Parlour palm.

SIZE: Solitary, slender, up to 2 m (6.5 ft), 0.8–1.5 cm (0.3–0.6 in) in diameter.

HABITAT: Moist or wet dense forest up to 1400 m (4600 ft), often on limestone.

DISTRIBUTION: Mexico, Guatemala, Belize.

CONSERVATION STATUS: Vulnerable in Guatemala, endangered in Mexico.

DESCRIPTION: Has 5–8 pinnate leaves, each about 0.3–1 m (1–3 ft) long. Has 11–21 leaflets on each side of rachis, linear-lanceolate, 15–30 cm (6 in–1 ft) long. Inflorescences are among the leaves, both sexes simple-branched on a long peduncle, which often reaches beyond the leaves. Has from a few to many rachillae, red-orange in fruit. Fruit are black, globose, 0.4–0.7 cm (0.15–0.3 in) in diameter. Eophyll is pinnate.

CULTIVATION: Grown in large numbers from seed for the indoor plant market. Tolerates low light and dry air conditions.

Chamaedorea ernesti-augustii

COMMON NAME: None known.

SIZE: Solitary, slender, up to 2 m (6.5 ft) tall, or more, 1–1.5 cm (0.4–0.6 in) in diameter.

HABITAT: Wet, dense forest up to 1000 m (3300 ft), but mostly at low altitudes, often on limestone.

DISTRIBUTION: Mexico, Guatemala, Belize, Honduras.

CONSERVATION STATUS: Insufficiently known.

DESCRIPTION: Has 5–8 bifid leaves. Blade is 25–60 cm (10 in–2 ft) long and 20–30 cm (8–12 in) wide, incised to nearly half its length, with toothed margins. Inflorescences are among the leaves, sometimes below the leaves in fruit, simple-branched. Have 15–25 rachillae in males, but are spicate or have up to 4 rachillae in females, the rachillae orange in fruit. Fruit are black, subglobose to ellipsoid, up to 1.5 cm (0.6 in) long.

CULTIVATION: A popular indoor and garden plant. Suitable for tropical to warm temperate areas. Hand-pollination is usually necessary for cultivated plants to set fruit.

Chamaedorea ernesti-augustii

Chamaedorea fragrans

Chamaedorea fragrans

COMMON NAME: None known.
SIZE: Clumping, up to 2 m (6.5 ft) tall, stems 0.5–1.5 cm (0.2–0.6 in) in diameter. Sometimes decumbent.
HABITAT: Moist or wet forest from 400–1000 m (1300–3300 ft).
DISTRIBUTION: Peru.
CONSERVATION STATUS: Endangered.
DESCRIPTION: Has 4–7 bifid leaves on short petioles. Blade has a distinctive narrow V-shape, is 40–50 cm (16–20 in) long, 15–20 cm (6–8 in) wide, incised to about three-quarters its length, with toothed outer margins. Inflorescences are below the leaves, often bursting through old persistent leaf sheaths. Both sexes are simple-branched on short peduncles with few rachillae. Fruit are globose-ellipsoid, black, 1.2 cm (0.5 in) long.
CULTIVATION: Propagated from seed or by division of clustered stems. An attractive pot or garden plant. Leaf tips turn brown when grown in cooler areas.

Chamaedorea geonomiformis

Chamaedorea geonomiformis

COMMON NAME: Necklace chamaedorea.
SIZE: Solitary stem up to 1.5 m (5 ft) tall, 0.5–1 cm (0.2–0.4 in) in diameter. Sometimes decumbent.
HABITAT: Dense, wet forest from 100–900 m (330–3000 ft), usually on limestone.
DISTRIBUTION: Mexico, Guatemala, Belize, Honduras, possibly Colombia.
CONSERVATION STATUS: Vulnerable.
DESCRIPTION: Has 5–10 bifid leaves. Blade is 15–30 cm (6–12 in) long and 15 cm (6 in) wide, incised to one-third (or half) its length, with outer margins shallowly toothed. Inflorescences are among the leaves, often below the leaves in fruit, on long peduncles. Are simple-branched with 3–6 rachillae (rarely 2 or spicate) in males, 2–3 rachillae (rarely spicate) in females, the rachillae orange-red in fruit. Fruit are black, globose, up to 0.8–1.2 cm (0.3–0.5 in) in diameter.
CULTIVATION: Sometimes confused with *C. ernesti-augustii*, which is generally a larger plant, because of a similarity of habit. Suitable for tropical to subtropical gardens or as a potted plant in a shaded position.

Chamaedorea glaucifolia

COMMON NAME: None known.
SIZE: Solitary stems, up to 5 m (16 ft) tall, 2–3.5 cm (0.8–1.4 in) in diameter.
HABITAT: Moist or wet forest from 500–1000 m (1600–3300 ft), often on limestone.
DISTRIBUTION: Mexico.
CONSERVATION STATUS: Endangered.
DESCRIPTION: Has 3–5 finely pinnate leaves, each 1.5 m (5 ft) or more long. Has 50–70 leaflets on each side of the rachis, clustered in groups, linear to linear-lanceolate, and 30–35 cm (12–14 in) long. Leaf rachis and petiole are glaucous. Inflorescences are below the leaves, on long peduncles, and solitary. Both sexes are simple-branched with up to 30 rachillae. Rachillae are red-orange in fruit. Fruit are black, globose, 0.7–1 cm (0.3–0.4 in) in diameter.
CULTIVATION: Suited to warm temperate to tropical climates. Tolerates higher light intensities than other species of *Chamaedorea*.

Chamaedorea glaucifolia

Chamaedorea klotzschiana

COMMON NAME: None known.
SIZE: Solitary stem, 1–4 m (3.3–13 ft) tall, 1.5–2.8 cm (0.6–1.1 in) in diameter.
HABITAT: Dense, wet forest from 500–1250 m (1600–4100 ft).
DISTRIBUTION: Mexico.
CONSERVATION STATUS: Endangered.
DESCRIPTION: Has 4–6 pinnate leaves, about 1 m (3.3 ft) or more long. Has 12–20 lanceolate leaflets on each side of rachis, 20–40 cm (8–16 in) long, clustered in groups of 2–4. Inflorescences are below the leaves, on long peduncles. They are simple-branched, with 12–20 rachillae in both sexes. Rachillae are red-orange in fruit. Fruit are globose-ovoid, black, up to 1 cm (0.4 in).
CULTIVATION: Tropical to warm temperate areas.

Chamaedorea klotzschiana

Chamaedorea metallica

COMMON NAME: None known.
SIZE: Solitary stem, 2–3 m (6.5–10 ft) tall,
1.3–1.5 cm (0.5–0.6 in) in diameter.
HABITAT: Dense, wet forest, from 50–600 m
(160–2000 ft), usually on limestone.
DISTRIBUTION: Mexico.
CONSERVATION STATUS: Endangered.
DESCRIPTION: Has 12–16 leaves, usually bifid,
but often variously pinnate, characteristically
metallic-blue-green. Bifid blade is incised to
about one third its length, or, if pinnately
divided, has 3–8 leaflets on each side of
rachis. Inflorescences are among the leaves,
often below the leaves in fruit, solitary, and
on long peduncles. Male are simple-branched
with 10–12 rachillae, female are spicate,
sometimes forked or with 3–4 rachillae (red-
orange in fruit). Fruit are globose-ellipsoid,
black, 1.2 cm (0.5 in) long.
CULTIVATION: A good indoor plant because it
tolerates low light intensities. Suitable for
tropical to warm temperate climates.

Chamaedorea microspadix

Chamaedorea metallica

Chamaedorea microspadix

COMMON NAME: None known.
SIZE: Clumping densely, up to 3 m (10 ft) tall, stems often leaning.
Stems 1 cm (0.4 in) in diameter.
HABITAT: Moist forest, at middle elevations, usually on limestone.
DISTRIBUTION: Mexico.
CONSERVATION STATUS: Vulnerable.
DESCRIPTION: Has 4–6 pinnate leaves up to about 1 m (3.3 ft) long.
Usually has 9 leaflets on each side of rachis, lanceolate and usually
sigmoid, up to 25 cm (10 in) long. The terminal pair are wider and
united into a bifid unit. Inflorescences are below the leaves, simple-
branched in both sexes, the female rachillae orange when in fruit.
Fruit are globose, orange-red, up to 1 cm (0.4 in) in diameter.
CULTIVATION: One of the more cold-hardy *Chamaedorea* species,
suitable for tropical to temperate climates. Will grow to large clumps
in the garden and will withstand nearly open sun, usually without
foliage damage.

Chamaedorea oreophila

syn. *Chamaedorea monostachys*
COMMON NAME: None known.
SIZE: Solitary stem, 1–3 m (3.3–10 ft) tall,
0.6–2 cm (0.25–0.8 in) in diameter.
HABITAT: Wet forest from 1000–1500 m
(3300–5000 ft), often on limestone.
DISTRIBUTION: Mexico.
CONSERVATION STATUS: Vulnerable.
DESCRIPTION: Has 5–13 pinnate leaves, up to
1 m (3.3 ft) long or more. Has 14–25 leaflets
on each side of rachis, narrowly lanceolate,
16–35 cm (6.5–14 in) long. Inflorescences are
spicate, among the leaves, on very long
peduncles which extend beyond the leaves.
They are solitary at a node in females, 4–8
per node in males. Infructescence is club-like
with densely packed fruit. Fruit are ovoid-
ellipsoid, red when ripe, up to 0.8 cm
(0.3 in) long.
CULTIVATION: Suitable for warm temperate to
tropical climates.

Chamaedorea pinnatifrons

Chamaedorea oreophila

Chamaedorea pinnatifrons

syn. *Chamaedorea concolor*
COMMON NAME: None known.
SIZE: Solitary stem, 0.5–4 m (1.5–13 ft) tall, 0.5–3 cm (0.2–1.2 in) in
diameter. Sometimes decumbent.
HABITAT: Dense, moist or wet forest, up to 2700 m (8900 ft).
DISTRIBUTION: Bolivia, Ecuador, Brazil, Peru, Colombia, Venezuela,
Panama, Costa Rica, Nicaragua, Honduras, El Salvador, Guatemala,
Mexico.
CONSERVATION STATUS: Not threatened.
DESCRIPTION: A highly variable species. Leaves are pinnate or bifid. If
pinnate, leaflets are sigmoid, with prominent nerves on upper surface.
Inflorescence is among or below the leaves, solitary, not exceeding the
leaves, usually simple-branched, with a various number of rachillae
(generally 5–21 in the male and 5–15 in the female). Fruit ripen from
green to yellow-orange, then to red and ageing to black. They are
ellipsoid to globose and up to 2 cm (0.8 in) long.
CULTIVATION: Various forms are in cultivation, some misnamed. A
Venezuelan form and Costa Rican form are commonly cultivated.

Chamaedorea pochutlensis

Chamaedorea pochutlensis

syn. *Chamaedorea karwinskyana*
COMMON NAME: None known.
SIZE: Densely clumping, stems sometimes leaning, 3–5 m (10–16 ft) tall, stems 2–3 cm (0.8–1.2 in) in diameter.
HABITAT: Moist forest from 50–2000 m (160–6500 ft).
DISTRIBUTION: Mexico.
CONSERVATION STATUS: Indeterminate.
DESCRIPTION: Sometimes confused with *C. costaricana*, but does not have ligules at the apex of the leaf sheath. Has 3–5 pinnate leaves, each up to 2 m (6.5 ft) long. Has 20–33 leaflets on each side of rachis, lanceolate, and up to 40 cm (16 in) long. Inflorescences are below the leaves, simple-branched, on peduncles 30–40 cm (12–16 in) long. Has 12–25 rachillae in the male, 12–18 rachillae in the female. Fruit are globose-ellipsoid, black, about 1.2 cm (0.5 in) long.
CULTIVATION: A cold-hardy *Chamaedorea*, able to tolerate nearly full sun.

Chamaedorea radicalis

Chamaedorea radicalis

COMMON NAME: None known.
SIZE: Solitary, the common form appearing stemless, the less common form with stems 3–4 m (10–13 ft) tall, 2.5–3 cm (1–1.2 in) in diameter.
HABITAT: Moist oak forest up to 1000 m (3300 ft).
DISTRIBUTION: Mexico.
CONSERVATION STATUS: Vulnerable.
DESCRIPTION: Has 4–8 pinnate leaves, up to about 1 m (3.3 ft) or more. Has 10–18 leaflets (or more) on each side of the rachis, linear-lanceolate, up to 40 cm (16 in) long. Inflorescence is on a long peduncle, among the leaves, in stemless plants often arising from the base. Male inflorescence is simply to moderately branched with 8–20 rachillae. Female may be spicate, forked or with up to 10 rachillae which are green in fruit. Fruit are ellipsoid to globose, green ripening to yellow, then orange and red, 1.2 cm (0.5 in) long.
CULTIVATION: Very cold-hardy. Tolerates both low light and open sun.

Chamaedorea sartorii

Chamaedorea sartorii

COMMON NAME: None known.
SIZE: Solitary stem, 3–4 m (10–13 ft) tall, 0.8–1.6 cm (0.3–0.6 in) in diameter.
HABITAT: Wet or moist forest, from 100–1300 m (330–4300 ft), often on limestone.
DISTRIBUTION: Mexico.
CONSERVATION STATUS: Indeterminate.
DESCRIPTION: Has 3–6 pinnate leaves up to about 1 m (3.3 ft) long. Has 5–10 leaflets on each side of the rachis, lanceolate and sigmoid, 20–40 cm (8–16 in) long. Inflorescence is among the leaves, often below the leaves in fruit. It is solitary, on a long peduncle, simple-branched, has 30 rachillae in the male, 4–8 rachillae in the female (orange in fruit). Fruit are ellipsoid-ovoid, black, up to 1.2 cm (0.5 in) long.
CULTIVATION: A popular ornamental suitable for tropical to warm temperate climates.

Chamaedorea seifrizii

Chamaedorea seifrizii

syn. *Chamaedorea erumpens*
COMMON NAME: Bamboo palm.
SIZE: Densely clumping, stems up to 3 m (10 ft) tall, 1–2 cm (0.4–0.8 in) in diameter.
HABITAT: Open or dense moist or wet woodland or forest, up to 500 m (1600 ft), often on limestone.
DISTRIBUTION: Mexico, Belize, Guatemala, Honduras.
CONSERVATION STATUS: Endangered in Mexico, status unknown elsewhere.
DESCRIPTION: Has 4–5 leaves per stem. Leaves are 0.7–1 m (28 in–3 ft) long, with 5–18 pairs of more or less lanceolate leaflets, variable in size with different forms, the apical pair wider and shorter than the others. Inflorescences are below the leaves, simple-branched in both sexes, short and breaking through the old leaf sheath. Female rachillae are orange in fruit. Fruit are globose, black, 0.8 cm (0.3 in) in diameter. The horticultural industry recognise *C. erumpens* as a broader-leafed species, but it is synonymous with *C. seifrizii*.

Chamaedorea stolonifera

COMMON NAME: None known.
SIZE: Producing creeping stolons from basal or near-basal nodes and densely clustering, 1–2 m (3.3–6.5 ft) tall. Stems are 0.5–0.8 cm (0.2–0.3 in) in diameter.
HABITAT: Wet forest from 600–800 m (2000–2600 ft), usually on limestone.
DISTRIBUTION: Mexico.
CONSERVATION STATUS: Endangered.
DESCRIPTION: Has 5–8 leaves. Blades are bifid, about 30 cm (12 in) long and 25 cm (10 in) wide, incised to two thirds their length, with toothed outer margins. Inflorescences are usually below the leaves, simple-branched, with peduncles up to 20 cm (8 in) long. Has 2–7 rachillae in the male, 2–4 rachillae in the female, rachillae red in fruit. Fruit are globose, black, 0.7–0.9 cm (0.3–0.35 in) in diameter.
CULTIVATION: Propagated readily by removing the stolons which have produced rooted new stems. Also (but rarely) propagated from seed.

Chamaedorea stolonifera

Chamaedorea tenella

Chamaedorea tenella

COMMON NAME: None known.
SIZE: Solitary, up to 2 m (6.5 ft) tall, sometimes decumbent. Stems approximately 0.5 cm (0.2 in) in diameter.
HABITAT: Dense, wet forest, from 100–1000 m (330–3300 ft).
DISTRIBUTION: Mexico, Costa Rica.
CONSERVATION STATUS: Endangered.
DESCRIPTION: Has 5–7 bright green bifid leaves. Blade is up to 20 cm (8 in) long and 10 cm (4 in) wide, incised to about one quarter its length, with toothed outer margins. Inflorescences are among the leaves, often below the leaves in fruit. They are spicate, on long peduncles, and orange-red in fruit. Fruit are black, globose, 0.6–1.2 cm (0.25–0.5 in) in diameter. Note that Hodel (1992) suggests that *C. tenella* may be a smaller form of *C. geonomiformis*.
CULTIVATION: Rare in cultivation. A tropical to warm temperate climate is required.

Chamaedorea tepejilote

COMMON NAME: None known.
SIZE: Solitary, sometimes clumping, 2–7 m (6.5–23 ft) tall or more. Stems 2–10 cm (0.8–4 in) in diameter.
HABITAT: Moist or wet forest, from sea level to 1600 m (5200 ft), often on limestone.
DISTRIBUTION: Mexico, Guatemala, Belize, Honduras, El Salvador, Nicaragua, Costa Rica, Panama, Colombia.
CONSERVATION STATUS: Unknown, probably not threatened.
DESCRIPTION: Variable. One of the more robust Chamaedoreas. Has 3–7 pinnate leaves, 1–2 m (3.3–6.5 ft) long. Yellow line down the underside of the petiole and onto the sheath. Usually has 12–25 leaflets on each side of the rachis, lanceolate and sigmoid, 16–70 cm (6.5–28 in) long. Inflorescences are below the leaves, solitary, simple-branched. Has 7–50 rachillae in the male, 5–20 rachillae in the female (orange-red in fruit). Fruit are ellipsoid to subglobose, green ripening black, usually 1–1.5 cm (0.4–0.6 in) in diameter.
CULTIVATION: Unopened male inflorescence is used as a vegetable in Mexico and Central America. The palm is cultivated for this crop. A widely-cultivated ornamental suitable for tropical to warm temperate climates. Tolerates a nearly open sunny position.

Chamaedorea tepejilote. with male inflorescence.

CHAMAEROPS

'kăm-ĕr-ŏps

*C*hamaerops is a monotypic genus, *Chamaerops humilis* being the sole representative. This hardy, clumping fan palm is found naturally along the coastal areas of the western Mediterranean and on the Atlantic coasts of Morocco and Portugal. The European or Mediterranean fan palm, as it is commonly known, is widely cultivated around the world. In its natural habitat near the sea, where it is subject to salty hot or cold winds, it grows on limestone and sandy soils which may be quite dry at times. Variable in habit and form, *C. humilis* may form several trunks in a clump, but it is most often low growing in its natural habitat.

Usually dwarf and clumping in the wild, *C. humilis* trunks can grow several metres tall under cultivation.

Floral abnormalities are frequent. Inflorescences are usually either all male or all female and on different plants, but occasionally they also bear bisexual flowers.

The European fan palm is best suited for temperate to subtropical areas although it will grow slowly in the tropics. It is hardy to drought and cold, and will withstand coastal winds without damage. However, it does not tolerate soggy soil. Propagated from seed, it grows relatively slowly.

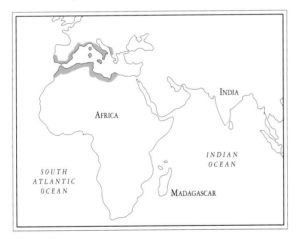

Chamaerops humilis

Chamaerops humilis

COMMON NAME: European fan palm, Mediterranean fan palm, windmill palm.

SIZE: Usually multiple trunks, 3–4 m (10–13 ft) tall.

HABITAT: Coastal areas.

DISTRIBUTION: Western Mediterranean countries.

CONSERVATION STATUS: Unknown.

DESCRIPTION: Trunks are covered in fibrous material. Compact crown of palmate leaves. Petiole margins have short thick spines. Leaf blade is divided (to more than halfway) into stiff segments, which are again split to various lengths. Inflorescences are moderately branched, enclosed in a large bract at the bud stage. Fruit are 1- to 3-seeded, globose to oblong, smooth-skinned and yellow or brown with pale dots.

CULTIVATION: Temperate to subtropical climates. Tolerates cold, salty air and drought.

Chamaerops humilis

CHAMBEYRONIA

shăm-bĕr-ˈō-nĭ-à

Chambeyronia is closely related to the genus *Archontophoenix*. The two species of *Chambeyronia* are moderate, single-trunked palms with prominent crownshafts and handsome curved pinnate leaves. Both species are endemic to New Caledonia, where they are found as emergent and semi-emergent palms of moist forests. *Chambeyronia macrocarpa* is widely distributed on a variety of soil types, from close to sea level to elevations of 1200 m (4000 ft). It is undoubtedly the most popular cultivated palm from New Caledonia and has proved its adaptability in temperate and tropical areas.

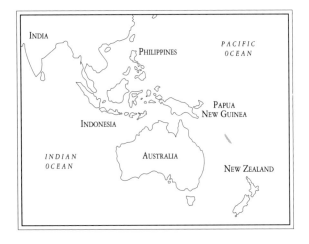

Chambeyronia macrocarpa

Chambeyronia macrocarpa

Chambeyronia macrocarpa

COMMON NAME: None known.
SIZE: Solitary trunk, up to 15 m (49 ft) tall, 25 cm (10 in) in diameter.
HABITAT: Emergent and semi-emergent palm in moist forests.
DISTRIBUTION: New Caledonia.
CONSERVATION STATUS: Rare.
DESCRIPTION: Trunk grey, smooth and evenly ringed. Crown has about 10 leaves, each new leaf being red and turning green in a week or so. Crownshaft is prominent, elongate and dark green. Petiole is short and the leaf long and arching to about 4 m (13 ft). There are about 38 pairs of leathery, pointed leaflets (the largest about 7 cm (2.8 in) wide and 1.5 m (5 ft) long), with prominent midribs. Inflorescences are below the crownshaft, moderately branched, and enclosed in bud by 2 bracts. Male and female flowers are borne on the same inflorescence in triads. Fruit vary from egg-shaped to almost round, are up to 4.6 cm (1.8 in), turning from green to red as they ripen.
CULTIVATION: A popular palm in temperate areas because of its cold tolerance. Seed germinates readily, followed by rapid growth.

CHRYSALIDOCARPUS

krĭs-à-lĭd-ō-ˈkărp-ŭs

Chrysalidocarpus is a genus of about 20 species, the best known being the golden cane palm, *Chrysalidocarpus lutescens*. *Chrysalidocarpus* palms originate in Madagascar, the Comores Islands and Pemba Island off the coast of Tanzania. Their natural habitats vary from coastal forests to mountain rainforest. *C. lutescens* is a hardy species naturally found on sand dunes and along waterways in Madagascar. It is a most adaptable species and has been very successful in cultivation in a wide range of climates.

Species vary in size, may be clustering or single stemmed, have prominent rings on the stems, and sometimes produce aerial branches, an unusual feature amongst palms. Leaves are arching and pinnate with the long, narrow, pointed leaflets being regularly arranged along the rachis, or in clusters with leaflets fanned, giving a plumose appearance to the leaf. Leaf sheaths are tubular at first then split opposite the petiole. They do not usually form a well-defined crownshaft, except in a few species. The inflorescence is well-branched, arises among the leaves, occasionally below the leaves with age, and is enclosed in two unequal-sized bracts when in the bud stage. Flowers are arranged in triads. Towards the outer ends of the flowering branches the flowers are usually male, either paired or solitary. Fruit are globose to ovoid or elliptical, smooth-skinned, have a fleshy mesocarp and contain only one seed.

Recent study of the palms of Madagascar has provided more evidence of the close affinity between the genera *Chrysalidocarpus, Neodypsis, Vonitra, Phloga* and *Dypsis*. Without tangible differences between the genera, it is likely that they will be combined under one name. In the absence of published references on these latest taxonomic changes, *Chrysalidocarpus* is treated here under its current name.

Chrysalidocarpus lutescens

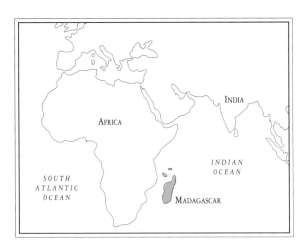

Chrysalidocarpus lutescens

syn. *Areca lutescens*

COMMON NAME: Golden cane palm, butterfly palm, yellow cane palm.

SIZE: Clumping, 5–10 m (16–33 ft) tall.

HABITAT: Sand dunes and along waterways.

DISTRIBUTION: Madagascar.

CONSERVATION STATUS: Rare.

DESCRIPTION: Green to yellow-orange ringed stems, 6–12 cm (2.5–5 in) in diameter. Forms many suckers, giving multiple stems of different heights. Long sheathing leaf bases have a whitish bloom when young. Pinnate leaves are up to 2 m (6.5 ft) long, green to yellow-orange petioles and rachis. Leaflets are green to yellow, and evenly spaced. Leaves are gracefully arching with a slight twist. Fruit are yellow when ripe, ovoid and 1–2 cm (0.4–0.8 in) long.

CULTIVATION: A very adaptable palm for tropical to temperate climates. One of the most widely-grown garden ornamentals. Grown from seed. Needs frost protection when young. Best in a sunny location where the leaves display their golden colour.

Chrysalidocarpus madagascariensis: multi-stemmed form.

Chrysalidocarpus lutescens

Chrysalidocarpus madagascariensis

syn. *Chrysalidocarpus lucubensis, C. madagascariensis* var. *lucubensis*

COMMON NAME: The solitary-trunked form is commonly called the lucuba palm.

SIZE: Clumping, up to 8 m (26 ft) tall or more. Solitary-trunked form (often called *C. lucubensis*) is 6–10 m (20–33 ft) tall and occasionally has 2 stems from the same plant.

HABITAT: Rainforest up to approximately 460 m (1500 ft).

DISTRIBUTION: Madagascar, Nossi-Be (island off the northwest coast of Madagascar).

CONSERVATION STATUS: Rare.

DESCRIPTION: Strongly-ringed narrow trunks, often swollen at the base. Leaves are pinnate, 2–3 m (6.5–10 ft) long, with numerous narrow tapering leaflets in groups or clusters along the leaf rachis, giving a plumose appearance. Leaves arise in 3 vertical rows on the trunk, the leaf bases sheathing. Branched inflorescences arise from the leaf axils just below the crown. Fruit are small, ovoid, around 1.5 cm (0.6 in) long, and brown when ripe.

CULTIVATION: A popular garden ornamental grown from seed. Fast growing in the tropics in deep rich soils with a good water supply, but also tolerates dryness. Suits subtropical regions, but is sensitive to frost.

Chrysalidocarpus madagascariensis: single-stemmed form.

CLINOSTIGMA

'klīn-ŏ-stĭg-mà

Clinostigma is a genus of about 13 species of tall single-trunked palms distributed from the Bonin and Caroline Islands to New Britain, the Solomon Islands, Vanuatu, Fiji Islands and Samoa. Found from sea level to mountain elevations in dense rainforest, particularly on ridge tops and hill crests. Their cultivation potential is likely to be in tropical regions only.

Trunks are ringed with closely-spaced leaf scars. There is a prominent crownshaft and sometimes long prickly stilt roots are present around the base. Leaves are pinnate, usually arching, the leaflets regularly arranged and often pendulous. The inflorescences mature below the crownshaft and are borne on short peduncles. They are usually well branched and completely enclosed in two bracts in the bud stage. Flowers are borne in triads. Fruit are ovoid to ellipsoidal, sometimes slightly flattened, with a smooth epicarp and a fibrous mesocarp.

Clinostigma exorrhizum

Clinostigma exorrhizum

COMMON NAME: Niuniu, niusowa (Fiji).
SIZE: Solitary trunk, up to 20 m (65 ft) tall and 35 cm (14 in) in diameter.
HABITAT: Moist forests on steep slopes, ridges and hill crests, from 230–1200 m (750–4000 ft). Most common at the upper levels where it receives high rainfall and persistent cloud cover.
DISTRIBUTION: Fiji Isands.
CONSERVATION STATUS: Rare.
DESCRIPTION: Spiny stilt roots to 3 m (10 ft). Crown has up to 12 pinnate leaves, up to 5 m (16 ft) long, with about 100 pairs of long, pendulous leaflets. Has a light green, glaucous crownshaft up to 1.2 m (4 ft) long. Inflorescence is up to 65 cm (26 in) long, well branched. Fruit are ovoid, up to 0.6 cm (0.25 in) long, red when ripe.
CULTIVATION: Potential as a cultivated palm is unknown. Its natural habitat indicates that it may be successful in tropical areas.

Clinostigma exorrhizum

COCCOTHRINAX

kŏk-ŏ-'thrȳ-năx

Coccothrinax is a genus of hardy, drought-resistant fan palms occurring on soils derived from limestone. About 49 species are distributed on the islands of the West Indies with the majority of species in Cuba. Many species are endemic to very small areas, and are the only representative of the genus in their particular area. Cross pollination between species means that some cultivated specimens may be hybrids.

Closely related to the genus *Thrinax*, *Coccothrinax* palms are small to moderate, usually solitary, but sometimes clustering palms. Their stems are covered with fibrous material derived from leaf sheaths. This may become a matted network, thread-like or spiny. As the palm ages, the fibrous material tends to fall off, revealing a bare, closely-ringed trunk. Leaves are small and palmate, with folded blades divided to about midway into narrow pointed segments, the tips of which are usually bifid. The inflorescence is moderately branched and shorter than the leaves. Flowers are bisexual. Fruit are small, round and purple-black when ripe.

Coccothrinax palms are popular in Florida and the West Indies as ornamental garden and potted plants. Propagated from seed that germinates in a few months, their growth is slow. They tolerate poor soils in tropical to subtropical climates and need partial shade when in juvenile stages.

Coccothrinax alta

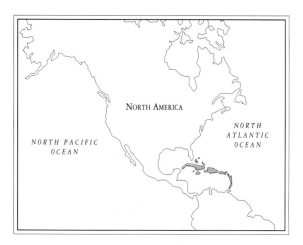

Coccothrinax argentata

Coccothrinax argentata

syn. *Coccothrinax garberi, C. jucunda*
COMMON NAMES: Silver palm, silver thatch palm, silvertop, Florida silver palm.
SIZE: Narrow, solitary palm, up to 6 m (20 ft) tall and 15 cm (6 in) in diameter.
HABITAT: Varies from open coastal areas to tropical hammock, coppice or pinelands.
DISTRIBUTION: Bahamas, Florida's southeastern coast and Keys (USA).
CONSERVATION STATUS: Rare in Florida, not threatened in the Bahamas.
DESCRIPTION: Open crown of about 16 fan leaves has many slightly-drooping segments. Tightly woven leaf sheaths have fine fibrous strands. Undersurface of the leaf is silvery in colour.
CULTIVATION: Best in shade in juvenile stage. Mature plants tolerate coastal salt spray, open sun and rather dry locations.

Coccothrinax barbadensis

syn. *Coccothrinax martiniensisi, C. australis, C. dussiana, C. sabana, C. boxii*
COMMON NAME: Thatch palm, Lesser Antilles silver thatch.
SIZE: Solitary trunk, up to 8 m (26 ft) tall and 10–15 cm (4–6 in) in diameter.
HABITAT: Forms colonies on dry, calcereous soils in coastal woodland and hills up to 200 m (650 ft).
DISTRIBUTION: Lesser Antilles.
CONSERVATION STATUS: Not threatened.
DESCRIPTION: Has an open crown of 15–20 palmate leaves. Trunk is covered in a net-like, tightly woven mat of brown fibres. Leaves are silvery white on the undersurface.
CULTIVATION: Seed germinates sporadically after 4 months or more. Requires shade in juvenile stage.

Coccothrinax crinita

COMMON NAME: Old man palm, mat palm.
SIZE: Solitary trunk, up to 10 m (33 ft) tall.
HABITAT: Serpentine soils on prairies or open mountain areas.
DISTRIBUTION: Endemic to Cuba.
CONSERVATION STATUS: Subspecies *crinata* is endangered, ssp. *brevicrinis* is rare.
DESCRIPTION: Palmate leaves are deeply divided into numerous segments, grey-green on undersurface. A characteristic of this species is the trunk covering of elongate fibrous strands from the leaf sheaths. These form a thick, light brown hair-like mat.
CULTIVATION: A garden ornamental that can withstand full sun.

Coccothrinax barbadensis

Coccothrinax miraguama

Coccothrinax miraguama

syn. *Coccothrinax accuminata, C. miraguano, C. yuraguana*
COMMON NAME: Miraguama.
SIZE: Solitary trunk, 4–6 m (13–20 ft) tall and 8–13 cm (3–5 in) in diameter.
HABITAT: Savanna and serpentine rocky hills.
DISTRIBUTION: Cuba.
CONSERVATION STATUS: Not threatened.
DESCRIPTION: Trunk is covered in a fine fibrous mesh when young, but later is clean and bare. Has about 30 palmate leaves in the open crown, deeply divided into numerous segments which are greyish on the undersurface. Several subspecies have been described due to variations in floral and leaf morphology.

Coccothrinax crinita

Cocos

'kō-kŏs

Cocos is a monotypic genus, with one widely-cultivated species. *Cocos nucifera*, the coconut palm, is the botanical symbol of the tropics. The origin of the coconut is probably the west Pacific, but this is uncertain since the palm has spread and been cultivated in the tropics and subtropics, and has become naturalised in many coastal areas. It is usually regarded as a strand (seaside) plant. However, it will grow and fruit in humid equatorial regions at altitudes up to 900 m (3000 ft).

Fruit have a smooth epicarp (the outer skin), fibrous mesocarp (the husk) and hard woody endocarp (the shell). The seed has a narrow layer of edible endosperm (the flesh) and a large central cavity partially filled with fluid (the coconut milk).

Dwarf varieties have become a popular selection for plantations because they simplify harvesting. Coconuts can withstand severe bad weather in coastal locations. Coconut products are a major commodity of trade throughout the world. They also provide a primary source of shelter, food and drink, and utensils to millions of people in the tropics.

Cocos nucifera

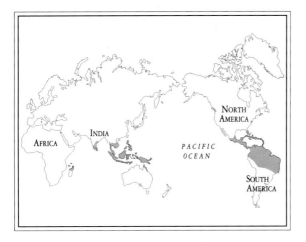

Cocos nucifera

Cocos nucifera

COMMON NAME: Coconut, coco palm.
SIZE: Single-trunked, up to 30 m (100 ft) tall.
HABITAT: Seaside locations.
DISTRIBUTION: Tropical and subtropical regions.
CONSERVATION STATUS: Not threatened.
DESCRIPTION: Pinnate leaves are about 5 m (16 ft) long, leaflets regularly arranged, numerous, and tapering to a split tip. Inflorescences are simple-branched, and arise among the leaves. Has 2 bracts, the upper one large, boat-shaped and woody. They enclose the inflorescence in bud. Fruit are large, green to brown to yellow, ovoid to ellipsoidal and 3-angled.
CULTIVATION: Many varieties are grown in the tropics and subtropics.

COPERNICIA

kŏp-ĕr-'nĭss-ē-à

Copernicia has 25 described species of handsome fan palms, three from the South American continent, two from Hispaniola (Haiti and the Dominican Republic) and the remainder endemic to Cuba. Many of the Cuban species also have adjoining localities and may have hybridised. Their natural habitats vary from open dry savanna or woodlands at relatively low elevations to areas subject to seasonal flooding.

With moderate to tall solitary trunks, these palms have large palmate to costapalmate leaves with the petiole sometimes short or absent. The stems are covered with persistent leaf sheaths or persistent dead leaves. Generally the trunk becomes bare with age. The leaf blades are round or wedge-shaped, divided (to approximately one quarter to one third) into folded pointed segments, the tips of which are bifid. The leaf surface may have a wax coating. In *Copernicia prunifera*, this wax is of economic importance and is processed to make the high quality carnauba wax. Inflorescences are well branched, arise among the leaves, are enclosed in a protective bract that persists after flowering, and usually extend beyond the leaves. Flowers are bisexual and fruit is ovoid or spherical.

The leaves are used for thatch and weaving, the trunk wood for fencing and building, and leaf fibre is used for making rope and brushes. The growth rate of these tropical palms is very slow, but as ornamentals they are interesting garden subjects, and some are strikingly unusual. Established plants usually tolerate seasonal drought. They can be planted as seedlings in open sunny locations.

Copernicia baileyana

Copernicia baileyana

Copernicia baileyana

COMMON NAME: Yarey.
SIZE: Large solitary trunk, 10–15 m (33–50 ft) tall and 66 cm (26 in) in diameter.
HABITAT: Savannas and woodlands.
DISTRIBUTION: Endemic to Cuba.
CONSERVATION STATUS: Not threatened.
DESCRIPTION: Thick trunk may be spindle shaped. Has persistent leaf and petiole bases in young trees only. Has large rigid, waxy, palmate leaves, over 1.6 m (5 ft) broad and deeply divided into more than 100 segments. Relatively short petioles are up to 1.3 m (4 ft) with the petiole base broad and sheathing around the trunk. Inflorescences are about 3 m (10 ft) long and densely tomentose. Fruit are round to ovoid, about 2 cm (0.8 in) long.

Copernicia berteroana

COMMON NAME: Yarey.
SIZE: Small to medium slender trunk, 4–5 m (13–16 ft) tall.
HABITAT: Lowland dry areas.
DISTRIBUTION: Endemic to the Dominican Republic.
CONSERVATION STATUS: Indeterminate.
DESCRIPTION: Petiole is up to about 90 cm (3 ft) long, usually waxy and with small spiny teeth along the margins. Sheathing leaf bases persist only on young trees. Circular leaf blades are over 1 m (3.3 ft) wide, deeply divided into about 90–100 segments, but not waxy on the upper surface and only lightly so on the undersurface. Has woolly hairs on the basal portion of the leaf blade. Inflorescences are densely tomentose and about 2 m (6.5 ft) long. Fruit are ovoid, about 2 cm (0.8 in) long.

Copernicia macroglossa

syn. *Copernicia torreana*
COMMON NAME: Cuban petticoat palm.
SIZE: Solitary trunk, up to 7 m (23 ft) tall.
HABITAT: Hilly regions and savannas.
DISTRIBUTION: Endemic to Cuba.
CONSERVATION STATUS: Not threatened.
DESCRIPTION: Trunk is covered with a large skirt of persistent dead leaves immediately below the dense crown of leaves. Species is unusual in having no petiole to its leaf, while the wide base of the leaf sheathes around the trunk. Leaves are wedge-shaped with the rounded outer edge shallowly divided into about 60 segments. Inflorescences are usually over 2 m (6.5 ft) long and densely tomentose. Fruit are ovoid, about 2 cm (0.8 in) long.

Copernicia berteroana

Copernicia prunifera

Copernicia prunifera

syn. *Copernicia cerifera, Corypha cerifera*
COMMON NAME: Carnauba, carnauba wax palm.
SIZE: Solitary slender trunk, 10–15 m (33–50 ft) tall.
HABITAT: Banks of rivers and streams and the borders of shallow lake basins.
DISTRIBUTION: Northeastern Brazil.
CONSERVATION STATUS: Not threatened.
DESCRIPTION: Older trunks are clean, with distinctive leaf scars. In young plants, the sheathing petiole bases persist. Spiny petiole over 1 m (3.3 ft) long. Leaf blades are circular and deeply divided into about 40–60 segments. Leaves densely waxy on both surfaces. Inflorescences are often over 2 m (6.5 ft) long and covered with a dense tomentum. Fruit are ovoid, up to 2.7 cm (1 in) long.
CULTIVATION: A commercially-significant palm for its wax. Carnauba wax is as an ingredient in polish, candles, cardboard and lipstick.

Copernicia macroglossa

CORYPHA

kŏr-'ē-fà

Corypha has eight species (perhaps less), and they are the largest palms of all. *Corypha utan*, or gebang, and *Corypha umbraculifera*, or talipot palm, are probably the best known in the genus and the most useful to humans. *Corypha* palms are distributed widely in the tropics, from southern India and Sri Lanka, across Southeast Asia and south to New Guinea and northern Australia. Usually found at low altitudes on open plains or in forest areas subject to monsoonal flooding, they can occur as scattered individuals or as dense stands. In Asia, they are often associated with human settlement and play an important role in providing raw materials for making thatch, baskets, umbrellas, hats, string and many other items. They also provide food in the form of starch from the stem pith, an alcoholic beverage from the fermented sugary sap, edible seed and edible leaf 'cabbage' from the pre-emergent leaf.

The trunks are massive, solitary and erect, and older trees are closely ringed with leaf scars. Young trees often display the leaf bases and petiole bases in a regular pattern, the leaf bases split just below the petiole. Leaves have massive, costapalmate blades and thick, long petioles, toothed along the margins. The leaves have a well-developed hastula on the upper surface, and the blades are divided (to about halfway) into single-fold segments. There are fine filaments between the segments in young plants. The well-developed costa often gives a distinctive twisting curve to the leaf blade. The inflorescence, which develops only after vegetative growth ceases, is an enormous terminal panicle containing literally millions of bisexual flowers. It develops from the apex of the tree and has a thick central stem which is an extension of the trunk. From this central stem several secondary branches are derived, which then branch again and again. The panicle thus contains thousands of rachillae. The whole inflorescence can be 7 m (23 ft) tall, covered in creamy-white flowers and developing approximately a quarter of a million round, single-seeded, fleshy fruit. *Corypha* palms are monocarpic, the tree dying after flowering and fruiting has been completed.

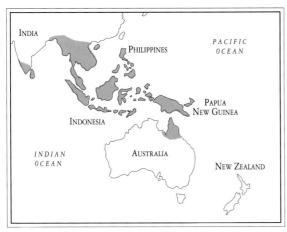

Corypha taliera

Corypha umbraculifera

COMMON NAME: Talipot palm.

SIZE: Large solitary trunk, up to 25 m (82 ft) tall, 60–90 cm (2–3 ft) in diameter.

HABITAT: Original habitat unknown, widely cultivated in India and Sri Lanka.

DISTRIBUTION: South India, Sri Lanka.

CONSERVATION STATUS: Known only in cultivation or semi-wild near human settlement.

DESCRIPTION: Closely ringed trunk, but with no obvious spiral pattern. Petiole is about 2 m (6.5 ft) or more long, with 2 auricles at the base. Leaf blades are massive, about 2 m (6.5 ft) long and 2.5 m (8 ft) wide, divided to about one third their depth into segments that are split at the apex. The inflorescence is an enormous panicle about 6 m (20 ft) tall with cream-coloured, plume-like flowering branches. Fruit are green-brown, round, 3–5 cm (1.2–2 in) in diameter.

CULTIVATION: Represented in Asian botanical garden collections. Was used in the past to provide a lasting writing paper for important documents. Tropical, slow growing.

Corypha utan: before forming a trunk.

Corypha umbraculifera: with a terminal inflorescence of cream-coloured flowers.

Corypha utan

syn. *Corypha elata*

COMMON NAME: Gebang, buri.

SIZE: Solitary trunk, up to 25 m (82 ft) tall, 35–100 cm (14–40 in) in diameter.

HABITAT: Lowland monsoonal forests and plains. Absent from equatorial, continuously wet areas. Often associated with human settlement.

DISTRIBUTION: Widely distributed from northern Australia, Indonesia, New Guinea, Southeast Asia to India.

CONSERVATION STATUS: Vulnerable in Peninsular Malaysia, not threatened elsewhere.

DESCRIPTION: Closely ringed trunk in a spiral pattern. Petiole 3–4 m (10–13 ft) long, armed with irregular teeth. Leaf blades are massive, more or less round, about 2–3 m (6.5–10 ft) across, divided (to about halfway or more) into numerous pointed segments. The inflorescence is an enormous panicle about 7 m (23 ft) tall with green to cream-coloured, plume-like flowering branches exuding a strong odour. Fruit are green, round, 2.5 cm (1 in) in diameter.

CULTIVATION: This tropical, slow-growing palm can take 20 years before a trunk develops. Seed germinates sporadically, but has long viability.

CYRTOSTACHYS

sĕr-tō-'stăk-ēs

Cyrtostachys is a genus comprised of about eight species, perhaps more, distributed in the Malay Peninsula, Sumatra, Borneo, New Guinea and across to the Solomon Islands. Only one, *Cyrtostachys renda*, is widely cultivated. Most species are found in lowland rainforest as undergrowth or canopy palms from sea level to 500 m (1600 ft) altitudes.

Solitary or clustering, *Cyrtostachys* may be moderate-sized or tall, the trunk ringed with leaf scars. Leaves are pinnate, their sheathing leaf bases forming a well-defined crownshaft. Petioles and leaf bases are glabrous or scaly. Leaflets are regularly arranged, stiff and ascending, sometimes drooping, with pointed tips. Inflorescences are below the crownshaft, are well branched and spreading, but completely enclosed in two bracts in the bud stage. Flowers are arranged spirally on the rachillae and are borne in triads. Rachillae are often brightly coloured. Fruit is ellipsoidal, black or dark purple, smooth-skinned and has one seed.

C. renda, the sealing-wax palm, is seen in the gardens and along the roadsides of Singapore and Malaysia. A difficult palm to cultivate outside its natural climate.

Cyrtostachys renda

Cyrtostachys renda

syn. *Cyrtostachys lakka*

COMMON NAME: Sealing wax palm, lipstick palm, pinang raja (Malaysia).
SIZE: Clumping, 3–5 m (10–16 ft) tall, sometimes 10 m (33 ft) or more, 5–7 cm (2–3 in) in diameter.
HABITAT: Lowland peat swamp forests.
DISTRIBUTION: Peninsular Malaysia, southern Thailand, Borneo, Sumatra.
CONSERVATION STATUS: Not threatened except in Sumatra and Kalimantan (Indonesian Borneo), where it is rare.
DESCRIPTION: Often has long stolons running along the ground. Leaves are about 1.5 m (5 ft) long, dark green above, paler beneath. Leaflets are held stiffly erect. Petioles and leaf bases are red. Fruit are ellipsoid with a narrow tip, black, and around 1 cm (0.4 in) long.
CULTIVATION: Propagated from suckers, stolons or seed. Slow growing. Requires a tropical moist climate free of cold nights and a consistent water supply. Soil should be neutral to slightly acid, and rich in humus. Easily suffers leaf damage in dryness, cold and winds.

Cyrtostachys renda

DICTYOSPERMA
'dĭk-tē-ō-ˌspĕrm-à

D*ictyosperma* is a monotypic genus, with *Dictyosperma album* being the sole representative. Since it is a variable species, several varieties have been described. Although nearly extinct in its natural habitat on the Mascarene Islands (from sea level to 600 m (2000 ft) or more), the princess palm, as it is known, is widely cultivated on these islands and elsewhere.

D. album is single-stemmed with a stout, dark grey to brown ringed trunk. It can be up to 15 m (50 ft) tall, but is usually shorter. The crown of pinnate leaves is fairly compact and individual leaves curve and twist, the newly-emergent but unopened leaf standing erect and tall. The slightly swollen crownshaft formed from the sheathing leaf bases may be green or brownish-green, whitish-green or white. Petioles are short, a similar colour to the crownshaft, and the leaf blades are up to approximately 3 m (10 ft) long. Leaflets are regularly arranged, closely spaced, and tapering to a point, sometimes split at the apex. Inflorescences arise below the crownshaft and several may be present at the one time. They are simply branched and enclosed in two bracts in the bud stage, the bracts falling once the inflorescence has matured. Flowers are borne in triads of one female and two male flowers, with male flowers dominating the outer portions of the rachillae. Fruit is ovoid to ovoid-ellipsoid, approximately 1.5 cm (0.6 in) long, smooth-skinned, black or purplish at maturity and has one seed.

Cultivated from the tropics to warm temperate zones, the princess palm is a popular ornamental. A location affording protection from cold temperatures and hot drying winds is preferred, although mature plants tolerate salty coastal winds. Fresh seed germinates readily in a few months. Plants grow best in a fertile, well-drained soil with abundant water. Varieties *album, aureum* and *conjugatum* are recognised by the colouring of their crownshafts and petioles. Young plants often have attractive colouring on their leaflet veins.

Dictyosperma album

Dictyosperma album

Dictyosperma album

COMMON NAME: Princess palm.

SIZE: Single-ringed trunk, stout, up to 15 m (50 ft) tall, but usually shorter.

HABITAT: Sea level to 600 m (2000 ft).

DISTRIBUTION: Mascarene Islands.

CONSERVATION STATUS: Endangered. Close to extinction in the wild.

DESCRIPTION: The swollen crownshaft may be green or brownish-green, whitish-green or white. Petioles are short, a similar colour to the crownshaft. The leaf blades, curved and with a twist, are up to 3 m (10 ft) long. Leaflets are regularly arranged, closely-spaced, and tapering to a point, sometimes split at the apex. Inflorescences arise below the crownshaft, are simply branched and enclosed in 2 bracts in the bud stage. Fruit are ovoid to ovoid-ellipsoid, about 1.5 cm (0.6 in) long, smooth-skinned, and black or purplish.

CULTIVATION: Tropics to warm temperate climates are suitable.

DYPSIS

'dip-sis

Dypsis palms are small, slender-stemmed palms from the rainforests of Madagascar. There are 21 species presently recognised, some quite exquisite with their dainty leaves. Habitats vary from the lowlands to mountain forests. Most *Dypsis* have narrow reed-like stems, which have been used by local people to make blowpipes. The *Dypsis* genus is closely related to *Chrysalidocarpus, Neodypsis, Vonitra* and *Phloga*. It is treated here as a separate genus, but will probably be united with these other four genera after taxonomic revision.

Dypsis species are small to moderate, clumping or solitary palms. All are without spines. A few species have a distinct crownshaft formed from the tubular leaf bases. Leaves are few and can be simple and bi-lobed, or pinnate with anything from a few to many segments. The leaflet shapes and arrangements vary from species to species. Some, like *Dypsis pinnatifrons*, have elegantly-arranged leaflets in groups. The inflorescence may be branched or unbranched, arises among the leaves and carries very small male and female flowers in triads. There are three subgenera separated because of differences in the male flowers. Fruit are small, ovoid to narrowly spindle-shaped, and red when ripe.

Dypsis palms are appreciated for their delicate beauty, but are not widely available to date. Seeds are said to germinate readily within two months. A warm moist environment with fertile, well-drained soil would be required.

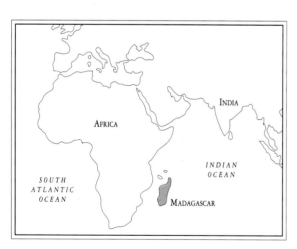

Dypsis hildebrandtii

Dypsis hildebrandtii

syn. *Trichodypsis hildebrandtii*

COMMON NAME: Tsirika.

SIZE: A dwarf, clumping palm, rarely exceeding 1 m (3.3 ft) tall.

HABITAT: Rainforest understorey in areas from 500–2000 m (1600–6500 ft).

DISTRIBUTION: Endemic to Madagascar.

CONSERVATION STATUS: Rare.

DESCRIPTION: Several slender stems in a clump. Has 4–10 leaves on each stem. Leaves usually 20–30 cm (8–12 in) long. Petiole 1–3 cm (0.4–1.2 in) long. Leaflets are sometimes bifid, or irregularly paired on each side of the rachis, sometimes in groups of 2 or, rarely, 3. Leaflets are slightly pleated with toothed ends, and the apical pair are joined. Fruit are narrowly oblong in shape, 1.1 cm (0.4 in) long and red when ripe.

CULTIVATION: This small ornamental requires tropical conditions and shade.

Dypsis hildebrandtii

Dypsis pinnatifrons

Dypsis pinnatifrons

syn. *Dypsis gracilis*

COMMON NAME: Lafa, hova, ambolo.

SIZE: Slender clustering or single stems, 1–8 m (3.3–26 ft) high.

HABITAT: Understorey to midstorey plant of rainforests up to 1400 m (4600 ft) altitude.

DISTRIBUTION: Endemic to Madagascar.

CONSERVATION STATUS: Rare.

DESCRIPTION: Stems 2–12 cm (0.8–5 in) thick. Pinnate leaves are about 1.3 m (4 ft) long with a reddish, downy tomentum on the tubular leaf sheaths and short petioles. The broad lanceolate leaflets are arranged in groups of 2–5 along the rachis. The branched inflorescence arises among the leaves. Fruit are oblong, 1.5 cm (0.6 in) long and red when ripe. Distinguished from *Phloga nodifera* on floral and fruit structure.

CULTIVATION: Requires a moist tropical climate with shade. Stems have been used in the making of blowpipes.

ELAEIS

'ē-lē-is

Elaeis has two species, the African oil palm, *Elaeis guineensis*, being the more important species commercially. *E. oleifera*, the American oil palm, a native of Central America and northern South America, has a creeping habit with its solitary trunk growing across or under the ground before turning upright and growing vertically for about 2–4 m (6.5–13 ft). Like its African cousin, it produces an oily fruit, which is crushed to extract edible oil. The African species is an upright grower, and has become a major plantation crop in Asia and Africa, overtaking the coconut as a commercial source of edible oil.

In tropical Africa, *E. guineensis* is found naturally in damp but not waterlogged alluvial soils along watercourses and is widespread on the edges of tropical rainforests. In the New World, *E. oleifera* is also found on damp, poorly-drained soils, the locations variously being in savannas, palm swamps and mangrove swamps. Malaysia and Indonesia have greatly increased their plantation areas of *E. guineensis* in recent years, so that palm oil is now the most important edible oil in world trade. One-third of the cultivated area of Malaysia is under the African oil palm. The best climatic conditions for plantation growing are within 10° of the equator. Although they will grow in tropical locations outside these limits, crop yield is reduced. Tissue culture and genetic engineering are being used to develop more productive strains and the American oil palm is being incorporated in this research.

Trunks of *Elaeis* are solitary and covered with persistent leaf bases. Mature trees have a dense crown of 30–50 pinnate leaves. The leaf sheath is tubular at first, later breaking down into a mass of fibres, those near the petiole being very spiny. The petiole is edged with fibrous spines. Leaflets are numerous, tapering to a point, and regularly arranged or slightly grouped. They arise in different planes, giving a plumose appearance to the leaf. Inflorescences are simple-branched, arise in the leaf axils of each leaf and are male or female, both types appearing on the same tree. In the bud stage, the inflorescences are enclosed in two protective bracts.

Elaeis guineensis

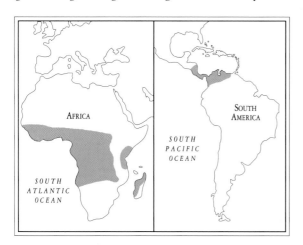

Occasionally an aberrant inflorescence will carry both male and female flowers. Pollination is by insect vector rather than wind. Male inflorescences have closely-bunched catkin-like rachillae bearing 600–1500 flowers. Female inflorescences have more numerous rachillae, each bearing 10–20 flowers. Each fertilised female flower produces one fruit which ripens over six months. One bunch contains a few hundred to a few thousand fruit. Fruit are more or less ovoid, smooth-skinned and orange-yellow in colour. The fleshy mesocarp is very oily and the seed (kernel) also contains oil.

For plantation growing of *E. guineensis*, seed at 17% moisture content is heated to 39°C for several weeks to break dormancy. After soaking in water, germination should begin within five days and be completed after 30 days. Seedlings of *E. guineensis*, planted at about 12 months old, take only two years to start producing fruit and six years for the bunch size to be large. Their productive life is about 25 years, although they will continue to produce reduced yields for about 50 years. On average, 8–15 fruit bunches are produced each year from each tree, with each bunch weighing from about 25–50 kg (55–110 lb). The oil extracted from each bunch is about 23% by weight. Yields are an enormous 10–30 tonnes of fresh fruit bunches per hectare per year. Thus it is not unusual for one hectare to yield five tonnes of crude oil per year. The uses for palm oil grow as palm oil technology and research grows. Most of the oil is used in food, principally in cooking oil, margarines, shortenings, vegetable ghee. However, other, non-edible uses include candle-making, soaps, lubricating greases and as epoxidised stabilisers in plastic and rubber products.

Elaeis guineensis

COMMON NAME: African oil palm.
SIZE: Solitary erect trunk, up to 20 m (66 ft) tall, 30–60 cm (1–2 ft) in diameter.
HABITAT: Damp alluvial soils along watercourses and on the margins of tropical rainforests.
DISTRIBUTION: Tropical western and central Africa, perhaps introduced into Madagascar.
CONSERVATION STATUS: Unknown in the wild. Widely cultivated.
DESCRIPTION: Petioles are about 1 m (3.3 ft) long, rachis 3 m (10 ft) long. Leaflets are grouped and arise in different planes, giving a plumose appearance. Inflorescences are short and dense, with fruit crowded in a bunch. Fruit are ovoid, orange-yellow, 3–4 cm (1.2–1.6 in) long.
CULTIVATION: In a tropical climate, plants will respond with rapid growth to an abundant water supply and added fertiliser.

Elaeis oleifera: in various stages of flowering and fruiting.

Elaeis guineensis

Elaeis oleifera

syn. *Corozo oleifera*
COMMON NAME: American oil palm.
SIZE: Solitary creeping trunk, 2–4 m (6.5–13 ft) tall.
HABITAT: Wet sandy soils in savannas, and in palm swamps and mangrove swamps.
DISTRIBUTION: Costa Rica to the lower Amazon River in Brazil.
CONSERVATION STATUS: Vulnerable.
DESCRIPTION: Petioles are around 1.5 m (5 ft) long, rachis 3 m (10 ft) long. Leaflets are regularly arranged and arise in the same plane. Inflorescences are short and dense, with fruit crowded in a bunch. Fruit are ovoid, orange-yellow, 2–3 cm (0.8–1.2 in) long.
CULTIVATION: In a tropical climate, plants will respond with rapid growth to an abundant water supply and added fertiliser.

EUTERPE

ēn-'tĕr-pē

Euterpe, which has recently grown through the inclusion of the genus *Prestoea*, has over 50 species. Distributed from the West Indies to Central America and South America (to Brazil and Peru), *Euterpe* shows a wide altitudinal range, some inhabiting lowland rainforests and swamps, while others are found on the high slopes of montane rainforest at over 3000 m (10 000 ft).

Solitary or clustering, *Euterpe* palms are small to large, the ringed trunk usually having a prominent crownshaft composed of elongate, tubular, sheathing leaf bases. Leaves are regularly pinnate with many narrow, lanceolate, pointed leaflets which tend to droop somewhat in a similar manner to *Howea forsteriana* or *Rhopaloblaste ceramica*. The arching leaves and pendant leaflets are characteristic of the genus. Inflorescences are simple-branched, arise among the leaves and are enclosed in bud by two bracts. By the time the bracts open and the inflorescence emerges, the leaf has fallen and the inflorescence is positioned below the crownshaft. Flowers are borne spirally in triads, one female flower between two male flowers, and the inflorescence branches are covered in a downy tomentum. Fruit are almost globose, smooth skinned and have one seed.

Euterpe palms are particularly useful to humans, the 'cabbage' being succulent and the main source of 'heart of palm' in the Americas. *Euterpe oleracea*, the açaí or assai palm, is cultivated widely in and around villages of the Amazon estuary of Brazil, where it supports a large palm heart industry. Its fruit are also used in making popular drinks and in flavouring ice creams.

Overexploitation of natural stands of the solitary-stemmed *E. edulis* has brought attention to the urgent need to manage natural palm groves and to bring new plants into cultivation. Fruits and unopened inflorescences are also edible. Trunk wood is used as a building material and leaves are used for thatch. The high altitude species are adaptable to subtropical and warm temperate climates, but generally do not tolerate frost.

Euterpe edulis

NORTH
ATLANTIC
OCEAN

SOUTH AMERICA

SOUTH PACIFIC
OCEAN

SOUTH
ATLANTIC
OCEAN

Euterpe edulis

Euterpe edulis

COMMON NAME: Assai palm.

SIZE: Solitary trunk, up to 33 m (100 ft) tall and 15 cm (6 in) or more in diameter.

HABITAT: Swampy ground in rainforests.

DISTRIBUTION: Brazil.

CONSERVATION STATUS: Vulnerable.

DESCRIPTION: Leaves are up to about 3 m (10 ft) long, the blade with about 70–80 leaflets each side of the rachis. Smooth olive green crownshaft is up to about 1.5 m (5 ft) long. Inflorescences are below the crownshaft, simple-branched, and with many rachillae. Fruit are dark purple.

CULTIVATION: Edible fruit and 'cabbage'. Overexploited in the wild. This tropical to subtropical ornamental requires high humidity and high temperatures for rapid growth.

GEONOMA

jē-ŏ-ˈnō-mȧ

Geonoma is a large genus of about 75 or more species, all rainforest understorey palms. There is an extensive range from southern Mexico, through Central America to southeastern Brazil and Paraguay. The centre of diversity appears to be western Colombia and adjacent Central America. *Geonoma* palms have a definite preference for tropical and montane rainforests with a wide altitudinal range. No species is found where annual rainfall is less than 1000 mm (40 in), and most occur where rainfall is 2000–5000 mm (80–200 in) annually.

Clumping or solitary, *Geonoma* species range from small to moderate size, sometimes with very short creeping or subterranean stems, sometimes with reed-like or tall erect cane-like stems. The leaf sheaths are thin, and split opposite the petiole. They eventually fall off in stemmed species to reveal a ringed stem. Leaves may be entire and bifid, or pinnate and regularly or irregularly divided. Inflorescence may arise among or below the leaves, may be spicate or simple-branched and carry both male and female flowers. The inflorescence is enclosed in bud by two or more bracts. Fruit is more or less globose, usually with a pointed apex. It is green, brown or purple-black when ripe and is often borne on bright-coloured branches. Some species are used for the edible 'cabbage', some for thatch. Many are potentially good ornamental plants with some hardiness to cool climates.

Geonoma longivaginata

Geonoma acaulis

COMMON NAME: None known.
SIZE: Acaulescent, variable size, leaves about 70–120 cm (28 in–4 ft) long.
HABITAT: Dense flood-free rainforest.
DISTRIBUTION: Western Amazon basin to the foot of the Andes — Colombia, Peru, Brazil.
CONSERVATION STATUS: Unknown.
DESCRIPTION: Pinnate leaves usually have 3–8 pairs of unequal segments, each more or less sigmoid in shape, narrowed at the base and tapering to a point at the apex. Apical segments are about 10–20 cm (4–8 in) long. Spicate inflorescence is 7–20 cm (3–8 in) long on a short peduncle. Fruit are almost globose, with a pointed apex, about 0.7 cm (0.3 in) long.

Geonoma acaulis

Geonoma longivaginata

COMMON NAME: None known.
SIZE: Clustering, 3–5 m (10–16 ft) tall, stems approximately 3 cm (1.2 in) in diameter.
HABITAT: Rainforest at low altitude.
DISTRIBUTION: Costa Rica.
CONSERVATION STATUS: Vulnerable.
DESCRIPTION: Petiole up to 70 cm (28 in) long. Leaf blade is more than 1 m (3.3 ft) long, about 70 cm (28 in) wide and irregularly pinnate. Leaflets are unequal and slightly falcate, variable in number, underside lighter than upper surface and brownish. Inflorescence is simple-branched, up to 30 cm (12 in) long. Fruit are subglobose, slightly pointed at the apex, and about 0.7 cm (0.3 in) long.

Geonoma longivaginata

Geonoma cuneata

syn. *Geonoma decurrens*
COMMON NAME: None known.
SIZE: Clustering, 0.5–2 m (20 in–6.5 ft) tall, stems 3–4 cm (1.2–1.6 in) in diameter.
HABITAT: Dense rainforests at low altitude.
DISTRIBUTION: Central America and adjacent northwestern South America: from Nicaragua to Colombia.
CONSERVATION STATUS: Vulnerable in Costa Rica and Panama, status unknown elsewhere.
DESCRIPTION: Petiole 10–25 cm (4–10 in) long. Leaf rachis is about 50 cm (20 in) long, blade entire or divided into 4–7 unequal segments. Inflorescence is spicate, 15–30 cm (6–12 in) long. Fruit are ovoid, slightly pointed, about 0.8 cm (0.3 in) long, and yellowish-green.

Geonoma cuneata

HEDYSCEPE

ˌhĕd-ē-ˈskē-pē

Hedyscepe is a monotypic genus, with *Hedyscepe canterburyana* being the sole representative. Native to Lord Howe Island, off the east coast of Australia, it is found at higher altitudes than the *Howea* palms, which are also endemic to the island. At 335–830 m (1100–2700 ft) overlooking the sea, the big mountain palms, or umbrella palms, as they are called, are emergent plants in the forests which cover the steep slopes and cliffs. They are in a stony soil of basalt origin, which is kept moist by frequent showers from low cloud cover.

Like the *Rhopalostylis* palms to which it is closely related, *Hedyscepe canterburyana* has a ringed trunk and a short prominent crownshaft. It is an attractive slow-growing palm suitable for warm temperate coastal areas. It does not tolerate frost, but withstands coastal winds well. Young leaves are easily scorched by hot sun and so require shade for best presentation.

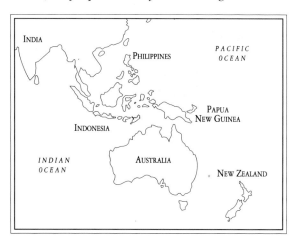

Hedyscepe canterburyana

Hedyscepe canterburyana

COMMON NAME: Big mountain palm, umbrella palm.

SIZE: Single trunk, up to 10 m (33 ft) tall in habitat. Cultivated plants attain about half this height.

HABITAT: Steep slopes and cliffs from 335–830 m (1100–2700 ft).

DISTRIBUTION: Lord Howe Island.

CONSERVATION STATUS: Vulnerable.

DESCRIPTION: Pale blue-green crownshaft is about 50 cm (20 in) long or more. Compact crown has about 8 stiffly-arched pinnate leaves, with very short and stout petioles. Has about 30 pairs of leaflets, dark green above and paler beneath. They are held erect, each tapering to a point. Inflorescence is below the crownshaft, well branched, and is enclosed by 2 papery bracts in the bud stage. Fruit are egg shaped, around 5 cm (2 in) long by 4 cm (1.6 in) wide, smooth-skinned and a dark, dull red when ripe.

CULTIVATION: Needs a warm temperate climate, does not tolerate frost.

Hedyscepe canterburyana

HETEROSPATHE

‚hĕt-ĕr-ō-'spā-thē

Heterospathe are solitary palms growing in rainforests from low to mountain elevations, sometimes remaining under and sometimes becoming part of the forest canopy. There are about 37 species of these tropical pinnate-leaved palms distributed in the Western Pacific from the Philippines, the Mariana Islands, the Caroline Islands and New Guinea to the Solomon Islands.

Ranging from dwarf to large, and occasionally clustering, *Heterospathe* have slender trunks without a crownshaft. The crown of leaves is fairly open and spreading with pendulous pinnate leaves, the newest leaf often being red or pinkish when young. Leaflets taper to a point or are abruptly pointed, with the leaf veins on the underside of the leaf tomentose or brown-dotted. Inflorescences are moderate- to well-branched panicles and arise among the leaves, but may be below the leaves by the time flowering occurs. The inflorescence in the bud stage is completely enclosed by a large bract, which may persist after the inflorescence has opened. Flowers are in triads (one female between two males) or pairs and there are single male flowers towards the outer ends of the rachillae. Fruit are one-seeded, globose to slightly elliptical, small to large, and orange to red when ripe.

Heterospathe palms are popular amongst collectors as garden plants, the newly-emerged leaves being particularly attractive. They have tropical requirements, but have been successfully grown in subtropical regions.

Heterospathe sp.

Heterospathe elata

COMMON NAME: Sagisi (Philippines).
SIZE: Solitary trunk, up to 12 m (40 ft) tall, about 20 cm (8 in) in diameter.
HABITAT: Lowland forests in moist soil.
DISTRIBUTION: Philippines, Moluccas, Guam, Palau Islands.
CONSERVATION STATUS: Unknown, probably vulnerable.
DESCRIPTION: Trunks are smooth with obscure rings. Leaves are 2–3 m (6.5–10 ft) and have a lateral twist. Petiole is 30–60 cm (1–2 ft) long with sharp margins but no spines. Inflorescence is 1–1.5 m (3.3–5 ft) long with a peduncle up to 60 cm (2 ft) long and creamish-white branches. Fruit are globose, ripen from green to white and then red, and are about 7 cm (2.8 in) in diameter.
CULTIVATION: The seed is used as a betel nut substitute in the Philippines. On some Philippine islands, the leaves are used to make sun hats. Leaf sheaths are used in basket making. Widely cultivated in the Philippines. Suitable for a tropical climate.

Heterospathe woodfordiana: the newly emergent leaf is bright red.

Heterospathe woodfordiana

COMMON NAME: Araramai (Solomon Islands).
SIZE: Solitary slender trunk, up to 3.5 m (12 ft) high.
HABITAT: Rainforest at moderate to high elevation.
DISTRIBUTION: Solomon Islands.
CONSERVATION STATUS: Unknown.
DESCRIPTION: Leaves are 2–3 m (6.5–10 ft) long with a long petiole. New leaves are deep red turning dark green. Brown and black blotches on leaf sheaths. Inflorescence is held erect. Fruit are bright red, ellipsoid, and around 1.2 cm (0.5 in) long.
CULTIVATION: A tropical climate is required.

Heterospathe woodfordiana

Heterospathe elata

HOWEA

'hŏw-ē-à

Howea palms are known in the nursery trade under the name of kentia palms. The two species are endemic to Lord Howe Island off the east coast of Australia. The more popular of the two is *Howea forsteriana*, the thatch palm, which is to date the most popular palm in the world for indoor decorative use. Its natural habitat is the lowland forest of Lord Howe Island, on sandy soils. *H. belmoreana* is found in the same localities and more abundantly at higher elevations to about 450 m (1500 ft) above sea level.

Solitary trunks of moderate height are marked with prominent rings and do not have a crownshaft. The leaf bases are well developed and wrap around the trunk, then split opposite the petiole and disintegrate into a mass of fibres. Petioles are short to moderately long. The pinnate leaf has numerous narrow, long, pointed leaflets regularly arranged. Inflorescences arise among the leaves, but are below the leaves by the time the fruit ripens. They are long arching spikes that become pendulous as they flower and fruit. The inflorescence is enclosed in the bud stage by a papery bract, which splits open and falls. The spike bears triads of flowers in a spiral arrangement. Fruit are ovoid, single-seeded, smooth-skinned, and turn from green to brown or reddish-brown as they ripen.

Plants need to be four to five years old before they demonstrate the graceful arching pinnate leaves so sought after. Both *H. forsteriana* and *H. belmoreana* are slow-growing attractive palms suitable for temperate to subtropical climates. Difficult to distinguish from each other until they are more advanced plants. *H. forsteriana* has leaflets that droop down from the rachis, while *H. belmoreana* has leaflets held erect from the rachis in an upright V-shape.

Indoor specimens tolerate cool positions and low light intensities if they are regularly refreshed by being moved outside into a shaded position. These palms are suitable as garden plants for subtropical coastal areas through to cool temperate regions. An industry has been built up on Lord Howe Island from harvesting the seed of these palms, germinating that seed in a nursery and exporting seedlings around the world. Seed germination is slow and is improved by bottom heat.

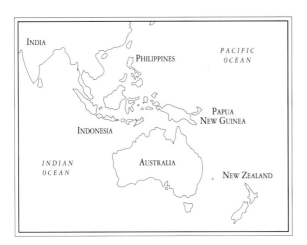

Howea belmoreana

Howea belmoreana

syn. *Kentia belmoreana*

COMMON NAME: Curly palm, sentry palm, kentia palm.

SIZE: Solitary trunk, 5–12 m (16–40 ft) tall, 10–15 cm (4–6 in) in diameter.

HABITAT: On volcanic soil up to approximately 450 m (1500 ft).

DISTRIBUTION: Lord Howe Island.

CONSERVATION STATUS: Rare.

DESCRIPTION: Leaves are 3–5 m (10–16 ft) long and strongly arching, with leaflets held in an erect V-shape. Inflorescences are single pendulous spikes. Fruit are ovoid, 2.5–3 cm (1–1.2 in) long, brown to red when ripe.

CULTIVATION: Suitable for a warm to cool temperate climate. Light frost tolerance.

Howea forsteriana on Lord Howe Island.

Howea forsteriana

syn. *Kentia forsteriana*

COMMON NAME: Kentia palm, thatch palm.

SIZE: Solitary trunk, 5–15 m (16–50 ft) tall, 8–15 cm (3.2–6 in) in diameter.

HABITAT: Lowland forest on sandy soils.

DISTRIBUTION: Lord Howe Island.

CONSERVATION STATUS: Rare.

DESCRIPTION: Leaves are 3–5 m (10–16 ft) long, with pendulous leaflets. Inflorescences are usually 3–5 pendulous spikes fused at the base. Fruit are ovoid, 3–4.5 cm (1.2–2 in) long, orange-brown to red when ripe.

CULTIVATION: Suitable for a warm to cool temperate climate. Light frost tolerance.

Howea belmoreana

HYDRIASTELE
ˌhȳ-drī-ˈăs-tĕl-ē

Hydriastele is a genus of about eight species found in New Guinea, the Bismarck Archipelago and The Australian palm *Hydriastele wendlandiana* grows in a range of situations, from swampy ground to well-drained slopes, from open to closed forest. The New Guinea species are found in rainforest at various elevations.

Hydriastele palms are small- to moderate-sized palms, most species clustering to form dense clumps with slender, conspicuously-ringed stems. Leaves are pinnate with leaflets often irregularly arranged on the rachis and sometimes in groups. Leaflets can be of unequal width with praemorse or tapering pointed tips. The terminal pair of leaflets are usually broad, often wedge-shaped and praemorse at the tips. The leaf sheaths wrap around the stem, forming a well-defined, elongate crownshaft, which is usually densely tomentose or scaly, and sometimes waxy. The inflorescence is simply branched, broom-like and arises below the crownshaft. It is enclosed in two or three large bracts in the bud stage, the bracts falling off once the inflorescence emerges. Rachillae bear flowers in triads. Fruit is one-seeded, globose to ovoid, small, and red to purplish when ripe.

Hydriastele microspadix

Hydriastele wendlandiana

COMMON NAME: None known.
SIZE: Solitary or clustering, up to 15 m (49 ft) tall but usually less, stems up to 12 cm (5 in) in diameter.
HABITAT: Open swamp woodland to well-drained slopes.
DISTRIBUTION: Northeastern Queensland and Northern Territory.
CONSERVATION STATUS: Vulnerable.
DESCRIPTION: Crown has up to 12 leaves. Has irregularly arranged pinnate leaflets, sometimes grouped, with pointed or truncate, praemorse tips.. Fruit are almost globose to slightly ovoid, up to 0.9 cm (0.4 in) long and red when ripe.
CULTIVATION: Adaptable to a wide range of situations in the tropics and subtropics. Can withstand periods of dryness. Does not like limestone soils.

Hydriastele wendlandiana

HYOPHORBE

ˌhȳ-ō-ˈfŏr-bē

Hyophorbe (syn. Mascarena) palms are endemic to the Mascarene Islands. There are five species: Rodriguez and Réunion Islands have one species each, and there are three on Mauritius and Round Islands. All species are now almost extinct in their natural habitat — forests up to about 700 m (2300 ft) above sea level, and probably also the coastal savanna. Commonly known as the bottle palm and the spindle palm (*Hyophorbe verschaffeltii*), they are handsome ornamentals highly valued in the nursery industry. Cultivated from seed (reputed to take some 5–8 months to germinate), these palms make good garden specimens in open sunny locations. They also appear to tolerate the salty winds in coastal areas quite well.

Solitary, moderate-sized palms, their trunk is of particular interest in some species for its swollen appearance (thus the common names). Leaves are pinnate with the sheathing leaf bases forming a prominent crownshaft. The inflorescence is a well-branched panicle, but is hornlike and erect in bud when it is enclosed by several bracts. Both male and female flowers are borne on the same inflorescence, in groups with one female flower surrounded by several male flowers. Flowers and fruit vary in colour with the species, and the floral characteristics are used to distinguish one species from another.

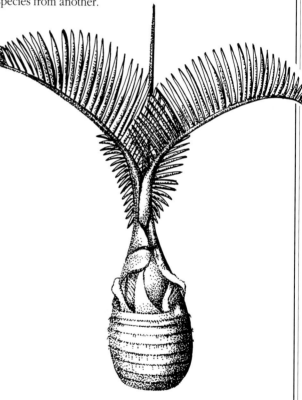

Hyophorbe lagenicaulis

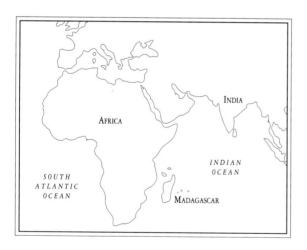

Hyophorbe lagenicaulis

syn. *Mascarena lagenicaulis, M. revaughanii*

COMMON NAME: Bottle palm.

SIZE: Solitary trunk, up to 6 m (20 ft) tall, but generally shorter. Bottle-shaped, with the thickest part often being 40–70 cm (16–28 in) in diameter.

HABITAT: Uncertain. Surviving specimens are in an open area of exposed rocks.

DISTRIBUTION: Round Island (Mascarene Islands).

CONSERVATION STATUS: Almost extinct in the wild. Only about 15 individuals on Round Island surviving.

DESCRIPTION: Usually 5–6 pinnate leaves that have a prominent twist. Inflorescence is horn-like and erect in bud, branched and bearing cream to yellow flowers. Fruit are ovoid, 1.8–2 cm (0.7–0.8 in) long and variously black to purple to orange when ripe.

CULTIVATION: Tropical climates are best as this palm is sensitive to cold.

Hyophorbe verschaffeltii

Hyophorbe lagenicaulis

Hyophorbe verschaffeltii

syn. *Mascarena verschaffeltii*

COMMON NAME: Spindle palm.

SIZE: Prominently-ringed, stout, solitary trunk, up to 5 m (16 ft) or more tall and approximately 25 cm (10 in) in diameter, variable in shape but often narrower at the base and below the crownshaft than in the middle region.

HABITAT: Volcanic soils of about 300 m (1000 ft) elevation and calcarenite limestone near sea level.

DISTRIBUTION: Endemic to Rodriguez Island (Mascarene Islands).

CONSERVATION STATUS: Almost extinct in the wild.

DESCRIPTION: Trunk appears triangular in its juvenile period and covered in sheathing leaf bases. Usually has 6–10 leaves, pinnate and strongly arching. Leaflets arise in different planes, giving a plumose appearance to the leaf. Inflorescence is horn-like and erect in bud, branched and bearing green to creamy yellow fragrant flowers. Fruit are oblong, 1.2–1.9 cm (0.5–0.8 in) long, black at maturity.

CULTIVATION: Exhibits some cold tolerance. Likes a sunny position.

HYPHAENE

hȳ-ʃē-nē

Hyphaene are commonly called doum palms. There have been many botanical descriptions of these palms, but they probably relate to only about ten species. They all have costapalmate leaves and frequently exhibit a characteristic dichotomous branching. Distribution is in southern and eastern Africa, Madagascar, around the Red Sea, coastal Arabia and the west coast of India. Found in arid and semi-arid climates, they grow naturally in areas where the water supply is poor or only seasonal. Thus they are usually found growing along coastal sand dunes, in seasonal watercourses and oases, or inland in the sandy soil of open dry plains. They are useful species to humans, their leaves being used for thatch, cordage and weaving, their wood for building, their young fruit as a food, and their sap for making an alcoholic beverage.

Hyphaene is a genus of variable palms in terms of their growth habit. *Hyphaene coriacea*, for example, can be densely clustering and can exhibit almost no trunk when growing on a sandy, infertile soil, whereas it will grow to a tall, branched tree on a fertile soil which retains more water. Fruit shape is similarly variable within species and appears to depend on the growing location of the palms. In general, *Hyphaene* palms have costapalmate leaves divided (to about one third their depth) into single-fold segments and usually with thread-like filaments hanging between the segments. There is a well-developed hastula on the underside of the leaf, but none on the upperside. The leaf blades are usually a silvery green with both surfaces covered with whitish wax. Petioles are long and thick with upward-pointing teeth along the margins. Leaf sheaths develop a split just below the petiole. Dead leaves and leaf bases eventually fall off, revealing a closely-ringed trunk. Inflorescences arise among the leaves and are moderately branched. *Hyphaene* palms are dioecious. Male flowers are in small groups of three, while female flowers are arranged singly. Each fruit is borne on a pedicel and usually has only one seed, but can have two or three. Fruit are large, very variable in shape, usually asymmetrical, and the smooth epicarp can be various shades of brown.

Seed germination can be assisted by removing the outer fibrous layer around the seed and placing the seed in a well-ventilated, moist environment where it will receive heat. The root system is vigorous and requires a well-drained medium. Plants will apparently take full sun at all stages.

Hyphaene coriacea

Hyphaene compressa

syn. *Hyphaene multiformis, H. incoje, H. kilvaensis, H. megacarpa, H. semiplaena*

COMMON NAME: Elala palm.

SIZE: Massive tree, up to 20 m (66 ft) tall, with trunks branching from ground level. Trunks are approximately 40 cm (16 in) in diameter at the base.

HABITAT: Coastal lowland and along the margins of watercourses.

DISTRIBUTION: Somalia to Mozambique.

CONSERVATION STATUS: Not threatened.

DESCRIPTION: Each trunk branches dichotomously 4–5 times, the trunk reducing in diameter each time until it is about 20 cm (8 in) below the crown. Usually has 16–32 crowns in total, each with about 15 leaves. Petiole is 0.8–1.2 m (32–48 in) long, with marginal teeth up to 2 cm (0.8 in) long. Leaf blade is strongly costapalmate, about 1.2 m (4 ft) across, divided (to about two thirds depth) into about 30 segments. It has a waxy surface and scattered black scales. Fruit are orange-brown to chestnut, usually 7–10 cm by 5–8 cm (2.8–4 in by 2–3.2 in), and extremely variable in shape. Usually have 2 depressed, flattened or sunken lateral faces, a dimpled epicarp, and an aromatic mesocarp.

Hyphaene compressa

Hyphaene coriacea

syn. *Hyphaene natalensis, H. turbinata, H. wendlandii, H. schatan, H. hildebrandtii, H. sphaerulifera, H. pyrifera, H. pleuropoda, H. parvula, H. pileata, H. tetragonoides.*

COMMON NAME: Doum palm, elala palm.

SIZE: Occasionally solitary, usually clustering, forming shrubby thickets up to about 5 m (16 ft) tall and up to 25 cm (10 in) in diameter.

HABITAT: Coastal regions on sand dunes where it stabilises the sand. Also beside creeks and, rarely, inland.

Hyphaene coriacea

DISTRIBUTION: From South Africa (Natal) north through tropical east Africa, Somalia and across to Madagascar.

CONSERVATION STATUS: Not threatened.

DESCRIPTION: Variable in habit, usually clustering with reclining trunks, branching once or twice. Petiole is up to 70 cm (28 in) long, covered in brown scales and wax, and armed with upward-pointing black triangular teeth about 1 cm (0.4 in) long. Leaf is strongly costapalmate, covered in wax and scattered black scales, divided (to a depth of one half to three quarters) into 15–20 segments. Fruit are very variable in shape, 3–6 cm (1.2–2.4 in) long, and egg-shaped to cottage loaf-shaped. The epicarp is dull but not deeply pitted.

CULTIVATION: Leaves are used in weaving. Sap is tapped to make an aloholic beverage.

Hyphaene petersiana

syn. *Hyphaene ventricosa, H. benguellensis, H. goetzei, H. aurantiaca, H. bussei, H. plagiocarpa, H. ovata, H. obovata*

COMMON NAME: Elala palm, doum palm.

SIZE: Erect, usually solitary trunk, up to 20 m (65 ft) tall, approximately 35 cm (14 in) in diameter.

HABITAT: Inland along stream banks and areas where there is a high water table and alkaline soils.

DISTRIBUTION: South Africa, Tanzania, Zaire, Angola, Namibia.

CONSERVATION STATUS: Unknown.

DESCRIPTION: Trunk is sometimes slightly swollen (from about 10 m (33 ft) above the ground) to about 50 cm (20 in). Petiole 1–1.8 m (3.3–6 ft) long with black, upward-pointing teeth along the margins. Costapalmate leaf blade has a curved costa. Blade is 1.5–1.9 m (5–6 ft) wide, divided (to one third or one half depth) into 35–40 segments, covered with a whitish bloom and dotted with small brown-black rounded scales. Branched inflorescences are usually over 1 m (3.3 ft) long. Ripe fruit are variable in shape, but always rounded with a smooth and polished surface that has minute inconspicuous pitting.

Hyphaene petersiana

IGUANURA
ĭg-wă-'nyŭ-rà

Iguanura genus is comprised of about 18 species of small, attractive, understorey rainforest palms. Their distribution is confined to Borneo, Peninsular Malaysia, southern Thailand and Sumatra. Widespread in Peninsular Malaysia in lowland forest, dense stands can occasionally dominate the undergrowth in a particular area. Species vary in size from the minute *Iguanura palmuncula*, with leaves the size of a hand, to *I. wallichiana* var. *major,* with large undivided leaves up to 2.5 m (8 ft) tall. Some are single-stemmed, others clumping, and all have interesting leaf shapes. Usually the leaf blade is divided into broad leaflets, irregularly placed along the rachis, and with the leaf margins jagged or toothed. New leaves are often a lovely pink. In the field they are readily distinguished from other similar-looking palms from the genera of *Pinanga*, *Areca* and *Nenga* by a combination of toothed leaf margin, inflorescences arising from among the leaves (except for *I. bicornis*), deeply sunken triads of flowers, and the fruit base carrying remnants of the flower. Crownshafts are also generally absent. There are a number of subspecies and varieties described by Kiew in 1976, and a selection are chosen here.

Iguanura species are decorative additions for a tropical shade house or, in cooler climates, a heated glass house. However, they are not widely grown. Seeds reportedly lose their viability quickly if grown outside the tropics. They will need bottom heat for best germination. Seedlings grow quickly but do require warmth, high humidity, plentiful water and good light.

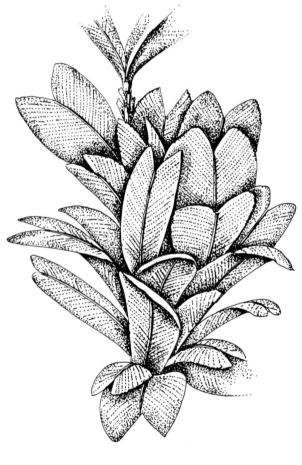

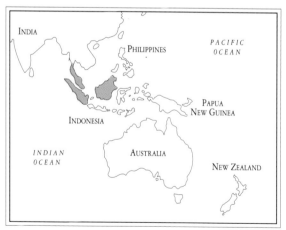

Iguanura wallichiana var. major

Iguanura bicornis

COMMON NAME: None known.
SIZE: Small, solitary stem, 1–2 m (3.3–6.5 ft) tall.
HABITAT: Rainforest understorey.
DISTRIBUTION: Peninsular Malaysia, southern Thailand.
CONSERVATION STATUS: Vulnerable in Peninsular Malaysia, status unknown in Thailand.
DESCRIPTION: Conspicuous crownshaft. Leaves are about 1.5 m (5 ft) long with 5–8 pairs of wedge-shaped leaves. Inflorescence is branched, always below the leaves. Fruit broadens from a narrow base to a double tip.

Iguanura bicornis

Iguanura wallichiana var. *major*

syn. *Iguanura* 'spectabilis'
COMMON NAME: None known.
SIZE: Clumping, 1.5–2.5 m (5–8 ft) tall.
HABITAT: Understorey of rainforests in damp or wet locations, on slopes and around streams, sometimes in large colonies.
DISTRIBUTION: Peninsular Malaysia.
CONSERVATION STATUS: Vulnerable.
DESCRIPTION: Petiole is around 15 cm (6 in) long. Leaf blade broad and undivided, about 75 cm (30 in) long, rounded at the apex with a deep cleft, then tapering to the base. Has jagged leaf margins. Inflorescence is branched and arises among the leaves, projecting beyond them. Fruit are about 2 cm (0.8 in) long.
CULTIVATION: This variety was collected and cultivated avidly in Victorian times. Has good horticultural potential.

Iguanura wallichiana var. *major*, often known as *Iguanura* 'spectabilis'.

Iguanura wallichiana var. *wallichiana*

syn. *Iguanura diffusa*
COMMON NAME: None known.
SIZE: Clumping, usually 1–2 m (3.3–6.5 ft) tall.
HABITAT: Rainforest understorey, along streams and on slopes, but not on dry ridges.
DISTRIBUTION: Sumatra, northern Malaysia, southern Thailand.
CONSERVATION STATUS: Vulnerable in Peninsular Malaysia, status unknown elsewhere.
DESCRIPTION: Pinnate leaves with 3–8 (usually 5) pairs of narrow leaf segments with jagged leaf margins. Branched inflorescences arise from among the leaves and project beyond. Fruit are about 1.2 cm (0.5 in) long.

Iguanura wallichiana var. *wallichiana*

JOHANNESTEIJSMANNIA

jo-hăn-ės-'tēs-mān-ē-à

*J*ohannesteijsmannia is a genus with four identified species. These magnificent palms, trunkless in all but one species, have enormous, tough, undivided, diamond-shaped leaves which are most striking, especially when viewed in their natural habitat — primary rainforest. *Johannesteijsmannia* are found from southern Thailand, Peninsular Malaysia, Sumatra to western Borneo.

Johannesteijsmannia palms lack a visible stem, except in *J. perakensis*, which develops a short trunk. Short stems may, however, be present underground. Leaves are at least 3 m (10 ft) long at maturity, and, in exceptional cases, twice that length. Leaf sheaths are short and break down into a fibrous interwoven mass as they age. Petioles, armed with small sharp spines, are continuous with the leaf midrib and there is a small hastula on the upper surface of young leaves at the insertion of the blade on the petiole. The leaf blade is entire, pleated, ribbed, and ranges from diamond-shaped to broadly lanceolate. The upper margins of the leaves are notched in a step-like fashion and the lower margins are thickened and armed with teeth-like spines similar to those on the petiole margin. Inflorescences arise among the leaves, but are usually partly obscured by leaf litter. They are short, branched, with the amount of branching and number of rachillae varying according to the species. Several tubular bracts enclose the unopened

inflorescence and remain conspicuous after they have split open. The cream-coloured scented bisexual flowers are solitary or arranged in groups of two to four. Fruit is rounded when it develops from one carpel, but occasionally lobed if it develops from two or three carpels. The outer layers dry and crack into corky, pyramidal warts, chestnut brown in colour. Seeds are globose and attached at the base.

Well-drained soil and shade are two consistent requirements for these understorey palms. Best suited to the humid tropics, they can be grown in a simulated tropical climate. Flowering and fruiting are apparently irregular and sporadic. Fresh seed germinate readily and growth is fast if the climate and soil are appropriate.

In Malaysia, *J. altifrons* leaves are collected for the excellent thatch they make. They are used for the walls and roofs of kongsi (communal) houses in logging camps and are reported to last for three to four years. In Peninsular Malaysia, they are commonly known as 'daun payung' or umbrella leaf palm.

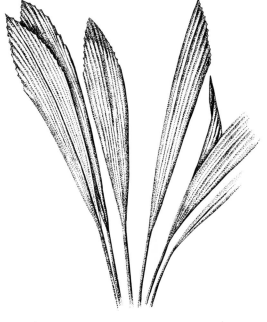

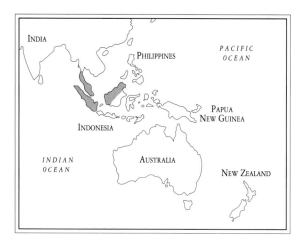

Johannesteijsmannia altifrons

Johannesteijsmannia altifrons

COMMON NAME: None known.

SIZE: Acaulescent, leaves 3–6 m (10–20 ft) tall.

HABITAT: Ridge-tops and hill slopes of primary rainforest (mostly in hill dipterocarp forest), generally above 300 m (1000 ft) altitude. Also found in low-lying heath forest on deeply podzolised soils. Can survive in selectively-logged forest, but not in secondary rainforest.

DISTRIBUTION: Sumatra, Peninsular Malaysia, southern Thailand, Borneo.

CONSERVATION STATUS: Vulnerable.

DESCRIPTION: Has relatively broad diamond-shaped leaves, variable in length and width, with blade up to about 3.5 m (11.5 ft) long and 1.8 m (6 ft) wide. Petiole up to 2.5 m (8 ft) long. Has 20–30 leaves in a crown. Very short spines on petiole and lower leaf margins. Inflorescence branches to 3 orders, and has 20–100 rachillae. Fruit are globose, around 4 cm (1.6 in) in diameter. Has 60–80 corky warts on fruit, each 0.7–0.9 cm (0.3–0.35 in) in height.

CULTIVATION: Best in a humid tropical climate, with deep shade.

Johannesteijsmannia perakensis

Johannesteijsmannia lanceolata

COMMON NAME: None known.

SIZE: Acaulescent, with erect leaves, up to approximately 3.5 m (11.5 ft) tall.

HABITAT: Steep slopes of a river in primary rainforest.

DISTRIBUTION: One location in Pahang province (Peninsular Malaysia).

CONSERVATION STATUS: Endangered.

DESCRIPTION: Leaves are lanceolate, 6–8 times as long as broad. Blade is up to 2.4 m (8 ft) long and 30 cm (1 ft) wide, covered with brown scurfy scales on the underside. Petiole is up to 1 m (3.3 ft) long. Inflorescence has 1 order of branching, with 3–6 thick rachillae. Fruit are up to 3.4 cm (1.4 in) in diameter, covered in about 90 corky warts about 0.25 cm (0.1 in) high.

CULTIVATION: Best in a humid tropical climate, with deep shade and a well-drained soil rich in humus.

Johannesteijsmannia lanceolata

Johannesteijsmannia magnifica

Johannesteijsmannia magnifica

COMMON NAME: None known.

SIZE: Acaulescent, with erect leaves, up to 5 m (16.5 ft) tall.

HABITAT: Steep slopes and ridge tops. In one location it is found from 150–500 m (500–1600 ft).

DISTRIBUTION: Peninsular Malaysia.

CONSERVATION STATUS: Endangered.

DESCRIPTION: Leaves are very broad compared to the other species. Blade is up to 3 m (10 ft) long and 2 m (6.5 ft) wide, covered with a white indumentum on the underside. Petiole is up to 2 m (6.5 ft) long with 2 yellow lines. Inflorescence has 5–6 orders of branching and 500–1000 rachillae. Fruit are up to 4 cm (1.6 in) in diameter, covered in about 150 corky warts up to about 0.25 cm (0.1 in) high.

CULTIVATION: Best in a humid tropical climate, with deep shade.

Johannesteijsmannia perakensis

COMMON NAME: None known.

SIZE: Trunk, up to 4 m (13 ft) tall and 15 cm (6 in) in diameter.

HABITAT: Hill slopes and ridge tops from approximately 175–850 m (575–2800 ft). Has survived selective logging of its rainforest habitat.

DISTRIBUTION: Peninsular Malaysia.

CONSERVATION STATUS: Vulnerable.

DESCRIPTION: Has relatively broad diamond-shaped leaves. Blade is up to about 3 m (10 ft) long and 1.6 m (5 ft) wide. Petiole is up to 1 m (3.3 ft) long, marked with 2 yellow lines. Very short spines on petiole and lower leaf margins. Inflorescence is sweet-smelling, divaricate, branching to 4 orders, with 50–100 rachillae. Fruit are globose, around 5 cm (2 in) in diameter. Has about 60 corky warts on fruit, about 0.9 cm (0.35 in) in height.

CULTIVATION: Best in a humid tropical climate, with deep shade and a well-drained soil rich in humus.

Johannesteijsmannia altifrons

KENTIOPSIS

'kĕn-tĭ-ŏp-sĭs

Kentiopsis is a monotypic genus, represented by the species *Kentiopsis oliviformis*, which is endemic to New Caledonia. In its natural habitat, the moist forest at the centre of the island, it is found on soils derived from acid rocks and basalt, from near sea level to 300 m (1000 ft) elevations, but in relatively few numbers.

Young plants have a superficial likeness to *Howea forsteriana*, but this is botanically a very different palm. Mature plants are up to 30 m (100 ft) tall, with a smooth grey trunk and a long swollen green crownshaft. There are about nine leaves in the open spreading crown, each with a short petiole and a long rachis (up to 3 m (10 ft)). On each leaf there are about 55 pairs of long pointed leaflets, dark green on top and paler beneath. The well-branched inflorescence arises below the crownshaft and carries male and female flowers. Fruit are ellipsoid, up to about 2 cm (0.8 in) long and red when ripe.

This is a palm that grows more successfully in cooler climates than its island habitat would indicate. It has potential as a temperate climate ornamental.

Kentiopsis oliviformis

Kentiopsis oliviformis

Kentiopsis oliviformis

syn. *Kentia oliviformis*

COMMON NAME: None known.

SIZE: Single, smooth, grey trunk, up to 30 m (100 ft) tall.

HABITAT: Moist forest from near sea level to 300 m (1000 ft).

DISTRIBUTION: New Caledonia.

CONSERVATION STATUS: Endangered.

DESCRIPTION: Green crownshaft is long and swollen. Open crown has about 8 pinnate leaves, each with a short petiole and a blade up to 3 m (10 ft) long. Leaflets taper to a point, are dark green on top and paler beneath. There are about 55 pairs on each leaf. The well-branched inflorescence arises below the crownshaft. Fruit are ellipsoid, up to about 2 cm (0.8 in) long and red when ripe.

CULTIVATION: Subtropical to temperate climate is required.

KERRIODOXA

kĕr-ī-ō-'dŏx-à

*K*erriodoxa was described in 1983 by John Dransfield, but had been collected 50 years earlier by A. G. F. Kerr as a possible species of *Livistona*. A beautiful large-leafed palm of horticultural potential, it is sufficiently different to have been named as a monotypic genus. Known in only two localities of southern Thailand, *Kerriodoxa elegans* occurs abundantly in the undergrowth on hill slopes in dry evergreen forest, at altitudes of about 100–300 m (330–1000 ft).

Kerriodoxa elegans is a solitary-stemmed small to moderate palm with trunks up to about 5 m (16 ft) high and 20 cm (8 in) in diameter. Leaf bases persist on the smooth, closely-ringed trunk, but fall off as the trunk gains height. There is no crownshaft. The leaf bases are sheathing at first, later splitting opposite the petiole. The dark green leaf blade is palmate and pleated, roughly circular in outline, approximately 1.5 m (5 ft) long by 2 m (6.5 ft) wide, with its undersurface chalky white. The blade is split shallowly (to uneven depths) into single-fold segments. There is a conspicuous hastula about 0.5 cm (0.2 in) high on the upper side of the leaf. *Kerriodoxa* is dioecious, male and female flowers being carried on different plants. Male inflorescences are well branched, about 45 cm (18 in) long and covered in a grey-brown tomentum. Female inflorescences are longer, up to about 75 cm (30 in) long, more simply and sparingly branched than the male, and also covered in a grey-brown tomentum. Fruit are white turning orange-yellow when ripe, almost globose (with a depressed base), approximately 4.5 cm (1.8 in) in diameter and 3 cm (1.2 in) long.

Seed of this beautiful palm has been distributed to many countries over the past few years, and *Kerriodoxa elegans* is now being grown in warm temperate climates and is also reportedly demonstrating some cold temperature tolerance.

Kerriodoxa elegans

Kerriodoxa elegans

Kerriodoxa elegans

COMMON NAME: None known.

SIZE: Solitary stems, up to about 5 m (16 ft) high and 20 cm (8 in) in diameter.

HABITAT: Hill slopes in dry evergreen forest, from 100–300 m (330–1000 ft).

DISTRIBUTION: Southern Thailand.

CONSERVATION STATUS: Unknown, probably vulnerable.

DESCRIPTION: Leaf blade is about 1.5 m (5 ft) long by 2 m (6.5 ft) wide. Undersurface is chalky white, palmate and pleated, roughly circular in outline, split shallowly to uneven depth. Has a hastula on the upper side of the leaf. Male inflorescence is well branched, about 45 cm (18 in) long, female inflorescence (on a different plant) is up to about 75 cm (30 in) long, but more simply and sparingly branched. Fruit are orange-yellow when ripe, almost globose (with a depressed base), about 4.5 cm (1.8 in) in diameter and 3 cm (1.2 in) long.

CULTIVATION: Tropical to warm temperate climate is required.

KORTHALSIA

kŏr-'thăl-sē-à

*K*orthalsia palms, commonly called ant rattans, are spiny, climbing and clustering vines, closely associated with ant colonies. They are distinguished from other rattans by their solitary hermaphroditic flowers borne on catkin-like branches (reminiscent of *Metroxylon*) and by the fact that they are hapaxanthic, each stem dying after flowering. Unlike other rattans, they branch dichotomously in the forest canopy. There are about 26 species distributed from Myanmar (Burma), the Andaman Islands, Vietnam, Laos and Cambodia, south to Sulawesi and New Guinea. The greatest diversity (15 species) is found in Borneo. Their natural habitat is in the lowland and hill rainforests, but not at high altitudes. They are also often found colonising secondary forest after logging or other disturbances.

Korthalsia palms are slender to robust vines, with the leaf sheaths armed and without a knee, as in many *Calamus* species. The ocrea, an extension along the stem beyond the petiole, is always conspicuous, sometimes like a net (as in *Korthalsia jala*), sometimes inflated, forming a chamber for ants (as in *K. echinometra*), and often spiny. Leaflets are usually diamond-shaped, sometimes lanceolate, always with the upper margins jagged. Sometimes they join the leaf rachis with a short stalk. The undersides are often a pale powdery colour. Leaves have a cirrus. This is a long whip-like extension to the tip of the leaf, which is armed with hook-like spines.

Several long pendulous inflorescences arise simultaneously from the axils of the uppermost leaves. Fruit have a fleshy mesocarp (unlike *Calamus*) and are covered with neat, brownish, overlapping scales.

Canes are collected for the rattan trade, but they are not as valuable as *Calamus* species because of their uneven nodes, and because the inner layer of the leaf sheath adheres to the cane surface, making it difficult to clean. *Korthalsia* are most often used as split cane for weaving baskets and binding. The diamond-shaped leaves of most species make these very desirable collector's palms, but as yet they are quite uncommon. Cultivation requires a tropical to subtropical climate with shade, plentiful water and good drainage.

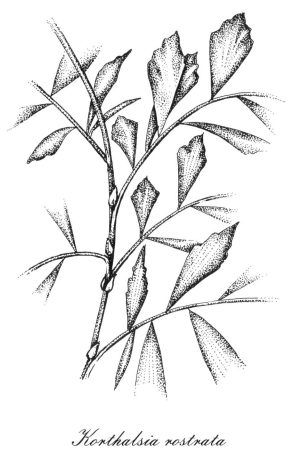

Korthalsia rostrata

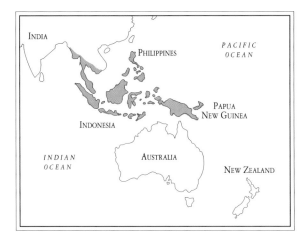

Korthalsia echinometra

Korthalsia echinometra

COMMON NAME: Ant rattan, rotan semut (Malaysia).

SIZE: Moderately robust, climbing to 40 m (130 ft) tall, clustering and branching, stems with sheaths up to 3 cm (1.2 in) in diameter.

HABITAT: Lowland and hill dipterocarp forests up to 1000 m (3300 ft) altitudes.

DISTRIBUTION: Widespread in Borneo, Sumatra, southern part of the Malay Peninsula.

CONSERVATION STATUS: Not threatened in Borneo, vulnerable in Peninsular Malaysia.

DESCRIPTION: Leaf sheaths are obscured by the long, bulbous, spiny ocreas which are up to 10 cm (4 in) long. Pinnate leaves are up to 1.8 m (6 ft) long, including a cirrus of about 70 cm (28 in). Leaflets are numerous and narrowly elongate, chalky white on the undersurface. Fruit are ovoid, 2.5 cm (1 in) long, and covered in reddish-brown overlapping scales.

LACCOSPADIX

lăk-ō-'spād-ix

Laccospadix is a monotypic genus, *Laccospadix australasica* being the sole representative. Commonly known as the Atherton palm, this small- to moderate-sized palm is endemic to the tropical rainforest of northeastern Queensland, Australia, from 100–1600 m (300–5200 ft). An understorey palm of the rainforests on the ranges and tablelands, it varies in habit from single-stemmed to multi-stemmed, the two forms sometimes occurring in the same locality.

Solitary trunks can reach 8 m (26 ft) tall, but are usually around 2–3 m (6.5–10 ft) in height. The slender trunks are covered with persistent leaf bases, which eventually fall off, leaving a clean, prominently-ringed surface. Trunks are a slender 5–10 cm (2–4 in) in diameter. The leaf bases are wide and wrap around the trunk, but split opposite the petiole and do not form a crownshaft. Petioles are slender and up to approximately 1 m (3.3 ft) long. The leaf blade is about 1–1.5 m (3.3–5 ft) long with numerous narrow, long, pointed leaflets. Newly emergent leaves are often reddish. Inflorescences arise among the leaves and are long arching spikes that become pendulous as they flower and fruit. The inflorescence is enclosed at the bud stage by a papery bract, which splits open and falls. The spike bears triads of flowers in a spiral arrangement, each triad composed of one female and two male flowers. Fruit are bright red, ovoid, approximately 1 cm (0.4 in) long.

Some difficulties have been encountered with growing this palm as seed can take a long time to germinate unless provided with warmth. Fresh seed should normally germinate within three to five months given bottom heat. These palms are suitable for warm temperate to temperate climates and will tolerate some frost. In the tropics and subtropics, *Laccospadix* needs the cooler night temperatures of high altitude areas to grow satisfactorily. Young plants require shade, a fertile, well-mulched soil and a good water supply. They make suitable indoor plants as their growth tends to be slow and they can tolerate low light levels.

Laccospadix australasica

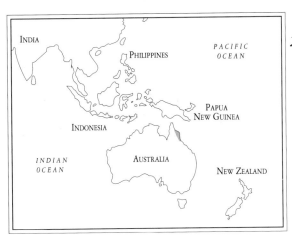

Laccospadix australasica

Laccospadix australasica

COMMON NAME: Atherton palm.

SIZE: Single-stemmed or multi-stemmed, usually 2–3 m (6.5–10 ft) tall. Stems 5–10 cm (2–4 in) in diameter.

HABITAT: Tropical rainforest from 100–1600 m (300–5200 ft).

DISTRIBUTION: Northeastern Queensland (Australia).

CONSERVATION STATUS: Not threatened.

DESCRIPTION: Stems are covered with persistent leaf bases, which eventually fall off, leaving a clean, prominently-ringed surface. Petioles are up to 1 m (3.3 ft) long, blade 1–1.5 m (3.3–5 ft) long with numerous long, narrow, pointed leaflets. Inflorescences are long arching spikes that arise among the leaves and become pendulous as they flower and fruit. Fruit are bright red, ovoid, about 1 cm (0.4 in) long.

CULTIVATION: Suitable for tropical to temperate climates. Needs cool night temperatures.

LATANIA

lă-'tăn-ē-à

Latania, commonly called the latan palms or latanier, are handsome fan-leaved palms. They are endangered in their natural habitat. Although all three species are common in cultivation, there are only a few individual specimens remaining on the islands of the Mascarene group. In times past they were used for thatch and construction by the local people, who harvested them from the cliffs, ravines and savanna country of the islands.

Latan palms are tall, rather stout, solitary-trunked palms with large, stiff, costapalmate leaves in a dense crown. The leaf blades are divided to about one third to half depth, the segments tapering to a point and often bifid. Leaf sheaths are narrow, and petioles are long and robust, often armed with short teeth close to the base. The leaves have a conspicuous hastula on the upperside, and the underside of the leaf has a grey-white waxy or downy covering. The leaf blades and petioles are tinged with blue, red or yellow in the three different species, a feature that is particularly distinctive in young plants before they grow a trunk. Inflorescences arise among the leaves, are shorter than the leaves, and are either male or female since latan palms are dioecious. Male inflorescences have a thick peduncle and up to 14 spike-like flowering branches, each the thickness of a finger. Female inflorescences have fewer, but thicker, spike-like branches and fewer flowers than the male. Fruits are large, oblong- to egg-shaped, smooth-skinned, and usually have three seeds, though sometimes they have only one or two.

Latans are best suited to tropical seasonally-wet climates, but are adaptable to subtropical and warm temperate climates. *Latania* palms are grown from seed, which germinates readily when fresh. They enjoy an open sunny position from the juvenile stages. They are capable of a fast growth rate if supplied with warm temperatures, fertile, well-drained soil and plenty of water. Hybridisation may occur where different *Latania* species are grown in proximity.

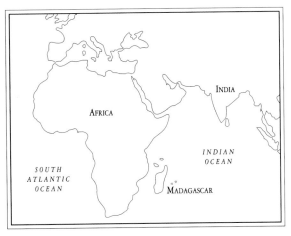

Latania lontaroides

Latania loddigesii

syn. *Latania glaucophylla*

COMMON NAME: Blue latan.

SIZE: Solitary trunk, up to 8 m (26 ft) tall, or more.

HABITAT: Coastal savanna.

DISTRIBUTION: Mascarene Islands.

CONSERVATION STATUS: Endangered. A few specimens still on Round Island and perhaps on Mauritius.

DESCRIPTION: Leaf bases and blue-green leaf blades are covered with a fluffy tomentum, which persists on the undersurface of the leaf as the palm gets older. Leaves are 2–3 m (6.5–10 ft) long, the blade about 1 m (3.3 ft) across. Inflorescence is up to 2 m (6.5 ft) long. Fruit are egg-shaped or pear-shaped, 5–7 cm (2–2.8 in) long, with a smooth seed.

CULTIVATION: Adaptable to a range of climates from tropical to warm temperate.

Latania loddigesii

Latania verschaffeltii

Latania verschaffeltii

syn. *Latani aurea* Hort.

COMMON NAME: Yellow latan.

SIZE: Solitary stout trunk, up to 16 m (52 ft) tall.

HABITAT: The edges of ravines and other areas of Rodriguez Island.

DISTRIBUTION: Rodriguez Island (Mascarene Islands).

CONSERVATION STATUS: Endangered.

DESCRIPTION: Very similar to *L. loddigesii*. Leaf bases, petioles and pale green leaf blades are covered with a fluffy tomentum, which persists on the undersurface of the leaf as the palm gets older. In young plants, the petioles and leaf veins are yellow to bright orange. Leaves are 2–3 m (6.5–10 ft) long, the blade up to 1.5 m (5 ft) across. Hastula is slightly rounded. Inflorescences are about 2.5 m (8 ft) long. Fruit are egg-shaped or pear-shaped, 4–5 cm (1.6–2 in) long. Seeds have a prominent ridge.

CULTIVATION: Adaptable to a range of climates from tropical to warm temperate.

LICUALA

lik-yū-'ā-là

Licuala is a genus of approximately 108 species of small- to moderate-sized palms with circular, usually divided, fan leaves. Some species with undivided leaves (e.g. *Licuala grandis* and *L. orbicularis*) are stunningly handsome. Other species have leaves divided into wedge-shaped segments. Commonly called licuala palms, the genus is distributed from India and southern China, through Myanmar (Burma), Thailand, Malaysia, Indonesia, the Celebes, the Philippines and across to New Guinea, northern Queensland, the Solomon Islands and Vanuatu.

Most are rainforest understorey plants, sometimes in large colonies dominating the vegetation. Some species occur as just a few solitary individuals scattered amongst other rainforest plants. In Borneo, which has the greatest diversity of licualas, it is common to find several different *Licuala* species in the same local habitat. The largest attains about 18 m (60 ft), but most species have short stems, only about 1 m (3.3 ft) or so in height. A few are stemless or have underground stems. Some form several clustering stems, others are solitary. Leaf petioles are usually edged with sharp teeth or short spines and the leaves have a small hastula on the upper surface but not the lower. Leaf sheaths persist and form a fibrous tangle around the stem or base of the plant. The leaf blade itself may be entire, or split along the ribs which radiate out like spokes of a wheel, thus producing many wedge-shaped segments. Sometimes the leaf does not appear strictly palmate as the central segment is borne on a short stalk-like extension of the petiole. Inflorescences are borne among the leaves and vary in both their length and their degree of branching from one species to another. Flowers are usually hermaphroditic. Fruit are small, vary in shape from one species to another, but are usually roundish and brightly coloured.

The leaves of some species are used for thatch and other domestic uses. The stems of some larger species are used to make walking sticks. *Licuala* palms are very popular as garden ornamentals. They are mostly tropical, but some grow well in subtropical areas when provided with shade, fertile well-mulched soil and adequate water.

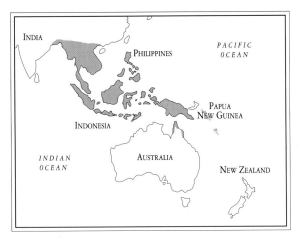

Licuala paludosa

Licuala grandis

COMMON NAME: None known.
SIZE: Solitary trunk, up to 4 m (13 ft) tall.
HABITAT: Undergrowth rainforest palm.
DISTRIBUTION: Vanuatu.
CONSERVATION STATUS: Rare.
DESCRIPTION: Has an undivided leaf blade up to 2 m (6.5 ft) across, deeply pleated and toothed along the margin. Inflorescence is openly branched, and longer than the leaves. Fruit are globose, red to orange when ripe, 1–1.5 cm (0.4–0.6 in) in diameter.
CULTIVATION: Widely cultivated as a garden ornamental. Propagated from seed, which germinates in a few months. Can be grown from the tropics to subtropical areas. Best in shade to semi-shade with protection from winds.

Licuala grandis

Licuala lauterbachii

Licuala lauterbachii

COMMON NAME: None known.
SIZE: Solitary stem, up to 6 m (20 ft) tall, or more.
HABITAT: Understorey palm of lowland rainforests.
DISTRIBUTION: New Guinea, Bougainville Island, Solomon Islands.
CONSERVATION STATUS: Unknown.
DESCRIPTION: Stem is about 6 cm (2.5 in) wide. Leaf petiole is 1–2 m (3.3–6.5 ft) long with spines along the margins. Leaf blade has many wedge-shaped, pleated leaflets, each with a truncate, toothed apex. Branching inflorescence has orange to red globose fruit 2–3 cm (0.5–1.2 in) in diameter.
CULTIVATION: Needs a tropical climate.

Licuala mattanensis

Licuala mattanensis

COMMON NAME: None known.
SIZE: Solitary stem, 1–2 m (3.3–6.5 ft) tall.
HABITAT: Rainforest understorey.
DISTRIBUTION: Low mountains of Sarawak (including Mt Mattang, 1000 m (3300 ft)), Borneo.
CONSERVATION STATUS: Rare.
DESCRIPTION: A small palmate palm with many narrow or few broad, wedge-shaped leaflets. Long narrow petioles. Leaf bases tend to persist and make for a ragged appearance on the stem. Unbranched inflorescence. Fruit are cigar-shaped.
CULTIVATION: Probably needs a tropical climate.

Licuala orbicularis

COMMON NAME: None known.
SIZE: No trunk. Large leaves, up to about 1.5 m (5 ft) long.
HABITAT: Rainforest understorey.
DISTRIBUTION: Borneo.
CONSERVATION STATUS: Endangered.
DESCRIPTION: A small palm with entire, stiffly-held, orbicular, pleated leaves with toothed margins. Long narrow petiole. Seldom fruits.
CULTIVATION: The leaf is used in Borneo for thatching material and many other domestic uses. Probably needs a tropical climate.

Licuala orbicularis

Licuala peltata

COMMON NAME: None known.
SIZE: Clumping or single stemmed, up to 5 m (16 ft) tall.
HABITAT: Moist forest understorey.
DISTRIBUTION: India, Bangladesh, Myanmar (Burma), Thailand.
CONSERVATION STATUS: Vulnerable in India and Bangladesh. Not threatened elsewhere.
DESCRIPTION: Has large circular leaves 1–1.5 m (3.3–6 ft) across and divided into many segments or undivided in 1 form.* Petiole is about 2 m (6.5 ft) long, with marginal spines. Inflorescence appears above the leaves. Has small globose, orange-red fruit, 2 cm (0.8 in) long.
CULTIVATION: Leaves are sometimes used by local people for rain hats and thatch. The form with undivided leaves is popular in palm collections in the tropics.
* The form from Thailand with undivided leaves has not been formally named. It has been incorrectly referred to as *Licuala elegans* and *Licuala peltata* var. *Sumawong*.

Licuala peltata

Licuala ramsayi

Licuala ramsayi

COMMON NAME: None known.
SIZE: Solitary trunk, up to 18 m (60 ft) tall, up to 20 cm (8 in) in diameter.
HABITAT: Lowland coastal swamp areas and along stream banks.
DISRIBUTION: Coastal areas of northeast Queensland (Australia).
CONSERVATION STATUS: Vulnerable.
DESCRIPTION: The largest species of *Licuala*. Ringed trunk. Has an open crown of about 12 or more circular leaves on long 2 m (6.5 ft) petioles. The leaf blades are up to 2 m (6.5 ft) across and divided into many closely-spaced, wedge-shaped segments with truncate toothed tips. Inflorescence is a branched panicle 1.5–2 m (5–6.5 ft) long. Fruit are small, globose, 1 cm (0.4 in) in diameter and orange to red when ripe.
CULTIVATION: Grows slowly and requires tropical to subtropical warm climate.

Licuala spinosa

syn. *Licuala horrida*
COMMON NAME: None known.
SIZE: Clumping, up to about 5 m (16 ft) tall, up to 8 cm (3.2 in) in diameter.
HABITAT: Edge of brackish mangrove swamps.
DISTRIBUTION: Thailand, Peninsular Malaysia, Philippines, Andaman Islands, Sumatra, Java, Borneo.
CONSERVATION STATUS: Not threatened.
DESCRIPTION: Forms dense thickets. Leaves are circular, about 1 m (3.3 ft) across and divided into many wedge-shaped segments, each with a truncate toothed apex. Branched long inflorescence. Has small, round to ovoid fruit, up to 1 cm (0.4 in) long and red when ripe.
CULTIVATION: Propagated from suckers or from seed. Tolerates open sunny positions. Used for roof thatch and food wrappers.

Licuala spinosa

LINOSPADIX

ˌlin-ō-ˈspād-ix

Linospadix is a genus of attractive small palms, including about 11 species in total, found in Australia and New Guinea. They are generally found in the undergrowth of tropical rainforest at moderate elevations. The exceptions are *Linospadix minor*, which is found at low elevations in northeastern Queensland (Australia), and *L. monostachya*, which extends to relatively low altitude areas of subtropical northeastern New South Wales (Australia). The latter is commonly known as the walking stick palm as its stems have been used for that purpose. Several taxa in Australia are yet to be described.

Linospadix palms may be solitary or clustering, but with only two or three narrow stems dominating a clump. Stems eventually become bare and show conspicuous rings. Leaf blades are entire and bifid, or are pinnately divided into segments of similar or differing widths on the same leaf. Leaflets may be tapering and pointed or truncate, and often have toothed or notched tips. Petioles may be short to long and are usually scaly. Leaf sheaths soon split opposite the petiole and, although the sheaths wrap around the stem, there is no real crownshaft. Dead leaves may persist for some time before falling. Inflorescences are unbranched, pendulous spikes arising singly among the leaves and enclosed by two papery bracts in the bud stage. Flowers are arranged spirally in triads, one female flower between two male flowers. Fruit are small, elliptical to cylindrical, single-seeded, often a beautiful coral pink to red colour when ripe. The pendulous spike of red fruit hanging from the crown of leaves is most attractive.

Protected and shaded positions are best for these palms as their leaves tend to be damaged by direct sunlight and dry wind. A tropical to subtropical climate in a cool moist location suits most species, but *L. monostachya* and *L. palmeriana* grow well in temperate areas. A well-drained soil rich in organic matter is best with extra mulching and a good water supply.

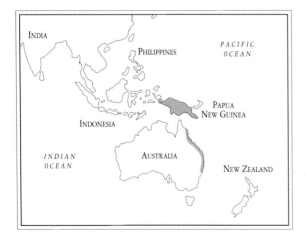

Linospadix monostachya

Linospadix microcarya

Linospadix microcarya

COMMON NAME: None known.
SIZE: Clumping, with slender stems 1–2 m (3.3–6.5 ft) tall and 0.5–1.5 cm (0.2–0.6 in) in diameter.
HABITAT: Rainforest understorey, from low elevations to 1100 m (3600 ft).
DISTRIBUTION: Northeastern Queensland (Australia).
CONSERVATION STATUS: Vulnerable.
DESCRIPTION: Loose crown of pinnate leaves up to 60 cm (2 ft) long (including the short petiole). Leaf segments are of variable width and are irregularly shaped. Has up to 12 pairs per leaf, with toothed ends, and with the terminal pair joined and fishtail-shaped. Inflorescence is spicate and pendulous, 30–40 cm (12–16 in) long. Fruit are small, globose, up to 0.8 cm (0.3 in) in diameter and yellow to red when ripe.
CULTIVATION: Propagated from seed or suckers. Tropical to subtropical climate is required. Shaded and moist conditions are best.

Linospadix monostachya

Linospadix minor

COMMON NAME: Walking stick palm.
SIZE: Clumping or single-stemmed, usually about 1 m (3.3 ft) tall, but up to 1.5 m (5 ft), stems up to 2 cm (0.8 in) in diameter.
HABITAT: Low to high altitude rainforest understorey.
DISTRIBUTION: Northeastern Queensland (Australia).
CONSERVATION STATUS: Not threatened. Common and widespread.
DESCRIPTION: Has a loose crown of pinnate leaves, each up to 1 m (3 ft) long including petiole of 10–20 cm (4–8 in). Leaf segments are broad and irregularly shaped, with 6–7 pairs per leaf. The ends are toothed, the terminal pair are joined and fishtail-shaped. Inflorescence is spicate and pendulous, 20–40 cm (8–16 in) long. Fruit are elliptical, up to 1.8 cm (0.7 in) long and yellow to red when ripe.
CULTIVATION: Tropical to subtropical (or warm temperate) climate is required. Shaded and moist conditions are essential.

Linospadix monostachya

COMMON NAME: Walking stick palm.
SIZE: Solitary stem, 1–4 m (3.3–13 ft) tall and 2–3 cm (0.8–1.2 in) in diameter.
HABITAT: Low to high altitude rainforest understorey.
DISTRIBUTION: Southeast Queensland and northeast New South Wales (Australia).
CONSERVATION STATUS: Not threatened. Common and widespread.
DESCRIPTION: Has a loose crown of pinnate leaves, each up to 1.2 m (4 ft) long including petiole of 20–30 cm (8–12 in). Leaf segments are variously broad to narrow and irregularly shaped. There are 5–30 pairs per leaf, with the ends pointed or toothed. The terminal pair are joined and fishtail-shaped. Inflorescence is spicate and pendulous, 1–1.5 m (3.3–5 ft) long. Fruit are ovoid to elliptical, up to 1.5 cm (0.6 in) long and bright red when ripe.
CULTIVATION: Subtropical to temperate climate is required. Tolerates cold. Shaded and moist conditions are best. Seed is difficult to germinate and fresh seed has limited viability.

Linospadix palmeriana

COMMON NAME: None known.
SIZE: Clumping, up to about 1.5 m (5 ft) tall. Stems are very slender, up to 1.5 cm (0.6 in) in diameter.
HABITAT: Rainforest understorey from near sea level to 800 m (2600 ft).
DISTRIBUTION: Northeast Queensland (Australia).
CONSERVATION STATUS: Not threatened. Restricted distribution but locally common.
DESCRIPTION: Has a loose crown of pinnate leaves, each up to 25–45 cm (10–18 in) long, including petiole of 15–30 cm (6–12 in). Leaf segments are triangular, 15–25 cm (6–10 in) long, with 1–2 pairs per leaf. They are broad where attached to the leaf rachis and taper to a point. Terminal pair are joined and fishtail-shaped. Inflorescence is spicate and pendulous, 15–25 cm (6–10 in) long. Fruit are elliptical, up to 1 cm (0.4 in) long and orange to red when ripe.
CULTIVATION: Cool subtropical to temperate climate is required. Tolerates cold. Shaded and moist conditions are best. Fresh seed has limited viability.

Linospadix minor

Linospadix palmeriana

LIVISTONA

li-vĭs-'tōn-à

Livistona is a genus of at least 28 species. They are distributed from the Ryukyu and Bonin Islands through Southeast Asia, New Guinea, the Solomon Islands, northern and eastern Australia, and also on the Horn of Africa and into Arabia. The majority of species are in Australia, where their habitats vary from tropical dry savanna woodland to gully bottoms in the middle of deserts which have a permanent underground water supply, to swamp forests, to around the edge of mangrove forests. In Peninsular Malaysia, *Livistona* species are found in both swampy lowland areas and in montane rainforests. The Chinese fan palm, *Livistona chinensis*, is widely planted around the world. The cabbage palm, *L. australis*, is popular in Australia, particularly since its natural habitat extends into temperate areas, while *L. rotundifolia* is popular in Southeast Asia.

Solitary tree palms, some growing very tall, the Livistonas have trunks that are often covered with persistent leaf bases. They later become bare and show the leaf base scars. Leaves are usually large, slightly to strongly costapalmate with a well-developed hastula on the upper surface and a small hastula (or none) on the lower suface. The blade is divided into many narrow single-fold segments which are split terminally. In a few species, segments may have several folds. The petiole usually has spines or teeth along the margins and may be expanded where it joins the sheathing leaf base. The inflorescences arise among the leaves, are well branched and are enclosed in the bud stage by several tubular, overlapping bracts. Flowers are bisexual and small, borne singly or in clusters along the rachillae. Fruit is single-seeded, round to egg-shaped, small- to medium-sized, and variously coloured, from red to brown, green, blue-green, or black when ripe.

Livistona australis

Livistona australis

syn. *Corypha australis*
COMMON NAME: Cabbage tree palm, cabbage palm.
SIZE: Solitary trunk, up to 35 m (100 ft) tall, up to 30 cm (1 ft) in diameter.
HABITAT: Temperate and subtropical coastal areas, including rainforest, banks of rivers and streams, swampy areas and moist gullies. Often forms large stands.
DISTRIBUTION: Eastern coast of Australia from central Queensland south into eastern Victoria.
CONSERVATION STATUS: Not threatened.
DESCRIPTION: Grey, rough, ringed trunk often has vertical fissures. Leaves are about 3–4 m (10–13 ft) long with a spined petiole. Blade is circular and 1–1.5 m (3.3–5 ft) across, divided (to about two thirds) into many stiff segments, which are drooping at the ends. Inflorescence is shorter than the leaves, flowers cream-coloured. Fruit are globose, around 2 cm (0.8 in) in diameter and red to brown or black when ripe.
CULTIVATION: Suits temperate to subtropical and tropical climates. Tolerates frost. Best in a semi-shaded position when young. Likes a deep fertile, well-drained soil.

Livistona chinensis

COMMON NAME: Chinese fan palm.
SIZE: Solitary trunk, up to 12 m (40 ft) tall, 30 cm (1 ft) in diameter.
HABITAT: Subtropical woodland.
DISTRIBUTION: Ryukyu and Bonin Islands, Volcano Islands, and islands off Kyushu (Japan).
CONSERVATION STATUS: Endangered.
DESCRIPTION: Rough, grey trunk. Has a short petiole, spiny towards the base. Large blade is deeply divided with many segments heavily drooping. Inflorescence is short. Fruit are irregular globose to ovoid, green to blue-green, about 2.5 cm (1 in) in diameter. The variety seen in the wild, var. *subglobosa*, has rounded fruit.
CULTIVATION: Tolerates cold. Suitable for temperate to tropical climates. A very popular garden palm, widely grown around the world.

Livistona chinensis

Livistona australis

Livistona decipiens

Livistona decipiens

COMMON NAME: Weeping cabbage palm.
SIZE: Solitary trunk, 10–15 m (33–50 ft) tall, up to 25 cm (10 in) in diameter.
HABITAT: Eucalypt forests and the edge of rainforests.
DISTRIBUTION: Central coast of Queensland (Australia).
CONSERVATION STATUS: Not threatened. Widespread and common.
DESCRIPTION: Has strongly costapalmate leaves, deeply divided almost to the costa into narrow segments which are pendulous, creating a weeping effect. Petiole is up to 3 m (10 ft) long and edged with spines. Inflorescence is shorter than the leaves. Fruit are globose, on short stalks, up to 1.8 cm (0.7 in) in diameter and black when ripe.
CULTIVATION: Will grow in tropical to temperate areas in moist well-drained soil.

Livistona drudei

COMMON NAME: None known.
SIZE: Solitary trunk, 15–30 m (50–100 ft) tall, 20–25 cm (8–10 in) in diameter.
HABITAT: Near streams and along the edge of paperbark swamps.
DISTRIBUTION: Coastal northern Queensland (Australia).
CONSERVATION STATUS: Endangered.
DESCRIPTION: Trunk is grey and almost smooth. Leaves are 3–4 m (10–13 ft) long and narrow. The spined petiole is purplish-black at the base. Leaf blade is about 1 m (3.3 ft) across, deeply divided into fine segments which are pendulous. Inflorescence only about 1 m (3.3 ft) long. Fruit are small, globose, black and 0.8–1.0 cm (0.3–0.4 in) in diameter.
CULTIVATION: A well-drained sandy soil is most suitable, particularly if rich in organic matter. Responds to feeding and regular watering. Does not transplant easily because of long root system. Subtropical to tropical areas are suitable, but it will grow slowly in a warm temperate climate.

Livistona mariae

COMMON NAME: Central Australian cabbage palm.
SIZE: Solitary trunk, up to 20 m (66 ft) tall, 30–40 cm (12–16 in) in diameter.
HABITAT: In the base of gorges where there is a permanent water supply.
DISTRIBUTION: Endemic to gorges of the Finke River and its tributaries in the MacDonnell Ranges of central Australia.
CONSERVATION STATUS: Rare.
DESCRIPTION: Crown of leaves is fairly dense, each leaf up to 4.5 m (15 ft) long. Has a large blade (over 2 m (6.5 ft) in diameter) divided (to about halfway) into numerous tapering segments, which droop at the tips. Leaves are bluish-green with a definite bloom to the undersurface. Petiole has marginal spines. Young leaves may have an intense reddish appearance. Inflorescence is much shorter than the leaves and well branched. Fruit are globose, 1.5–2 cm (0.5–0.8 in) long and black when ripe.
CULTIVATION: Suitable for subtropical to temperate areas and for inland dry areas provided there is an adequate water supply. Tolerates cold and frosts.

Livistona drudei

Livistona muelleri

COMMON NAME: Cairns fan palm.
SIZE: Solitary trunk, 2–10 m (6.5–33 ft) tall, but can be up to 20 m (65 ft), 30–40 cm (12–16 in) in diameter.
HABITAT: Open forest, savanna grassland and seasonally-wet forest.
DISTRIBUTION: Cape York Peninsula and northeastern Queensland (Australia).
CONSERVATION STATUS: Not threatened.
DESCRIPTION: Persistent leaf bases. Has a compact crown of stiff, dull green leaves 2–3 m (6.5–10 ft) long, paler green on the undersurface. Blade is divided (to about halfway or more), but segments generally do not droop. Petiole has curved spines. Inflorescence is shorter than the leaves. Fruit are globose to ovoid, bluish-black and 0.6–1 cm (0.2–0.4 in) long.
CULTIVATION: Grows slowly.

Livistona rotundifolia

syn. *Saribus rotundifolius*

COMMON NAME: Anahaw palm (Philippines), footstool palm.
SIZE: Solitary trunk, up to 18 m (60 ft) tall.
HABITAT: Lowland rainforest.
DISTRIBUTION: Philippines, the Indonesian Islands.
CONSERVATION STATUS: Not threatened. Widespread.
DESCRIPTION: Leaf sheath and petiole bases are chestnut brown. Trunk is conspicuously marked with brown to green annular rings. Leaves are circular, only shallowly divided when young and softly drooping at the tips. Older leaves are more deeply divided, the segments broad with a blunt tip. The whole leaf, not just the tips, droops slightly. Petiole is spiny near the base. Fruit are globose, about 2 cm (0.8 in) in diameter, turning red then black when ripe.
CULTIVATION: Leaves are fire-resistant and can be shaped into a cone to make a kettle for boiling water. Leaves are used for thatch and wrapping material. Wood is used for building material and making hand tools. 'Cabbage' is edible. Needs a a tropical climate.

Livistona mariae

Livistona muelleri

Livistona rotundifolia

LODOICEA

lŏd-ō-'ē-sē-à

Lodoicea is a monotypic genus. *Lodoicea maldivica*, the coco-de-mer or double coconut, is an oddity in the palm world. Endemic to just two of the Seychelles Islands, Praslin and Curiense, this palm is found only on the hill slopes and valleys away from the flatter coastal areas.

Mature plants are tall, solitary, robust palms to 25 m (80 ft) in their native habitat, but usually much less in botanical collections. Coco-de-mer is a dioecious palm with the female inflorescences being huge and of bizarre shape. The fruit is enormous with a female palm carrying up to 500 kg (1100 lb) of fruit, each fruit taking five to seven years to mature. The bi-lobed seed resembles a double coconut when cut in cross-section, thus the name.

Seeds can weigh 20 kg (44 lb) each and continue to be sought after as an oddity with legendary aphrodisiac properties. Certainly the seed's suggestive shape and size makes it a tourist commodity in the Seychelles.

Lodoicea is very slow growing and requires a tropical climate and deep soil. The seed, slow to germinate, sends out an extremely long radicle and the sinker root may go down to 4 m (13 ft) or more. Trees take 30–60 years to flower and are reputed to be extremely long-lived, perhaps 300 years or more. This palm has been difficult to establish in botanical gardens around the world.

Lodoicea maldivica

Lodoicea maldivica

COMMON NAME: Coco-de-mer, double coconut.
SIZE: Solitary, robust trunk, up to 25 m (80 ft) tall in habitat, usually much less in cultivation.
HABITAT: Hill slopes and valleys.
DISTRIBUTION: Seychelle Islands.
CONSERVATION STATUS: Unknown, probably vulnerable.
DESCRIPTION: Leaves are strongly costapalmate, with pendulous segment tips. The leaf sheaths split opposite the petiole and a triangular cleft develops at the base of the petiole. Dioecious. Female inflorescences are huge and of a bizarre shape. Seed are of an enormous size and weigh up to 20 kg (44 lb).
CULTIVATION: Tropical climate is required. Grows slowly.

Lodoicea maldivica

LYTOCARYUM
'lyt-ō-,kăr-ē-ŭm

Lytocaryum (syn. *Microcoelum*) is a genus of three closely-related species, all found in Brazil in forests, woodlands or open fields, from 800–1800 m (2600–6000 ft). The three species are *Lytocaryum hoehnei*, *L. insigne* and *L. weddellianum*, the latter a widely-used ornamental.

Lytocaryum is a solitary palm with a closely-ringed slender trunk, rarely exceeding 3 m (10 ft) tall. Leaf bases tend to persist near the crown and are brown and densely hairy. Petioles are short to elongate with fibrous margins. The rachis is arched, with about 50 pairs of very slender, closely-spaced, regularly-arranged, tapering leaflets. Inflorescences arise among the leaves, are simple-branched and are enclosed by a large leathery to woody bract in the bud stage. Flowers are borne in triads of one female and two male flowers. Fruit are globose to ovoid, single-seeded, turning green to brown with a red-orange tinge when ripe. The epicarp and mesocarp dry and split open while still attached to the rachillae.

Suited to subtropical and warm temperate climates, *Lytocaryum* palms make fine ornamentals. Adaptable to low light intensities found indoors, *L. weddellianum* is one of the most suitable palms for indoors. Propagation is from seed, which may need bottom heat to germinate.

Lytocaryum weddellianum

Lytocaryum weddellianum

Lytocaryum weddellianum

syn. *Microcoelum weddellianum, Cocos weddelliana, Syagrus weddelliana*

COMMON NAME: None known.
SIZE: Slender trunks, 1–3 m (3.3–10 ft) tall and 5–10 cm (2–4 in) in diameter.
HABITAT: Campos or open fields.
DISTRIBUTION: Brazil.
CONSERVATION STATUS: Endangered.
DESCRIPTION: Has sheathing leaf bases with blackish-brown hairs. Petiole is 30–40 cm (12–16 in) long. Rachis is around 70 cm (28 in) long, with numerous fine, drooping leaflets, grey-green on the undersurface. Inflorescence is up to 1 m (3.3 ft) long with yellow flowers. Fruit are ovoid, beaked, orange-brown and are about 1.7 cm (0.7 in) long.
CULTIVATION: Tolerates light frosts. Best in semi-shade. Suitable as an indoor plant.

METROXYLON

mĕt-ˈrŏx-i-lŏn

Metroxylon palms are commonly known as the sago palms. This genus is composed of large to massive tree palms which accumulate starch in the pith of their trunks. In one of the five species, *Metroxylon sagu*, this starch is a traditional source of carbohydrate. The five species are found in five separate areas of Micronesia and Melanesia, are botanically quite variable, but are distinguishable by differences in their inflorescence or in their fruit shape. *M. sagu* is very widespread and naturalised in lowland swamps in many parts of Malaysia, Indonesia, Mindanao and New Guinea. The sago made from the stem starch is a staple for many communities. The pinnate leaves are an important source of thatch; the leaf petioles, when split, are used for weaving house walls and partitions and the trunks are used for house rafters. *M. sagu* is an important starch crop and new plantations are being sown in Borneo on swampy ground generally considered unsuitable for other uses.

Solitary or clustering, the stems are usually partly obscured by the old leaf bases and persistent dead leaves. Leaf sheaths split opposite the petiole, and both may be armed with spines in whorls. Leaves are pinnate with leaflets regularly arranged or in groups and fanned within the groups, giving a plumose appearance. Leaves may also be armed with short spines along the main veins and margins. The inflorescences are branched and arise among the leaves in pleonanthic species, or are terminal and compound with multiple branches in hapaxanthic species. Flowers are borne in dyads of one male flower and one flower containing both male and female parts. Fruit are round to pear-shaped, usually large and single seeded, the outer covering covered with rows of straw- to chestnut-coloured scales.

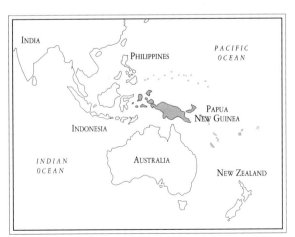

Metroxylon salomonense

Metroxylon sagu

syn. *Metroxylon rumphii*

COMMON NAME: Sago palm.

SIZE: Clustering, trunks 8–20 m (26–65 ft) high, 15–60 cm (6 in–2 ft) in diameter.

HABITAT: Freshwater swamps, valleys and along streams.

DISTRIBUTION: New Guinea, Indonesia, Malaysia, Philippines.

CONSERVATION STATUS: Unknown, probably not threatened.

DESCRIPTION: Leaves up to 7 m (23 ft) long or more. In some forms of the species, leaf sheaths and petioles bear spines, others are spineless. Is hapaxanthic, each trunk dying after flowering and fruiting is complete. Scaly fruit are globose, up to about 5 cm (2 in) in diameter.

CULTIVATION: Plantations on swampy ground take about 4 years before the stems can be harvested for sago starch. Tropical climate is required.

Metroxylon sagu

Metroxylon salomonense

Metroxylon salomonense

syn. *Coelococcus salomonensis, Metroxylon bougainvillense*

COMMON NAME: Heavy nut palm, ivory nut palm.

SIZE: Single trunk, 9–20 m (30–65 ft) tall, up to 120 cm (4 ft) diameter.

HABITAT: Swampy lowland areas, or wet heavy clay soils on slopes and ridges up to 800 m (2600 ft).

DISTRIBUTION: New Guinea, Solomon Islands, Bougainville Island, Santa Cruz Islands, Vanuatu.

CONSERVATION STATUS: Rare on Vanuatu, status unknown elsewhere.

DESCRIPTION: Leaves are 9–11 m (30–36 ft) long with long yellowish spines. Persistent leaf bases and dead leaves make an untidy 'skirt'. This monocarpic species has a terminal inflorescence up to 4 m (13 ft) high. Has large, scaly, apple-shaped fruit, 8–9 cm (2.2–3 in) across.

CULTIVATION: Leaves are harvested for roofing thatch. In the past, the ivory-hard seed was harvested for button-making. Tropical climate is required. Life of the tree is 12–13 years.

Metroxylon warburgii

syn. *Coelococcus warburgii*

COMMON NAME: None known.

SIZE: Solitary trunk, 6–7 m (20–23 ft) tall, up to 30 cm (1 ft) in diameter near the base.

HABITAT: Swamps and drier well-drained slopes.

DISTRIBUTION: Vanuatu, Santa Cruz Islands.

CONSERVATION STATUS: Rare on Vanuatu, status unknown on Santa Cruz.

DESCRIPTION: Leaves are deciduous, about 3 m (10 ft) long, with spiny leaf bases. This monocarpic species has a terminal inflorescence up to 3 m (13 ft) high. Scaly, pear-shaped fruit are up to 12 cm (5 in) by 9 cm (3.5 in).

CULTIVATION: This is commonly cultivated. Leaves are harvested to make a durable thatch. Tropical climate is required.

Metroxylon warburgii: with terminal infructescence.

NEODYPSIS
nē-ō-'dĭp-sĭs

Neodypsis comprises about 15 species of palms endemic to Madagascar. At the moment, they are separated from the genus *Chrysalidocarpus* solely on the characteristic of ruminate endosperm. It is likely that once more taxonomic work is done, both genera will be gathered — together with *Vonitra*, *Phloga* and *Dypsis* — into the one genus. Several species are ornamental, *Neodypsis decaryi*, *N. lastelliana* and *N. leptocheilos* being widely grown. In Madagascar, the low- to mid-altitude (0–1000 m (0–3300 ft)) rainforests of the east coast and the northerly Sambirano region provide the moist habitat needed for the tall-growing *N. lastelliana*, distinguished by its rusty brown tomentum on the crownshaft.

N. leptocheilos is a newly-named palm, similar to *N. lastelliana*, which has been commonly known as *N. lastelliana* var. *darianii* or *N. darianii*. It is more hardy to cool temperatures and a drier climate than *N. lastelliana*, and can be most easily distinguished from it by a petiole that grows to about 17 cm (7 in) long. *N. decaryi*, the triangle palm, so named because of its three-sided leaf arrangement, is found in a small patch of forest in the southeast of Madagascar, an area transitional between wet and dry forest domains. Other species are found in forests from sea level to 2000 m (6500 ft).

Solitary or clustering, *Neodypsis* palms vary from small to tall erect palms with ringed trunks. Leaf sheaths may be smooth or covered in white wax or a scaly indumentum. They are usually split opposite the petiole and a crownshaft is not always well developed. Leaves are pinnate with narrow leaflets regularly arranged or grouped and fanned within the group, each with a prominent midrib on the upper surface. Inflorescences are usually large, moderately branched and arise among the leaves, often maturing below the leaves as leaves drop off with age. A tubular bract encloses the inflorescence in bud, then splits longitudinally and falls off once the flowers are open. Flowers on the numerous rachillae are borne in shallow pits in triads. Fruit are smooth-skinned, ovoid to globose, and single-seeded.

Cultivation appears possible in tropical to warm temperate climates, as *Neodypsis* palms exhibit some cold tolerance. For those species described below, fresh seed germinates readily and growth can be fast in a warm climate with fertile well-drained soil.

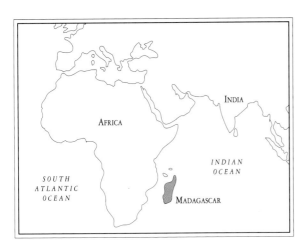

Neodypsis decaryi

Neodypsis decaryi

COMMON NAME: Triangle palm.

SIZE: Solitary trunk, up to 10 m (33 ft) tall, or more, and 50 cm (20 in) in diameter.

HABITAT: Transitional forest between wet and dry domains.

DISTRIBUTION: Southeast Madagascar.

CONSERVATION STATUS: Vulnerable.

DESCRIPTION: Leaf sheaths are arranged in 3 overlapping rows or ranks giving the trunk a triangular shape. Young petioles and sheaths are covered in a rusty brown tomentum. Trunk and older leaf bases are grey-green with a whitish bloom. Leaves are pinnate, regularly arranged, grey-green, arching strongly near the apex. Petiole short. Fruit are egg-shaped, olive green, 2 cm (0.8 in) long.

CULTIVATION: Adaptable to various climates from tropical to warm temperate. Prefers an open sunny location.

Neodypsis lastelliana

Neodypsis lastelliana

COMMON NAME: Redneck palm.

SIZE: Solitary ringed trunk, 15–20 m (50–65 ft) tall and 25–40 cm (10–16 in) in diameter.

HABITAT: Moist rainforest from sea level to 1000 m (3300 ft).

DISTRIBUTION: East coast and northerly Sambirano region of Madagascar.

CONSERVATION STATUS: Rare.

DESCRIPTION: Trunk is white with leaf scars about 3 cm (1.2 in) apart. Tubular leaf sheaths form a crownshaft and are covered with a thick, rusty brown tomentum. Petiole is lacking. Leaves are pinnate, 3 m (10 ft) long or more, leaflets regularly arranged. Inflorescences arise among the leaves, maturing below the crownshaft. Fruit are egg-shaped, around 2 cm (0.8 in) long.

CULTIVATION: Tropical to subtropical climate is preferred. Likes a partially-shaded to open sunny position.

Neodypsis decaryi

NORMANBYA

nŏr-'măn-bē-à

Normanbya is a monotypic genus. *Normanbya normanbyi* is the sole representative, and is endemic to the rainforests of northeastern Queensland, Australia. It is a solitary, pinnate-leaved palm, growing in moist coastal forests where the annual rainfall is 3000 mm (120 in). Found close to rivers and streams, sometimes in very swampy ground, it needs deep rich soil and a tropical climate for fast growth. However, the Queensland black palm, as it is commonly known, will grow slowly in warm temperate areas if it has a good water supply in summer and is not subjected to frost.

The very hard, almost black wood has been used by Australian Aborigines for spear shafts and is used today in specialty woodwork. *Normanbya* is reputedly difficult to germinate and grow. Newly-germinated seed sends down long roots before a leaf emerges above ground.

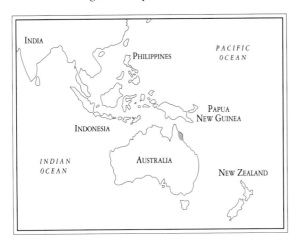

Normanbya normanbyi

Normanbya normanbyi

COMMON NAME: Queensland black palm.
SIZE: Solitary smooth trunk, up to about 20 m (65 ft) tall, 15 cm (6 in) in diameter.
HABITAT: Moist, sometimes swampy ground in rainforests.
DISTRIBUTION: Northeastern Queensland (Australia).
CONSERVATION STATUS: Vulnerable.
DESCRIPTION: Leaves are pinnate, up to 2 m (6.5 ft) long. In mature plants, leaflets radiate in all directions, creating a plumose appearance. Leaflets are dark green above and whitish beneath, with the tips praemorse. Crownshaft is pale green to grey. Inflorescence is below the crownshaft and is enclosed in 2 bracts in the bud stage. Infructescence is pendulous and usually heavily laden with large, salmon-pink to red fruit. Fruit are large, ovoid, and around 4 cm (1.6 in) long.
CULTIVATION: Tropical to subtropical climate is required, but the palm can grow slowly in a warm temperate frost-free climate.

Normanbya normanbyi

NYPA

'nē-pà

Nypa is a monotypic genus. Its single representative, *Nypa fruticans,* is the well-known mangrove palm of the Western Pacific. Found in river estuaries and on the soft muddy banks of smaller waterways, the 'nipah' palm grows in large stands from the Ganges Delta in India, east through Myanmar (Burma), Thailand, Malaysia, Indonesia, Borneo, north to the Philippines and Ryukyu Islands and south to New Guinea, the Solomon Islands and northern Australia. Recently it has been introduced to West Africa and found on the Central American coast in Panama, where it was probably introduced. Fossil records suggest that it was among the earliest monocotyledons.

Clumping, and 4–9 m (13–30 ft) tall, the stems are underground or prostrate and dichotomously branching. Large pinnate, slightly twisting leaves form an erect crown. The inflorescence arises among the leaves and is protected by two tubular bracts in the bud stage. On the end of the long peduncle is a dense head of female flowers and lateral branches ending in short spikes of male flowers. The inflorescence is unique in the palm family. The unusual globular fruiting head, 30–45 cm (12–18 in) across, is composed of angular, brown fruit compressed together, each about 7.5 cm (3 in) across, the whole fruiting head at the end of a long peduncle.

The creeping habit assists the spread of nipah palms, as does the fruit, which can float on tidal or flood waters.

It is an economically important palm, not least for its role in the stabilisation of river and coastal soils. Its leaves are used as thatch, and the sap of the inflorescence is tapped for its sugar, which can also be made into an alcoholic beverage. Young seeds are boiled in syrup and the endosperm is eaten as a sweetmeat. Nipah has strictly tropical requirements and readily grows from seed in marshy land and tidal mudflats.

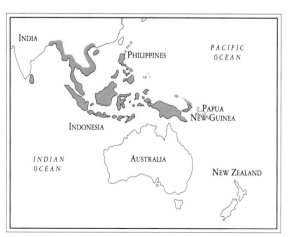

Nypa fruticans

Nypa fruticans

Nypa fruticans

COMMON NAME: Nipah, mangrove palm.

SIZE: Clumping, 4–9 m (13–30 ft) tall, stems underground or prostrate.

HABITAT: River estuaries and on soft muddy banks of smaller waterways.

DISTRIBUTION: India, Myanmar (Burma), Thailand, Malaysia, Indonesia, Borneo, Philippines, Ryukyu Islands, New Guinea, the Solomon Islands, northern Australia.

CONSERVATION STATUS: Not threatened.

DESCRIPTION: Large pinnate, slightly twisting leaves. Inflorescence has a long peduncle with a dense head of female flowers and lateral branches ending in short spikes of male flowers. The globular fruiting head, 30–45 cm (12–18 in) across, is composed of angular, brown fruit compressed together, each about 7.5 cm (3 in) across.

CULTIVATION: Requires a tropical climate and muddy soil.

Nypa fruticans: in fruit.

Nypa fruticans: inflorescence.

ONCOSPERMA

ŏn-'cō-spĕrm-à

Oncosperma is a genus of densely clumping, spiny palms from Southeast Asia. There are five species, one endemic to Sri Lanka, two endemic to the Philippines and the two others widespread in Southeast Asia, including Sulawesi, the Philippines and the Moluccas. The species have a variety of habitats from coastal swampy land with brackish water to higher hill slopes. Although well represented in the botanical gardens of Southeast Asia, these palms are not common in private collections. Part of the reason may be that they have long, black, sharp spines on their trunks, crownshafts, petioles and midribs. As the plant ages, the lower parts of the trunks shed their spines and leaf scars, and become smooth. The ring scars are easily seen on the upper part of the trunks below the short crownshaft. Leaflets are numerous, strongly drooping from the rachis. Branched inflorescences arise below the crownshaft with the flowers in triads of two male and one female flower, the male dominating the distal portions of rachillae. Inflorescences are enclosed in bud by two tubular, leathery to woody bracts, and held erect. Fruits are purple to black and globose.

Grown sometimes in parks and near the water's edge, some form huge, magnificent clumps. Seeds germinate rapidly (in a few weeks), but plants can also be grown from basal suckers. A tropical climate is required for successful cultivation.

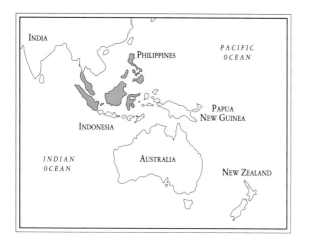

Oncosperma tigillarium

Oncosperma horridum

COMMON NAME: Bayeh, bayas.
SIZE: Clumping, up to 20 m (65 ft) tall, often with only 4–6 stems.
HABITAT: Hillsides, up to 500 m (1650 ft) elevation.
DISTRIBUTION: Peninsular Malaysia, Sumatra, Borneo, Philippines.
CONSERVATION STATUS: Unknown.
DESCRIPTION: Trunks become smooth with age and are more stout than the nibung palm. Pinnate leaves are held stiffly vertical, with leaflets drooping only at the tips. Fruit are globose, black and 1.7 cm (0.7 in) in diameter.
CULTIVATION: Needs a tropical climate. Trunks are used for building material and the new shoots are used as a vegetable.

Oncosperma tigillarium

Oncosperma horridum

Oncosperma tigillarium

syn. *Oncosperma filamentosum*
COMMON NAME: Nibung palm.
SIZE: Densely clumping, up to 25 m (80 ft) tall, or more.
HABITAT: Lowlands below 50 m (165 ft). Found on the edge of mangrove forest (in brackish soil) near the coast and occasionally on poor sandy soil.
DISTRIBUTION: Sumatra, Borneo, Java, Peninsular Malaysia.
CONSERVATION STATUS: Not threatened.
DESCRIPTION: The massed crowns of leaves give a characteristic sculptured appearance. Leaves arch and leaflets droop heavily. Crownshaft has abundant tomentum and spines. Fruit are dark purple, 0.5–0.7 cm (0.2–0.3 in) in diameter.
CULTIVATION: Needs a tropical climate. Stems are used for building material, leaf sheaths for basket-making and the basal shoots are a tasty vegetable.

PELAGODOXA

'pĕl-à-gō-,dŏx-à

*P*elagodoxa is an unusual monotypic genus. *Pelagodoxa henryana* is a rarity in its natural habitat, found at about 135 m (440 ft) in dense humid rainforest on the Marquesas Islands. In 1983, a closely-affiliated palm, which may be found to be conspecific after further study, was found on the island of Vanua Lava in Vanuatu in dense secondary rainforest at about 250 m (820 ft) altitude.

P. henryana has been successfully grown in tropical gardens, particularly in the Pacific. Propagation is from seed, which is not readily available or easily germinated. A warm tropical climate, shade, a plentiful water supply and high humidity are cultivation requisites. Protection from wind is necessary to keep the leaves from splitting.

Pelagodoxa henryana

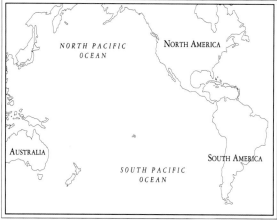

Pelagodoxa henryana

COMMON NAME: Enu, vahani (local).
SIZE: Narrow trunk, up to 7 m (23 ft) tall, often wider at the base.
HABITAT: Dense humid rainforest at 135 m (440 ft).
DISTRIBUTION: Marquesas Islands, Vanuatu.
CONSERVATION STATUS: Rare on the Marquesas, endangered on Vanuatu.
DESCRIPTION: Trunk often has stilt roots. Crown has about 10 leaves. Leaf blade is entire, about 2 m (6.5 ft) long and less than 1 m (3.3 ft) wide, pinnately ribbed, with toothed margins. It is shortly bifid at the tip, but otherwise undivided unless split by wind. Moderately branched inflorescence is among the leaves. Flowers in triads. Fruit are large and globose, up to 15 cm (6 in) in diameter, with a thick warty skin. Only about 12–16 fruit are usually produced.
CULTIVATION: Needs a tropical climate.

Pelagodoxa henryana

PHLOGA

'flō-gà

Phloga is a genus of two species. Both are delightful decorative palms found in the undergrowth of rainforest on the eastern side of Madagascar, from 0–2000 m (0–6500 ft) elevation. Like *Dypsis* palms, they are in much need of further taxonomic study. *Phloga* palms are not well known in cultivation, but have great potential as ornamentals and would be a rewarding addition to any collection.

Phloga nodifera is single-stemmed, reaching 2–3 m (6–10 ft). *P. gracilis* suckers to four to eight stems and reaches 4–8 m (13–26 ft), the stems thicker and fruit larger than in *P. nodifera*. Both species have numerous delicate, irregularly pinnate leaves, which are especially elegant. The leaflets are lanceolate, abruptly pointed and curved down at the tips. Leaf sheaths are tubular, but there is no well-defined crownshaft. The petiole is absent or very short. The long, branching inflorescences (often several in various stages of development) are borne below the leaves. In the bud stage, they are held erect and enclosed in two bracts. Flowers are in triads of one female and two male flowers, with male flowers dominating toward the distal portions of the rachillae. Fruit are single-seeded, narrowly ellipsoidal, smooth-skinned and bright red when ripe.

Phloga gracilis

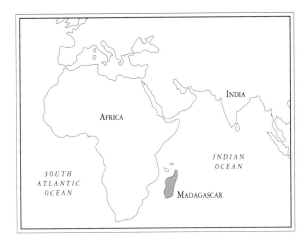

Phloga gracilis

COMMON NAME: None known.

SIZE: Slender, clumping palm, 4–8 m (13–26 ft) tall and 2.5–5 cm (1–2 in) in diameter.

HABITAT: Rainforest undergrowth from 300–2000 m (1000–6500 ft).

DISTRIBUTION: Madagascar.

CONSERVATION STATUS: Possibly extinct. Cannot be found in the wild.

DESCRIPTION: Has 4–8 stems per clump. Stems ringed. Pinnate leaves are about 1 m (3.3 ft) long. Leaflets are longer and narrower than in *P. nodifera*, in near-opposite groups of 3–5 leaflet pairs along the rachis, the distal leaflets much smaller and shorter than those proximal and in the centre of the rachis. Fruit are wider and longer than *P. nodifera*, about 1.2 cm (0.5 in) long and red when ripe.

CULTIVATION: Needs a warm humid climate, but exhibits some cold hardiness.

Phloga nodifera

syn. *Phloga polystacchya, Dypsis nodifera*

COMMON NAME: None known.

SIZE: Slender stem, 2–3 m (6.5–10 ft) tall and 2–4 cm (0.8–1.6 in) in diameter.

HABITAT: Rainforest undergrowth from sea level up to 1400 m (4500 ft).

DISTRIBUTION: Madagascar.

CONSERVATION STATUS: Not threatened.

DESCRIPTION: Stems ringed. Pinnate leaves are about 1 m (3.3 ft) long. Leaflets are short, in near-opposite groups of 2–4 leaflet pairs along the rachis. The terminal group of about 14 are fanned attractively. Fruit are narrow, 0.7–0.9 cm (0.3–0.4 in) long and red when ripe. *P. nodifera* closely resembles *Dypsis pinnatifrons*. It is readily distinguishable by its ruminate seed (*D. pinnatifrons* has homogenous seed).

CULTIVATION: Needs a warm humid climate, but exhibits some cold hardiness.

Phloga gracilis

Phloga nodifera

PHOENICOPHORIUM
'fe-nik-ō-,for-ē-um

*P*hoenicophorium (syn. *Stevensonia)* is represented by the species *P. borsigianum.* A highly ornamental palm with large undivided leaves, it is found naturally in the Seychelles where it grows in abundance in secondary forest from sea level to about 300 m (1000 ft). *P. borsigianum* has been able to form pure stands with the leaves making a close canopy about 12 m (40 ft) high, which virtually excludes any direct light from the forest floor. These palms need a warm tropical climate with good moisture and shade in the early stages of growth. Propagation is from seed, which requires warmth for germination.

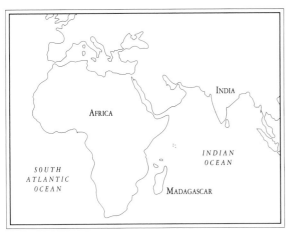

Phoenicophorium borsigianum

Phoenicophorium borsigianum

syn. *Stevensonia borsigiana*
COMMON NAME: Latanier feuille.
SIZE: Solitary trunk, 10–16 m (33–52 ft) tall and 8–10 cm (3–4 in) in diameter.
HABITAT: Secondary forest from sea level to about 300 m (1000 ft).
DISTRIBUTION: Seychelles Islands.
CONSERVATION STATUS: Unknown.
DESCRIPTION: Trunk, leaf sheath, petiole, and rachis bear black spines when young. Leaf blades are entire (unless split by the wind), pinnately ribbed, with a bifid tip, the margins splitting into narrow, ribbed lobes that are bifid at the tips. The well-branched inflorescences arise among the leaves, but mature below the leaves. Inflorescence enclosed in two long bracts in the bud stage, the lower bract persisting. Flowers in triads. Fruit are small, ovoid to oblong, single-seeded, 0.8–1 cm (0.3–0.4 in) long and red when ripe.
CULTIVATION: Needs a tropical climate.

Phoenicophorium borsigianum

PHOENIX

'fe-nix

*P*hoenix is a strictly Old World genus, with about 17 species ranging from Taiwan, Hong Kong and the Philippines, across the Malay Peninsula and Sumatra, through India and the Middle East and across Africa to the Atlantic islands off the west coast of Africa. Fossil records show a distribution that extended into Europe and North America. Most species are known as date palms, *Phoenix dactylifera* being of particular importance in the food supply of the Middle East and northern Africa. The majority of species are found in semi-arid regions where they often gain their water supply from underground sources. A few species are found in tropical monsoonal areas.

Growth habit varies from dwarf or creeping to tall robust trees. *Phoenix* palms may be solitary or clustering, and their trunks are often covered in spirally-arranged, persistent leaf bases. Leaves do not readily fall when they die, so it is common to see a number of dead leaves below the crown. Leaves are pinnate and distinctively induplicate — the leaflets make a V in their attachment with the rachis. Other distinctive features of *Phoenix* leaves are the presence of a terminal leaflet and of spines which are modified lower leaflets. Leaflets are regularly arranged or variously grouped, have a prominent midrib on the undersurface and taper to a sharp point. *Phoenix* palms are dioecious, with male and female inflorescences, although superficially similar,

being on separate plants. Arising among the leaves, inflorescences are simple-branched, enclosed by a bract while in the bud stage, the bract falling after the inflorescence has opened. Flowers are arranged spirally along the rachillae. Fruit is usually single-seeded, ovoid to oblong, smooth-skinned with a fleshy mesocarp. It is the fleshy part of the fruit which is edible.

Suitable for a wide range of climates, the date palms have become popular ornamentals. They generally tolerate poor soils in an arid environment. Fresh seed usually germinates readily. Young plants can grow in an open sunny location and dry winds provided they are watered well. Most species also tolerate cold. They can also be grown in warm to cool temperate areas. *Phoenix* palms hybridise freely and seed may not be 'true to type' if other *Phoenix* species are in the vicinity.

The date palm, *Phoenix dactylifera*, of great economic and dietary importance in the Middle East and northern Africa, is now cultivated in California as a successful fruit crop.

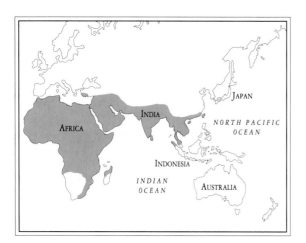

Phoenix canariensis

Phoenix canariensis

COMMON NAME: Canary Islands date palm.
SIZE: Solitary thick trunk, up to approximately 15 m (50 ft) or more tall and 70 cm (28 in) in diameter.
HABITAT: Dry open slopes on soils of volcanic origin.
DISTRIBUTION: Canary Islands.
CONSERVATION STATUS: Unknown.
DESCRIPTION: Distinctive pattern of leaf scars on the trunk. Leaves are up to 6 m (20 ft) long with numerous long, stiff, sharply-pointed leaflets. Inflorescence branches are yellow. Fruit are oblong, 2 cm (0.8 in) long and yellow when ripe.
CULTIVATION: Adaptable to tropical, subtropical or temperate climates. Very frost hardy.

Phoenix dactylifera

Phoenix dactylifera

COMMON NAME: Date palm.
SIZE: Solitary trunk, up to 30 m (100 ft) tall. Clustering (unless suckers removed).
HABITAT: Warm arid regions where it draws water from underground sources or nearby watercourses.
DISTRIBUTION: North Africa, the Middle East, India.
CONSERVATION STATUS: Not threatened.
DESCRIPTION: Has a distinctive pattern of leaf scars on the trunk. Leaves are grey-green, up to 3 m (10 ft) long, with numerous stiff, sharply-pointed leaflets, often borne in pairs in 1 or 2 planes. Fruit are oblong, 4–7 cm (1.6–2.8 in) long and yellowish brown or reddish when ripe. Fleshy mesocarp is sweet.
CULTIVATION: Commercially cultivated for the fruit. Grown from selected suckers cut from older plants.

Phoenix paludosa

Phoenix paludosa

COMMON NAME: Mangrove date palm.
SIZE: Can form dense thickets. Narrow trunks up to about 4 m (13 ft) or more tall and 5–8 cm (2–3 in) in diameter.
HABITAT: Low-lying wet areas adjacent to mangrove swamps.
DISTRIBUTION: Sumatra, India, Peninsular Malaysia, Thailand.
CONSERVATION STATUS: Vulnerable in Peninsular Malaysia and Sumatra. Status unknown elsewhere.
DESCRIPTION: Leaf sheath is covered with coarse fibres. Leaves are twisted and drooping. Leaflets are green above and grey beneath. They are grouped, and arise in different planes. Petioles have long spines. Fruits are ovoid, about 1 cm (0.4 in) long and orange or black when ripe.
CULTIVATION: Has edible 'hearts'. Leaves are used for fencing, thatch and umbrellas. A small amount of edible starch can be obtained from the trunk. Needs a tropical to subtropical climate. Sensitive to cold.

Phoenix canariensis

Phoenix reclinata

COMMON NAME: African wild date.

SIZE: Clustering, narrow trunks up to 15 m (50 ft) tall and 25–30 cm (10–12 in) in diameter.

HABITAT: Usually along the banks of streams and close to watercourses. Sometimes coastal or in very dry habitats.

DISTRIBUTION: Tropical and southern Africa.

CONSERVATION STATUS: Unknown.

DESCRIPTION: Often develops 10–20 stems in a cluster, the trunks growing at an angle away from the other trunks. Leaves are 2–3 m (6.5–10 ft) long, twist and arch strongly and form a more open crown than in most other species. Inflorescences are enclosed in bud in a boat-shaped bract. Fruits are ovoid, orange-yellow to brown and about 1.5–2.0 cm (0.6–0.8 in) long.

CULTIVATION: Fruit is edible. Adaptable to a wide range of climates from tropical to temperate. Tolerates frost.

Phoenix reclinata

Phoenix roebelenii

Phoenix roebelenii

COMMON NAME: Dwarf date, pygmy date.

SIZE: Slender trunk, up to 2 m (6.5 ft) tall, sometimes more.

HABITAT: River banks.

DISTRIBUTION: Northeast India, Myanmar (Burma).

CONSERVATION STATUS: Unknown.

DESCRIPTION: Peg-like persistent leaf bases on the trunk. Crown is dense, the leaves about 2 m (6.5 ft) long, gently curved and drooping. Leaflets are glossy green, very slender, evenly spaced and drooping. Fruit are small, ovoid, purple-black when ripe and often produced in abundance.

CULTIVATION: Edible fruit. Adaptable to a wide range of climates from tropical to temperate. Tolerates cold. Can be grown in shade or open sunny locations. Suitable as an indoor plant.

Phoenix sylvestris

COMMON NAME: Indian wild date, sugar date palm.

SIZE: Solitary trunk, up to 12 m (40 ft) tall, and approximately 40 cm (16 in) in diameter.

HABITAT: Coastal and inland plains.

DISTRIBUTION: India.

CONSERVATION STATUS: Unknown.

DESCRIPTION: Very like *P. canariensis*, but the crown is more compact and the leaves are bluish-green and 3–4 m (10–13 ft) long. Fruit are oblong, 2 cm (0.8 in) long and dark red when ripe.

CULTIVATION: In India, the peduncle is tapped for the sugary sap, which is boiled down to make jaggery (palm sugar). Fruit are also edible. Leaves are used for weaving various articles and making brooms. Adaptable to tropical, subtropical or temperate climates. Tolerates frost.

Phoenix sylvestris

PHYTELEPHAS
fyt-ĕl-ĕ-fas

*P*hytelephas (which includes *Palandra*), *Ammandra* and *Aphandra* are the three genera in the subfamily Phytelephantoideae, which contains the so-called 'ivory' palms. The subfamily is worthy of a brief introduction because of its extraordinary differences from palms in other subfamilies. The superficial resemblance of the fruiting head to that of *Nypa* led these palms to be included in the same group, but the floral and fruit structure is quite different. Whereas each fruit of *Nypa* is single-seeded, derived from one carpel of a three-carpellate flower, in *Phytelephas* each fruit is four- to ten-seeded and derived from syncarpous, multi-carpellate flowers. There are 15 species described in the subfamily (one each in *Ammandra* and *Aphandra*, and 13 in *Phytelephas*), but there will probably be fewer recognised after more work is completed on this interesting group. Distribution is in Panama and northern South America. All palms in this subfamily produce very hard seed which is used for ivory carving, particularly for making ivory buttons.

Phytelephas are moderate to large palms, solitary or clustering, sometimes lacking a visible trunk. Leaf bases persist and break down to a mass of fibres. The trunk may eventually be bare and is marked by old leaf bases. Leaves are pinnate, leaflets arranged regularly or in groups, and arising in two planes from the rachis. Leaflets are reduplicate, forming an upside down V in cross-section. *Phytelephas* palms are dioecious, the male and female inflorescences being on different plants. Inflorescences arise among the leaves. The female inflorescence is a large head of flowers held close to the stem, each flower having conspicuous long, fleshy sepals and petals. The male inflorescence is an elongate spike. Male flowers are unusual for the hundreds of stamens they contain, up to 1000 per flower in *Phytelephas aequatorialis*. Fruit are borne in large headlike clusters, the individual fruits more or less rounded, four- to ten-seeded, and covered with large, woody, pointed warts.

Seed germinate readily if fresh, but are otherwise extremely slow to germinate. Seed dormancy may be broken with heat treatment such as hot water soaking or exposing the seed to open sunlight. *Phytelephas* are generally reputed to grow slowly, but have been reported as growing relatively fast in a tropical climate with a good water supply. They are rarely seen in botanical collections.

Phytelephas decasperma
(female inflorescence)

Phytelephas aequatorialis

Phytelephas aequatorialis

COMMON NAME: Ivory palm.
SIZE: Solitary trunk, up to 4 m (13 ft) tall.
HABITAT: Rainforest up to 1600 m (5200 ft).
DISTRIBUTION: Ecuador.
CONSERVATION STATUS: Unknown.
DESCRIPTION: Trunk is covered with leaf bases and eventually becomes bare. Old inflorescences persist below the crown. Leaves are nearly 6 m (20 ft) long. Petiole short. There are more than 100 leaflets on each side of the rachis, irregularly arranged in 2 planes and often in groups of 2–5. Male inflorescence is more than 30 cm (1 ft) long, with fruiting heads about 30 cm (1 ft) across.
CULTIVATION: Provides vegetable ivory. Needs a tropical climate.

PIGAFETTA

'pĭg-à-ˌfĕt-à

*P*igafetta is a monotypic genus, with *Pigafetta filaris* from Sulawesi, the Moluccas and New Guinea the sole representative species. This fast-growing, handsome tropical palm can become massive with its solitary trunk reaching up to 50 m (160 ft) in its natural habitat. Described as a pioneer palm, it grows on disturbed land, old landslips and cleared land that is reverting to secondary forest. It is also found on riverbanks and in montane rainforests 300–1500 m (1000–5000 ft) above sea level where any disturbance has broken the forest canopy. Its small seed germinate rapidly and seedlings apparently require constant moisture and high light intensities. These requirements have made growing *Pigafetta* somewhat difficult outside the tropics. *P. filaris* is, however, growing well in the subtropical environment of the Mt Coot-tha Botanic Gardens, Brisbane (Australia). Juvenile plants need protection from wind, but respond to direct sunlight with hardy growth.

Pigafetta filaris

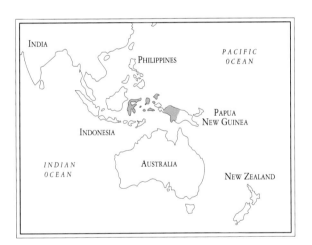

Pigafetta filaris

COMMON NAME: Pigafetta palm, wanga.
SIZE: Solitary, clearly-ringed trunk, up to 50 m (160 ft) tall.
HABITAT: Disturbed forest.
DISTRIBUTION: Sulawesi, the Moluccas, New Guinea.
CONSERVATION STATUS: Unknown.
DESCRIPTION: Leaves are up to about 6 m (20 ft) long, pinnate, strongly curved and with gold-coloured spines on the leaf rachis, petioles and the leaf sheaths. Leaf sheath is split opposite the petiole. Leaflets are long, numerous, and armed with short bristles on the margins and main veins. Dioecious. Inflorescences are moderately branched large panicles, maturing below the leaves. Fruit are globose, 1 cm (0.4 in) in diameter, yellowish, and have a patterned skin of scales.
CULTIVATION: Suitable for a tropical to subtropical climate.

Pigafetta filaris

PINANGA

pin-'ăng-à

P*inanga* is one of the largest genera of palms, with over 120 known species. There are sure to be more as yet not studied. They vary from very small colony-forming plants with stems less than 30 cm (1 ft) high to large trees that form part of the rainforest canopy. Most, however, are in the 2–5 m (6.5–16 ft) range and form part of the low to mid-storey layer of humid rainforests. Distributed throughout India, Taiwan, the Malay Peninsula, the Philippines, Indonesia and New Guinea, their greatest diversity is to be found in Borneo.

Stems may be solitary or clustering, or sometimes apparently lacking altogether. Usually they exhibit a well-developed, and sometimes brightly-coloured, crownshaft formed by the sheathing tubular leaf bases. Below the crownshaft, rings mark the stem where the leaves have neatly fallen away. Some *Pinanga* palms have stilt roots to support their narrow stems and long leaves. In some species, a broken or fallen stem will layer, producing roots from the leaf scars along the stem. Many *Pinanga* species sucker freely, thus forming spreading clumps with many leaves. The variation in leaf form is perhaps one of the most attractive features of this genus. Some have broad segments with pinnate venations, others are narrowly pinnate. Almost all have a terminal united pair of leaflets. Some have delightfully mottled leaves, others have pale or pinkish newly-emergent leaves, which become greener as they mature. The inflorescence is below the crownshaft, except in acaulescent species in which it arises among the leaf bases. It is usually short, unbranched or simple-branched, and bears triads of flowers throughout the entire length of the rachillae. The inflorescence in bud is enclosed by a membranous bract (prophyll). Fruit are variously shaped from globose to an elongate spindle, and are bright crimson, scarlet, orange or black, or, occasionally, brown or green when ripe. Often the rachillae are a bright red-orange.

Pinanga palms are popular in cultivation in tropical climates or with the use of a hothouse to simulate a tropical microclimate. Seeds usually germinate readily in a few weeks and young plants grow quickly given a warm, moist, shaded environment. A few species tolerate subtropical climates, but most are definite tropicals with little hardiness to cold or dryness.

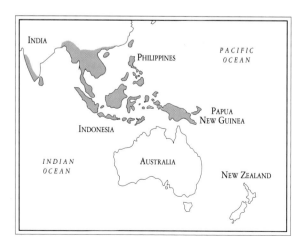

Pinanga maculata

Pinanga coronata

syn. *Pinanga kuhlii*

COMMON NAME: Pinang (Indonesia).
SIZE: Clustering stems, 5–7 m (16–23 ft) tall.
HABITAT: Rainforest from lowlands to 1500 m (5000 ft) altitude.
DISTRIBUTION: Sumatra, Java.
CONSERVATION STATUS: Unknown. Probably not threatened.
DESCRIPTION: A highly variable growth habit. Leaves are often lightly mottled. Leaflets vary in width, but are usually wide. Inflorescences are branched, the rachillae red. Fruit turn from red to black as they ripen, are egg-shaped and about 1.2 cm (0.5 in) long. Note that *P. coronata* and *P. kuhlii* were considered separate species, but they form a continuum from low to high altitude in their natural habitat.
CULTIVATION: Adaptable in cultivation to tropical and subtropical climates. A very popular garden and pot plant. Propagation from suckers is difficult.

Pinanga densiflora

COMMON NAME: Pinang (Indonesia).
SIZE: Clustering thin stems, up to about 4 m (13 ft) tall.
HABITAT: Close to watercourses from 300–800 m (1000–2600 ft).
DISTRIBUTION: Sumatra.
CONSERVATION STATUS: Unknown. Probably not threatened.
DESCRIPTION: Leaves have a beautiful dark green mottle on lighter green background. Leaflets are of variable width, irregularly placed and with pointed tips (except for the truncate and toothed terminal pair). Mottling is less evident in mature plant. Crownshaft is red in juvenile plants. Fruit are ovoid, arranged spirally on the rachillae, pink becoming black, and about 1.2 cm (0.5 in) long.
CULTIVATION: Cultivation is from suckers, and is reputed to be difficult.

Pinanga coronata (syn. *P. kuhlii*)

Pinanga densiflora

Pinanga disticha

Pinanga disticha

syn. *Areca disticha*

COMMON NAME: Pinang (Indonesia).
SIZE: Small clumping palm, up to approximately 1.2 m (4 ft) tall.
HABITAT: Common in forest undergrowth from the lowlands to elevations of 1200 m (4000 ft).
DISTRIBUTION: Peninsular Malaysia, Sumatra.
CONSERVATION STATUS: Rare in Sumatra, vulnerable in Peninsular Malaysia.
DESCRIPTION: Has fine brown stems, sometimes with axillary shoots from upper leaf scars. Has bifid leaves, sometimes further divided into more leaflets. Leaf mottling varies from distinct and intense to barely discernible or absent. Inflorescences are spicate. Fruits are oblong, about 1 cm (0.4 in) long and red when ripe.
CULTIVATION: Needs a warm tropical to subtropical climate with a good water supply. It also needs shade and high humidity.

Pinanga limosa

COMMON NAME: None known.
SIZE: Solitary small palm, usually 1–2 m (3.3–6 ft) tall, sometimes more.
HABITAT: Undergrowth palm from the lowlands up to mountain rainforest at 1200 m (4000 ft).
DISTRIBUTION: Peninsular Malaysia, Borneo.
CONSERVATION STATUS: Vulnerable in Sarawak and Peninsular Malaysia.
DESCRIPTION: Stem is around 1.5 cm (0.6 in) in diameter and pale in colour. Leaves are very variable in shape, from entire bifid to pinnate with irregularly-placed wide tapering leaflets and a united terminal leaflet pair. Often intermediate forms exist and sometimes various leaf arrangements exist on the same plant. Inflorescences are spicate. Fruits are held in 2 rows and are elliptical, about 1.5 cm (0.5 in) long and white, pale yellow or waxy pink in colour, ripening to black.
CULTIVATION: Needs a warm climate with a good water supply, shade and high humidity.

Pinanga maculata

syn. *Pinanga barnesii*
COMMON NAME: Tiger palm.
SIZE: Solitary trunk, up to about 5 m (16 ft) tall.
HABITAT: Mountain rainforest understorey from 300–800 m (1000–2600 ft). Often found near streams.
DISTRIBUTION: The island of Luzon (Philippines).
CONSERVATION STATUS: Indeterminate. Probably endangered. Seeds and/or plants have been overcollected by palm collectors. Habitat area is threatened with destruction.
DESCRIPTION: Leaves are about 1.5–2 m (5–6.5 ft) long with wide, irregularly-placed, truncate (sometimes mottled) segments with toothed outer margins. Leaves are paler on underside. Crownshaft is purple-brown in colour. Fruits are arranged spirally on the rachillae. They are ovoid, 2.1–2.8 cm (0.8–1.1 in) long, red turning to black when ripe.
CULTIVATION: Needs a warm climate with a good water supply, shade and high humidity.

Pinanga limosa

Pinanga malaiana

syn. *Seaforthia malaiana*
COMMON NAME: Legong (Malaysia).
SIZE: Solitary stemmed or clumping, approximately 2–5 m (6–16 ft) tall.
HABITAT: Widespread from lowlands to mountain rainforests, up to about 900 m (3000 ft).
DISTRIBUTION: Peninsular Malaysia, Sumatra.
CONSERVATION STATUS: Vulnerable in Peninsular Malaysia, not threatened in Sumatra.
DESCRIPTION: Moderately sized Pinanga with a prominently-ringed green stem (about 4 cm (1.5 in) in diameter) and a light brown to bronze crownshaft. Long, flat, broad pinnate leaves have narrow, evenly-divided leaflets. Inflorescence is pendulous and consists of 2–5 simple branches, which turn pink to red as the fruit (in 2 rows) ripens, through to a pale pink to purple red. Fruit are large, ovoid, up to about 2.5 cm (1 in) long.

Pinanga patula

COMMON NAME: Pinang (Indonesia and Malaysia).
SIZE: Forms clumps up to 4 m (13 ft) tall, from underground stems.
HABITAT: In rainforest undergrowth up to about 800 m (2600 ft).
DISTRIBUTION: Peninsular Malaysia, Sumatra, Borneo.
CONSERVATION STATUS: Insufficiently known in Sarawak, vulnerable in Peninsular Malaysia, no data in Sumatra or Kalimantan.
DESCRIPTION: Has thin brown-green stems with prominent leaf scars. Short pinnate leaves have broad pointed leaflets, the terminal pair broad. Crownshaft is silvery-green. Inflorescence has 3–4 simple branches which turn red as the ovoid fruit (1.5 cm (0.6 in) long), turn from green to red and finally black when ripe.
CULTIVATION: Can withstand open sun, but does better with some shade.

Pinanga malaiana

Pinanga maculata (syn. *P. barnesii*)

Pinanga patula

Pinanga pilosa

Pinanga pilosa

syn. *Pseudopinanga pilosa, Pinanga pilosa* var. *gracilior*

COMMON NAME: None known.
SIZE: Small clustering palm, up to about 1 m (3.3 ft).
HABITAT: Undergrowth of montane rainforest, from 1000–3000 m (3300–10000 ft).
DISTRIBUTION: Borneo.
CONSERVATION STATUS: Insufficiently known in Sarawak, not threatened in Sabah.
DESCRIPTION: Fine green stems are prominently marked with widely-spaced leaf scars. Crownshaft not well developed. Leaves are mottled green, divided into 3 or 4 pairs of broad, tapering leaflets, the terminal pair broad. Inflorescence of several simple branches is below the leaves. Fruit are arranged spirally on the rachillae. They are small and pointed, yellow at maturity.
CULTIVATION: Needs a tropical climate with a good water supply, shade and high humidity.

Pinanga polymorpha

Pinanga polymorpha

syn. *Pinanga brewsteriana, P. glaucescens, P. robusta*

COMMON NAME: None known.
SIZE: From very small up to 2 m (6.5 ft) tall or more.
HABITAT: Forms large colonies in moist areas of mountain rainforests above 500 m (1700 ft).
DISTRIBUTION: Peninsular Malaysia, Sumatra.
CONSERVATION STATUS: Vulnerable in Peninsular Malaysia, indeterminate in Sumatra.
DESCRIPTION: Stems are slender, lower nodes may develop roots. Extremely variable in leaf shape and plant size. Small plants are more likely to have entire bifid leaves while taller plants may have a pinnate leaf with broad irregularly-placed segments, slightly glaucous beneath. Inflorescence has 2–3 simple branches. Fruit are dark green, oblong, about 1.2 cm (0.5 in) long and ripen to black.
CULTIVATION: Needs a warm climate with deep shade and protection from wind.

Pinanga simplicifrons

Pinanga scortechinii

COMMON NAME: None known.
SIZE: Solitary, rarely clumping, 2–5 m (6.5–16 ft) tall.
HABITAT: Lowlands to mountain rainforest, up to about 900 m (3000 ft).
DISTRIBUTION: Endemic to Peninsular Malaysia.
CONSERVATION STATUS: Vulnerable.
DESCRIPTION: Stem is about 2.5 cm (1 in) in diameter with a well-developed bronze-brown crownshaft. Long pinnate leaves have many narrow pointed leaflets. Inflorescence has 5–6 simple branches held erect. Fruits are arranged spirally and close together on the rachillae. They are oblong-ovoid, about 1.5 cm (0.6 in) long, turning from white to pink and ruby-red when ripe.

Pinanga scortechinii

Pinanga simplicifrons

COMMON NAME: None known.
SIZE: Small slender stems, up to 60 cm (2 ft) tall, occasionally up to 120 cm (4 ft).
HABITAT: Lowland forest. Sometimes in locations subject to periodic flooding.
DISTRIBUTION: Sumatra, Peninsular Malaysia, Sarawak, Brunei.
CONSERVATION STATUS: Vulnerable in Peninsular Malaysia. Status unknown elsewhere.
DESCRIPTION: Leaves are entire and elongate, deeply bifid. Occasionally divided into broad leaflets. Crownshaft is up to 30 cm (12 in) long. Short inflorescence, about 2.5 cm (1 in) long, is unbranched, enclosed by the persistent bract. Fruit are sickle-shaped, turning from green to red as they ripen, and are about 1.7 cm (0.7 in) long.
CULTIVATION: Little known in cultivation.

PRITCHARDIA

prĭt-'chărd-ē-à

Pritchardia has 33 species from the Hawaiian Islands and four species from other Pacific islands, including Fiji, Tonga, the Danger Islands, the Cook Islands, the Tuamoto Archipelago and the Solomon Islands. As more taxonomic work is done, the number of species is likely to be reduced. Botanical garden specimens are confusing at times, some being the product of hybridisation and showing features at variance with those of their nominal parent. Most from the Hawaiian Islands, known collectively as lo'ulu palms, are difficult to cultivate outside their native islands, and many are rare and endangered species. A few species are known to be extinct in the wild, while others have only a few known individual plants left in habitat. The species from Fiji and Tonga, on the other hand, are easier to cultivate and have gained popularity in subtropical and tropical areas. Interestingly, the Hawaiian *Pritchardia* palms are grown more successfully in warm, frost-free temperate areas than in subtropical and tropical areas. This is probably because their natural habitats are mostly the mountainous terrain of the wetter windward sides of the islands at altitudes of around 500 m (1600 ft), but sometimes up to 1400 m (4600 ft) where the temperatures are considerably cooler than down on the flat coastal plains. Often they grow in near soil-less situations on precipitous cliffs with their roots firmly attached and invading porous volcanic rock.

Pritchardia palms are moderate, solitary, tree palms with clean, ringed trunks and no crownshaft. Leaves are costapalmate and distinctly pleated, often almost circular, the stiffly-held blades divided (to up to half their depth) into tapering pointed segments split at the tip. The leaf sheath is tomentose and disintegrates into a mass of fibres. Petioles are long and smooth, without spines or teeth. Inflorescences arise among the leaves and in some species hang down well below the crown. The peduncle is relatively long with the flowering branches held in a fairly tight cluster at the end. The inflorescence is enclosed in the bud stage by a large bract and several smaller bracts. Flowers are bisexual, scattered singly along the rachillae, with the petals being deciduous, a characteristic of this genus. Fruit are small, globose to ovoid, have a thin mesocarp and carry one seed.

Pritchardias are grown as ornamentals from seed that germinates within a few months. *Pritchardia* palms are unfortunately susceptible to the lethal yellowing disease and so are best planted in areas free of this disease.

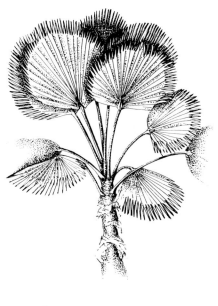

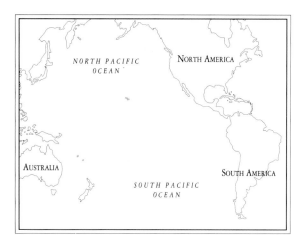

Pritchardia pacifica

Pritchardia martii

COMMON NAME: Lo'ulu palm.
SIZE: Solitary trunk, 3–10 m (10–33 ft) tall.
HABITAT: Volcanic slopes, ridges and cliff faces from 360–1000 m (1200–3300 ft).
DISTRIBUTION: Hawaiian Islands.
CONSERVATION STATUS: Not threatened.
DESCRIPTION: Dense crown of leaves. Petiole is about 1 m (3.3 ft) long, leaf blade 1 m (3.3 ft) across and shallowly divided to about one third depth, with a silvery grey undersurface. Inflorescence is shorter than the leaves and flowers are yellow. Fruit are egg-shaped, 4–5 cm (1.6–2 in) long.
CULTIVATION: Suitable for warm temperate frost-free areas.

Pritchardia martii

Pritchardia thurstonii

COMMON NAME: None known.
SIZE: Solitary trunk, up to about 8 m (26 ft) tall, occasionally up to 15 m (50 ft), approximately 20 cm (8 in) in diameter.
HABITAT: Dense colonies on limestone soils in hot dry locations.
DISTRIBUTION: Fiji.
CONSERVATION STATUS: Unknown.
DESCRIPTION: Petiole is about 1 m (3.3 ft) long. Leaf blade is slightly paler on the underside, 1 m (3.3 ft) across and shallowly divided to about one third its depth. Inflorescence is pendulous and longer than the leaves. Fruit are globose, 0.7 cm (0.3 in) in diameter and deep red when ripe.
CULTIVATION: Suitable for tropical and subtropical areas.

Pritchardia pacifica

COMMON NAME: Fijian fan palm.
SIZE: Solitary trunk, up to 10 m (33 ft) or more tall, 30 cm (1 ft) in diameter.
HABITAT: Unknown in the wild state.
DISTRIBUTION: Commonly cultivated in Tonga, Western Samoa and Fiji.
CONSERVATION STATUS: Unknown.
DESCRIPTION: Dense crown of about 20 leaves. Petiole is about 1 m (3.3 ft) long, leaf blade is 1 m (3.3 ft) across and shallowly divided to about one third its depth. Inflorescence is shorter than the leaves, and flowers are yellow-green. Fruit are globose, about 1.2 cm (0.5 in) in diameter and dark brown.
CULTIVATION: Suitable for tropical to subtropical areas.

Pritchardia pacifica

Pritchardia remota

COMMON NAME: Lo'ulu palm.
SIZE: Slender solitary trunk, 4–5 m (13–16 ft) tall, approximately 15 cm (6 in) in diameter.
HABITAT: High valleys in moist deep soil at the foot of basalt cliffs, from 200–800 m (650–2600 ft).
DISTRIBUTION: Nihoa Island (Hawaiian Islands).
CONSERVATION STATUS: Endangered.
DESCRIPTION: Petiole is about 1.5 m (5 ft) long, leaf blade is 1.5 m (5 ft) across and deeply divided to about halfway. Inflorescence is shorter than the leaves. Fruit are globose to slightly ovoid, up to 2 cm (0.8 in) long and pale green-brown.
CULTIVATION: Suitable for warm temperate areas and reported to tolerate light frosts.

Pritchardia thurstonii

Pritchardia remota

PSEUDOPHOENIX

ˌsēu-dō-ˈfē-nix

*P*seudophoenix has four recognised species, all found on the Caribbean island of Hispaniola. One species, *Pseudophoenix sargentii*, is found also in Florida, Cuba, the Bahamas, Honduras, Belize and Mexico. They are hardy palms, occurring on well-drained sandy soils or porous limestone in areas with low rainfall.

Solitary palms of moderate size, *Pseudophoenix* palms have prominently-ringed trunks which may be swollen for some of their length. The crown has about ten pinnate leaves. The sheathing leaf bases split opposite the petiole and form a short, slightly swollen, waxy, grey-green crownshaft. Leaflets are numerous, stiffly held, irregularly arranged in groups and fanned within the groups. Inflorescences arise among the leaves, and are well-branched panicles. Most flowers are bisexual and are borne singly in spirals on the rachillae, a few male flowers borne at the distal ends. Fruit are globose or with two or three lobes, smooth-skinned, one- to three-seeded and waxy red.

Pseudophoenix sargentii

Pseudophoenix sargentii

Pseudophoenix sargentii

COMMON NAME: Sargent's palm, buccaneer palm.
SIZE: Ringed trunk, 4–8 m (13–26 ft) tall and approx. 40 cm (16 in) in diameter, swollen at the base or some higher point along the trunk.
HABITAT: Along the seaside on well-drained limestone or sandy soils, usually protected from direct sea winds. Often in places subject to frequent inundation by sea water.
DISTRIBUTION: Hispaniola, Florida, Cuba, the Bahamas, Honduras, Belize, Mexico.
CONSERVATION STATUS: Not threatened.
DESCRIPTION: Leaves are blue-green, 1.5–3 m (5–10 ft) long. Leaflets are stiffly held, arising at different angles, singly or in groups of a few. They are grey-green or silvery on the undersurface. Fruit are globose, red, single-seeded, or with 2 or 3 lobes and as many seeds. They are up to about 1.7 cm (0.7 in) in diameter.
CULTIVATION: Variable in growth habit. Grows best in well drained sandy soil with a limestone content. Tolerates salty soils, salt spray and frosts.

PTYCHOSPERMA

ˌtȳ-kō-'spĕrm-à

*P*tychosperma is mainly distributed in New Guinea, with many of the 28 known species coming from the rainforests of the mountainous southeastern tip. Other species are found in the Moluccas, the Caroline Islands, the Solomon Islands, the D'Entrecasteaux, Bismarck and Louisiade Archipelagos, and northern Australia. A revision of the genus by Essig in 1978 provides the latest detailed information. However, more species have since been described and, it is thought, more are yet to be discovered. Essig has described four subgenera and two sections of one subgenus, each having a distinct distribution range and habitat.

Ptychosperma palms are small to moderate in size, with a solitary stem or clustering to many smooth-ringed stems. The crown is composed of relatively few rather short pinnate leaves. The leaf bases are sheathing, forming a prominent crownshaft which may have a scaly or tomentose covering. The apex of the sheath opposite the petiole may have a ligule-like appendage. In most species, the leaflets are elongate, with an obliquely praemorse or chewed-looking apex, or a notched apex. In a few species, the leaflets are fishtail- or wedge-shaped with a concave apex. Leaflets vary in number, may be regularly or irregularly arranged, or grouped into clusters along the rachis. The inflorescence is a short-stemmed panicle (the amount of branching varies) arising below the crownshaft. Tthe flowers are carried in triads.

Near the tips of the rachillae the flowers are often male only. The inflorescence in bud is enclosed by two (occasionally more) overlapping bracts. Fruits are usually 1–2 cm (0.4–0.8 in), round to ovoid, single-seeded, with a fleshy mesocarp. Some species have purple-black fruit carried on red branches, others have orange or red fruit. Seeds of most species have five longitudinal grooves.

One of the most successful palms in cultivation in the tropics is the Macarthur palm, *Ptychosperma macarthurii*, which is used extensively in the street landscaping of Singapore. *Ptychosperma elegans*, the solitaire palm, is also popular in the tropics and subtropics as a garden landscape subject. Hybridisation is common within the *Ptychosperma* palms, and it is often difficult to put a definite name to some of the plants grown by the nursery trade because plants have taken on characteristics of both parent species. In general, *Ptychosperma* palms require tropical to subtropical warm climates. Propagation is by seed, but can also be from basal suckers.

Ptychosperma macarthurii

Ptychosperma burretianum

COMMON NAME: None known.

SIZE: Slender solitary palm, 3–8 m (10–26 ft) tall, 3 cm (1.2 in) in diameter.

HABITAT: Rainforest on low hills.

DISTRIBUTION: Normanby Island, D'Entrecasteaux Archipelago.

CONSERVATION STATUS: Unknown.

DESCRIPTION: Leaf sheath has a prominent ligule-like appendage up to 4 cm (1.6 in) long. Leaves are 2–2.5 m (6.5–8 ft) long. Leaflets are regularly arranged, about 11 on each side of the rachis, each up to 26 cm (10.5 in) long and 14 cm (5.5 in) broad, with a concavely praemorse apex. Inflorescence is well branched, and has conspicuous bracts subtending the branches. Branches are bright red when in flower and fruit. Fruit are purple-brown, round to ovoid and 1.5 cm (0.6 in).

CULTIVATION: Warm tropical climate, a semi-shaded position and a good water supply.

Ptychosperma burretianum: purple-brown fruit.

Ptychosperma elegans

COMMON NAME: Solitaire palm.

SIZE: Slender solitary trunk, up to 12 m (40 ft) tall, 6–8 cm (2.5–3 in) in diameter.

HABITAT: Coastal rainforest up to 600 m (2000 ft) on the mountain slopes.

DISTRIBUTION: Northeastern Australia.

CONSERVATION STATUS: Not threatened.

DESCRIPTION: Leaf sheath has no ligule-like appendage. Leaves are about 3 m (10 ft) long, with about 5–10 in the crown. Has about 28 leaflets on each side of the rachis, regularly arranged. They are long, narrow and tapering, up to 1 m (3.3 ft) long, and have an obliquely praemorse apex. Inflorescence is well branched. Fruit are round to ovoid, 0.8–1.5 cm (0.3–0.6 in) and red when ripe.

CULTIVATION: Tropical to subtropical climates and to a variety of soil types.

Ptychosperma elegans

Ptychosperma lineare

COMMON NAME: None known.

SIZE: Sometimes a single stem, usually suckering, up to 10 m (33 ft) tall in its natural habitat, usually less in cultivation. Stems are 4–8 cm (1.6–3.2 in) in diameter.

HABITAT: Low-lying rainforest or swamp forest close to rivers or the coast.

DISTRIBUTION: Southeastern New Guinea.

CONSERVATION STATUS: Unknown.

DESCRIPTION: As for *P. macarthurii*, except the fruit is black when ripe, not red, and the leaflets are generally narrower.

CULTIVATION: Needs a tropical to subtropical climate.

Ptychosperma lineare

Ptychosperma macarthurii

COMMON NAME: Macarthur palm.

SIZE: Sometimes a single stem, especially when young. Usually suckering to many stems. Up to 10 m (33 ft) tall in its natural habitat, usually less in cultivation. Stems are 4–8 cm (1.6–3.2 in) in diameter.

HABITAT: Low-lying rainforest, swamp forest, mangroves, and hill slopes up to 400 m (1300 ft).

DISTRIBUTION: Southern central New Guinea, Torres Strait Islands, eastern Cape York Peninsula (Australia).

CONSERVATION STATUS: Unknown. Probably not threatened.

DESCRIPTION: Leaf sheath has a prominent ligule-like appendage up to 4 cm (1.6 in) long. Leaves are up to 2 m (6.5 ft) long. Leaflets are arranged regularly or grouped, with about 25 on each side of the rachis. Each is up to 60 cm (2 ft) long and 6 cm (2.4 in) wide in the middle, with an obliquely praemorse apex. Inflorescence is well branched, has a covering of brown scales and has conspicuous bracts subtending the branches. Fruit are bright red, round to ovoid, and 1.2–1.7 cm (0.5–0.7 in) long.

CULTIVATION: Can be grown in subtropical conditions and warm temperate climates, but is sensitive to cold. Is adaptable to a range of soils and to open sunny locations. Responds with vigorous growth to a fertile, well-drained soil and plenty of water.

Ptychosperma macarthurii

Ptychosperma microcarpum

COMMON NAME: None known.
SIZE: Solitary or clustering, up to 9 m (30 ft) tall, stems 4–13 cm (1.6–5 in) in diameter.
HABITAT: Lowland rainforest, river banks or swamp forest in savanna country.
DISTRIBUTION: Central New Guinea.
CONSERVATION STATUS: Unknown.
DESCRIPTION: Leaf sheath has a prominent ligule-like appendage up to 15 cm (6 in) long. Has 6–8 leaves in the crown. Leaves are up to about 2.5 m (8 ft) long. Has 35–50 leaflets on each side, up to about 55 cm (20 in) long, deeply notched and praemorse at the apex. They are regularly arranged and usually in distinct alternating clusters along the rachis. Inflorescence well-branched. Fruit are round to ovoid, 1.2–1.4 cm (0.5–0.6 in) long and red when ripe.
CULTIVATION: Needs a warm tropical climate and a good water supply.

Ptychosperma sanderanum

COMMON NAME: None known.
SIZE: Clustering, up to 4 m (13 ft) tall, stems 2.5–5 cm (1–2 in) in diameter.
HABITAT: Original habitat not known.
DISTRIBUTION: Probably southeastern Papua New Guinea.
CONSERVATION STATUS: Known only in cultivation.
DESCRIPTION: Very like *P. macarthurii* except that leaflets are very narrow and elongate, the apex narrow, praemorse and notched. Has 40–50 leaflets on each side of the rachis. Leaves are up to about 1.7 m (5.5 ft) long. Flowers and fruit are very densely arranged on the well-branched inflorescence. Fruit are ovoid, up to 1.8 cm (0.7 in) long and red when ripe.
CULTIVATION: Needs a warm tropical to subtropical climate. Is sensitive to cold.

Ptychosperma microcarpum

Ptychosperma sanderanum

Ptychosperma schefferi

COMMON NAME: None known.
SIZE: Solitary to clumping, up to 7 m (23 ft) tall, stems 5–6 cm (2–2.4 in) in diameter.
HABITAT: Moist locations near the beach or coastal creeks.
DISTRIBUTION: Central northern coast of New Guinea.
CONSERVATION STATUS: Unknown.
DESCRIPTION: Leaf sheath has ligule-like appendages up to 6.5 cm (2.6 in) long. Short petiole, 8–11 cm (3.2–4.5 in) long. Leaves are approximately 2 m (6.5 ft) long. Leaflets are regularly arranged, with 22–25 on each side of the rachis. They are up to 45 cm (18 in) long and 9.5 cm (3.8 in) broad, with the apex obliquely praemorse. Inflorescence is well branched, orange-yellow in fruit. Fruit are ovoid, up to about 2 cm (0.8 in) long and dark red, turning black-purple when ripe.
CULTIVATION: Needs a warm tropical climate and a good water supply.

Ptychosperma schefferi

RAPHIA

'răf-ē-à

Raphia palms are massive, and generally inhabit swamplands in humid tropical Africa. One of the approximately 20 species is also found in tropical America, where it may have been introduced, and one species is found in Madagascar. They are very useful palms to humans, the emerging leaflets being stripped of fibre to be used for weaving various articles, basketware and twine. Leaf bases of some species break down to a mass of long fibres which accumulate on the trunk. These are harvested as 'piassava' and are used to make brushes and ropes. *Raphia* wood has also long been used in west Africa for house building, the petioles in furniture making, and the leaves for thatch. A more recent development in Nigeria is to use wood and leaves of *R. hookeri* to make the pulp for paper manufacture. The stems of several species are tapped for sugary syrup, which is used to make a wine. The fruit mesocarp provides a source of cooking oil.

Most species of *Raphia* have trunks and develop suckers to form dense clumps. Trunks vary in height with the different species and are usually covered in persistent fibrous leaf bases. A few species develop subterranean trunks and one species has a solitary trunk. Their leaves are the largest of all land plants and are sometimes up to 25 m (82 ft) long. The pinnate leaves have a variety of leaflet arrangements, sometimes irregular, sometimes grouped and fanned within the group, giving the leaf a plumose appearance. The one leaf may display a variety of leaflet arrangements. Leaflets are often whitish beneath and have short spines along the midribs and margins. Inflorescences are well branched, of massive size and are pendulous in all but two species, *R. australis* and *R. regalis*, in which the inflorescence is erect and above the leaves. Male and female flowers are borne on the same inflorescence, but the females tend to be placed basally while the male flowers are in the middle and distal portions of the rachillae. *Raphia* palms are hapaxanthic: flowering occurs just once after the trunk has completed its vegetative growth. Inflorescences are produced simultaneously in the axils of the uppermost leaves. Fruit are usually light brown, large, elliptical, single-seeded, the mesocarp thick and oily, and the epicarp covered with scales.

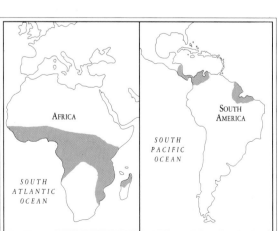

AFRICA

SOUTH AMERICA

SOUTH PACIFIC OCEAN

SOUTH ATLANTIC OCEAN

Raphia australis

Raphia australis

COMMON NAME: Giant raphia.

SIZE: Single trunk, up to 12 m (40 ft) tall and 40 cm (16 in) in diameter.

HABITAT: Swampy forest, often found growing in water.

DISTRIBUTION: South Africa, Mozambique.

CONSERVATION STATUS: Unknown.

DESCRIPTION: Has extra 'breathing' roots that grow upward above water level (similar to mangrove roots), but are also present when the palm is growing out of water. Leaves are up to 18 m (59 ft) long, dark shiny green on upper surface, waxy and glaucous on undersurface. Broad leaflets are arranged in 2 rows along the rachis, with fine spines on the upper surfaces and larger spines near the leaflet bases. Petioles are orange, and grooved on the basal portion. Inflorescence is up to 3 m (10 ft) long, composed of many short, broad partial inflorescences. Fruit are ellipsoid, about 9 cm (3.6 in) long, gold to reddish brown, and covered with rows of scales.

CULTIVATION: Is adaptable to various soil types and grows in swampy to dry locations. Bottom heat is recommended to stimulate seed germination. The petioles are used by local people for building house walls and water rafts. Plants take 20–30 years to mature before flowering.

Raphia australis

Raphia farinifera

syn. *Raphia ruffia*

COMMON NAME: None known.

SIZE: Various forms, some with stems up to 10 m (33 ft) tall, others only 1.5 m (5 ft) tall, all densely clumping.

HABITAT: Swamplands and along rivers.

DISTRIBUTION: East and Central Africa, probably introduced into Madagascar.

CONSERVATION STATUS: Not threatened.

DESCRIPTION: Trunk covered in shredding leaf bases. Leaves are up to 10 m (33 ft) long (15 m (50 ft) in the taller form). Leaflets are shiny green on the upper surface, glaucous on undersurface. Mid-vein on the upper surface is armed with spines. Huge inflorescences appear to be composed of many short, broad partial inflorescences, each partly concealed by a large triangular bract. Fruit are top-shaped, 6–8.5 cm (2.5–3.5 in) long and 3.5 cm (1.5 in) wide, with a short, pointed beak. They are brown and covered in 9–12 rows of scales.

CULTIVATION: Is adaptable to subtropical climates as long as the soil is kept wet.

Raphia farinifera

Raphia hookeri: showing the spiny and fibrous leaf bases.

Raphia hookeri

COMMON NAME: Nduvui (Sierra Leone), adobe (Ghana), oguru (Nigeria) and other vernacular names in West Africa.

SIZE: Single trunk up to 10 m (33 ft) tall, 30 cm (1 ft) in diameter. Occasionally has a few suckers, but does not form a dense clump.

HABITAT: Swampy forest.

DISTRIBUTION: West Africa, from Guinea and Sierra Leone east to Nigeria and Cameroon, south to Gabon and perhaps Angola.

CONSERVATION STATUS: Unknown.

DESCRIPTION: Leaves are up to 12 m (40 ft) long, dark green on upper surface, waxy and glaucous on undersurface. Leaflets are about 1.5 m (5 ft) long and 4 cm (1.6 in) wide, tapering, with fine spines on the upper surfaces and larger spines near the segment bases. Inflorescence is up to 2.5 m (8 ft) long, composed of many short, broad, partial inflorescences. Fruit are top-shaped or ellipsoid, from 6–12 cm (2.4–5 in) long and 4–5 cm (1.6–2 in) wide, with a pointed beak. They are brown and covered with 12–14 rows of scales.

CULTIVATION: Tapped for its sugary sap, which is used to make palm wine. The 'piassava' is used to make brooms, rope, cordage, and mats. Needs a tropical climate and wet soil.

RAVENEA

'răv-ĕn-ˌe-ȧ

Ravenea is a genus with ten species. Eight are endemic to Madagascar and two are from the Comores Islands. *Ravenea* palms occur in tropical lowland and montane rainforest up to 2000 m (6500 ft). One species is found in a dry forest area of Madagascar.

Ravenea vary from small, slender palms to large, robust solitary palms with pinnate leaves, usually with a characteristic strong arch in the rachis close to the leaf tip. One species, *Ravenea madagascariensis*, has a useful, durable and flexible trunk, whereas the huge *R. robustior* is a source of sago starch from the trunk pith.

Leaf sheaths are densely tomentose and disintegrate opposite the petiole, becoming fibrous. Leaflets are usually numerous, long, stiff and taper to a point. Inflorescences arise among the leaves, one or morel from each leaf axil, all enclosed within a number of persistent bracts. *Ravenea* are dioecious. Fruit are globose, usually brightly coloured and with a pebbly skin.

In general, *Ravenea* palms tolerate a range of climates and have excellent potential in the nursery industry.

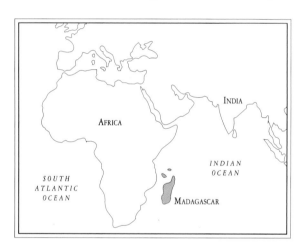

Ravenea rivularis

Ravenea rivularis

Ravenea rivularis

COMMON NAME: Majestic or majesty palm.

SIZE: Solitary trunk, up to about 25 m (80 ft) tall and 40 cm (16 in) in diameter.

HABITAT: Rainforest areas, along river banks and in swampy areas.

DISTRIBUTION: Madagascar.

CONSERVATION STATUS: Vulnerable.

DESCRIPTION: Has a dense and spreading crown of about 20–25 pinnate leaves, each about 2–2.4 m (6–8 ft) long and with a twist in the rachis. Leaves abscise neatly, leaving distinctive scars on the trunk. Fruit are small, globose, 0.7–0.8 cm (0.3 in) in diameter and red when ripe.

CULTIVATION: Seed reportedly loses its viability quickly, though fresh seed should germinate readily. Growth is rapid in a range of climates from subtropical to warm temperate. Is hardy to full sun and exhibits some frost tolerance. It is not suitable indoors, although it is sometimes promoted as an indoor plant. Requires fertile, well-drained soil. Reported as yellowing and requiring frequent additions of fertiliser in the limey soils of Florida.

Reinhardtia
rȳn-hărd-tē-à

*R*einhardtia (syn. *Malortiea*) is a highly ornamental New World genus with six known species. All but one are small undergrowth palms found in tropical rainforests. The latest discovered, *Reinhardtia paiewonskiana*, has a slender trunk of 6–12 m (20–40 ft) which reaches for the canopy in the moist forests of Hispaniola and the Dominican Republic in the West Indies. The other species inhabit lowland rainforest from Mexico through Central America to northern Colombia. *R. elegans* and *R. gracilis* var. *tenuissima* are found at higher altitudes of 1000–1500 m (3300–5000 ft).

Reinhardtia palms are small, except for one species. They are solitary or loosely clustering and have slender stems. Often partially covered with fibrous leaf sheaths, the stems eventually become bare and show conspicuous leaf scars. Stems sometimes have stilt roots at the base. Leaves are undivided with pinnate ribs and a short notch at the leaf apex, or are regularly divided and pinnate, with anything from a few to many leaflets. Leaflets are sometimes 'windowed', having small slit-like holes close to the rachis, and sometimes have a toothed or serrate apex. Leaf sheaths are tubular, becoming fibrous, and are particularly prominent opposite the petiole, where they project upwards into a ligule-like structure which becomes frayed as the leaf ages. Petioles are usually slender. Inflorescences are solitary, arise among the leaves, are usually on a long peduncle and are spicate or

simple- to moderate-branched. In the bud stage, the inflorescence is enclosed in two tubular, papery bracts that persist after splitting open. Flowers are spirally arranged and borne in triads of two male and one female flower, with only male flowers at the distal ends of the rachillae. After flowering, the rachillae change colour from green to red. Fruit are small, ovoid to ellipsoid, single-seeded, deep purple to black and smooth-skinned.

Suitable for tropical to subtropical climates, *Reinhardtia* species are grown from seed which germinates readily. The clumping species may be also propagated from suckers. Some are known for their exquisite leaf forms and are much sought after by palm collectors. In cultivation they require shade and humidity for luxuriant growth, and need abundant moisture in a well-drained soil rich in humus. Some tolerate light frosts, but in general they prefer a warm environment.

Reinhardtia gracilis var. gracilis

Reinhardtia gracilis var. gracilior

Reinhardtia gracilis

COMMON NAME: Window palm.
SIZE: Clustering (rarely solitary), up to 3 m (10 ft) tall, but usually 1–2 m (3.3–6.5 ft), stems 1.4 cm (0.6 in) in diameter.
HABITAT: Rainforest understorey, often on steep slopes. *R. gracilis* var. *tenuissima* found at altitudes of about 1000 m (3300 ft).
DISTRIBUTION: *R. gracilis* var. *gracilis* Belize, Guatemala, Honduras; var. *gracilior* Belize, Guatemala, Honduras, Mexico; var. *rostrata* Costa Rica, Nicaragua; var. *tenuissima* Mexico.
CONSERVATION STATUS: Unknown for all varieties except var. *tenuissima* which is threatened, but the exact status is unknown.
DESCRIPTION: A variable species which has 4 recognised varieties. Brown fibrous leaf sheaths. Has a pinnate leaf with 2–4 regularly-placed leaflets, broadly wedge-shaped, with a toothed apex, each with openings or 'windows' along the rachis between the veins. Inflorescence is variable in length and degree of branching. Fruit are ovoid, 1.2–1.6 cm (0.5–0.6 in) long. In var. *gracilior*, leaflets are small with 8–11 nerves on each side of the rachis. Var. *rostrata* has 11–15 nerves on each side of the rachis. Varieties are separated by leaf characteristics, inflorescences and number of stamens.
CULTIVATION: These shade-loving palms need a warm, moist, shaded location. Good ornamental pot plants.

Reinhardtia simplex

Reinhardtia latisecta

COMMON NAME: None known.
SIZE: Clumping, usually with 8–9 stems, up to 8 m (26 ft) high, each stem up to about 6 cm (2.4 in) in diameter.
HABITAT: Rainforest understorey.
DISTRIBUTION: Belize, Guatemala.
CONSERVATION STATUS: Indeterminate.
DESCRIPTION: Has about 10 leaves per crown. Sheath is about 25 cm (10 in) long, petiole 35–45 cm (14–18 in). Leaf blade is pinnate, 45–75 cm (18–30 in) long, with 2 or more pairs of differing size, the terminal pair very large and with a toothed apex. Leaflets have openings or 'windows' along the rachis between the veins. Inflorescence is up to 1.2 m (4 ft) long and simple-branched. Fruit are red, turning black at maturity, egg-shaped, and around 2 cm (0.8 in) long.
CULTIVATION: Needs a tropical climate with good shade and high humidity.

Reinhardtia simplex

COMMON NAME: None known.
SIZE: Clustering, with a few stems up to 120 cm (4 ft) high, 0.6 cm (0.25 in) in diameter.
HABITAT: Rainforest understorey. Usually at less than 300 m (1000 ft), but can be up to 700 m (2300 ft).
DISTRIBUTION: Belize, Costa Rica, Honduras, Nicaragua, Panama.
CONSERVATION STATUS: Endangered in Costa Rica and Panama, status unknown elsewhere.
DESCRIPTION: Slender petiole is about 15 cm (6 in) long. Leaf is undivided or has a pair of slender segments below the main apical segment. Main segment is about 17 cm (7 in) long by 12 cm (5 in) wide, with 11–12 nerves, a serrate margin and very shortly-cleft apex. Smaller segments are much narrower, taper and also have serrate margins. Inflorescence is simple-branched. Fruit are ovoid and 1.2 cm (0.5 in) long.
CULTIVATION: A shade-loving ornamental.

Reinhardtia latisecta

RHAPIS

'rāy-pis

Rhapis is a genus with about 12 species, amongst which are two of the most highly-prized ornamental palms. *Rhapis humilis* and *R. excelsa*, commonly known as the lady palms, are slow-growing palmate-leaved palms popular as garden plants or pot plants (for outdoor or indoors). They are distributed from southern China southwards through Vietnam, Laos and Cambodia to southern Thailand. One undescribed species of *Rhapis* is found in Sumatra. Botanically little studied to date, their natural habitat has been described as the undergrowth of dry evergreen forest. In southern Thailand and northernmost Sumatra, they grow in forests on limestone hills.

Rhapis are small, clustering palms. Their stems are slender and reed-like, and usually covered with persistent leaf bases which break down to a web of fibres. Older stems eventually become bare and exhibit conspicuous rings. Vegetative suckers will multiply over a number of years to produce many stems, sometimes spreading through stoloniferous growth into large clumps. Leaves are palmate, the blade usually divided (to the base) into segments, each with several ribs and minutely-toothed margins. Segments are tapering and the tips may be pointed or truncate. Petioles are elongate and very slender, and there is a small hastula on the upper surface of the leaf where it joins the petiole. Segments vary in number and width. Male and female inflorescences are on different plants, arise among the leaves, project from the leaf sheath, are simple-branched in the female and well branched in the male. The inflorescence is enclosed in the bud stage by two papery bracts. Flowers are borne singly in a spiral arrangement on the rachillae. Fruit are small, globose to egg-shaped and usually single-seeded, but may be two- or three-seeded, 0.7–1 cm (0.3–0.4 in) long. They are purplish-brown or white when ripe.

The Japanese horticultural industry has developed many dwarf varieties of *R. excelsa*, some with variegated leaves. Culture is by division of vegetative suckers as seed is generally unreliable in reproducing parent characteristics true to form. A porous potting mixture, with added fertiliser and humus, and a cover of heavy shade are the preferred growing conditions. A good water supply and humidity encourage luxuriant growth. Highly adaptable plants, *Rhapis* palms can be grown from the tropics to cool temperate climates.

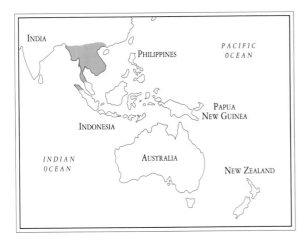

Rhapis multifida

Rhapis excelsa

COMMON NAME: Lady palm, bamboo palm.
SIZE: Stems up to 3 m (10 ft) tall and
1.5–2.5 cm (0.6–1 in) in diameter. Forms
large clumps.
HABITAT: Uncertain.
DISTRIBUTION: Southern China.
CONSERVATION STATUS: Unknown.
DESCRIPTION: Leaf sheaths break down to a
coarse, loose, net-like web of fibres. Usually
has 4–10 segments per leaf, the tips tapering,
obliquely truncate and toothed. Fruits are
small, globose, white, and about 0.7 cm
(0.3 in) in diameter.
CULTIVATION: Suits subtropical to cool
temperate climates. Propagated from basal
suckers or from seed.

Rhapis humilis

Rhapis humilis

COMMON NAME: Slender lady palm.
SIZE: Stems up to 5 m (16 ft) tall and
1.5–2.5 cm (0.6–1 in) in diameter. Forms
large clumps.
HABITAT: Uncertain.
DISTRIBUTION: Probably southern China.
CONSERVATION STATUS: Unknown.
DESCRIPTION: Leaf sheaths break down to a
tight, closely-woven, net-like web of fine
fibres. Usually has 10–30 narrow, drooping
segments per leaf, the tips tapering almost to
a point. All plants in cultivation are male, thus
the inflorescence does not develop fruit.
CULTIVATION: Suits subtropical to cool
temperate climates. Propagated from basal
suckers.

Rhapis subtilis

COMMON NAME: None known.
SIZE: Slender stems, 1–2 m (3.3–6.5 ft) tall and
1.0–1.5 (0.4–0.6 in) in diameter. Forms large
clumps.
HABITAT: Tropical rainforest.
DISTRIBUTION: Laos, Thailand.
CONSERVATION STATUS: Unknown.
DESCRIPTION: Slender stems. Leaf sheaths have
fine, soft fibres. Leaf is variable in size and
segment number, the tips tapering to a point.
CULTIVATION: Needs a tropical to subtropical
climate. Propagated from seed. Seedlings are
very variable. Not suitable as an indoor plant.

Rhapis subtilis

Rhapis excelsa

RHOPALOBLASTE

rō-ˌpăl-ō-ˌblăs-tē

Rhopaloblaste is comprised of seven described species. Distributed in the Nicobar Islands, Peninsular Malaysia, Singapore, the Moluccas, New Guinea and the Solomon Islands, they are tropical rainforest plants growing at low altitudes. Grown in tropical Southeast Asia, *Rhopaloblaste ceramica*, *R. augusta* and *R. singaporensis* are particularly attractive ornamentals worthy of wider cultivation. *Rhopaloblaste* species are solitary, tall, slender palms, with only one exception, *R. singaporensis*. It is a clumping palm which grows up to about 4 m (13 ft). The ringed trunks of this genus are often enlarged at the base. Leaf sheaths are tubular and usually form a distinct crownshaft. The pinnate leaves are reduplicate, and drooping. Leaflets are narrow, tapering and split at the apex. Inflorescences arise below the crownshaft and are well branched. The inflorescence is enclosed at the bud stage by two overlapping bracts which fall shortly after splitting open. Flowers are borne in triads. Fruit is ovoid to subglobose, orange-yellow to red at maturity and single-seeded.

Rhopaloblaste ceramica

Rhopaloblaste ceramica

syn. *Bentinckia ceramica, Rhopaloblaste hexandra, Ptychoraphis ceramica*

COMMON NAME: None known.

SIZE: Solitary slender trunk, 15–20 m (50–65 ft) tall.

HABITAT: Emergent in tropical rainforests.

DISTRIBUTION: Molucca Islands.

CONSERVATION STATUS: Unknown.

DESCRIPTION: Leaves are about 3 m (10 ft) long, held at the horizontal with long leaflets drooping limply. Crownshaft prominent. Has several paniculate inflorescences below the crownshaft. Fruit are ovoid, 3–3.5 cm (1.2–1.4 in) long and scarlet when ripe.

CULTIVATION: Suitable as a tropical garden ornamental.

Rhopaloblaste ceramica

RHOPALOSTYLIS

rō-ˌpăl-ō-ˈstȳ-lis

Rhopalostylis is a genus closely related to *Hedyscepe*. This genus has just two species, one of which has two recognised varieties. *Rhopalostylis* palms are the most southerly of all palms, inhabiting the coastal and near coastal forests of Norfolk and Raoul Islands, mainland New Zealand, and the Chatham Islands to the east of the South Island of New Zealand. They are most numerous in moist areas and along watercourses, but isolated individuals grow in drier locations.

Mature plants are tall, with a prominently-ringed green to grey trunk and a short, bulbous crownshaft. The crown of about 14 pinnate leaves is compact, the leaves pointing stiffly upwards, slightly arched. Leaves become pendulous in plants growing in shaded positions. The petioles are very short and leaf bases sheath to form a crownshaft, which is sometimes split opposite the petiole. Leaflets are placed not quite opposite along the rachis, are forward pointing and taper to a point. Inflorescences arise below the crownshaft and are enclosed by two bracts in the bud stage, the bracts splitting and then falling. The inflorescence is on a short peduncle, is well branched, spreading and drooping as flowering and then fruiting occur. Flowers are borne in triads of one female and two male flowers, with male flowers dominating the distal portions of the rachillae. Fruit are globular to ellipsoid, smooth-skinned and red when ripe.

Rhopalostylis palms are best grown in a protected shaded or semi-shaded position. Fresh seed germinates within a few months. A fertile, well-drained soil and plentiful water supply will encourage growth. They can be grown in subtropical to warm temperate areas, but growth is always rather slow.

Rhopalostylis sapida

Rhopalostylis baueri var. *baueri*

syn *Rhopalostylis baueri*
COMMON NAME: Norfolk palm, Norkolk Island nikau.
SIZE: Solitary trunk, up to 15 m (50 ft) tall and 20 cm (8 in) in diameter.
HABITAT: Understorey and emergent plant. Subtropical forest from sea level to approximately 300 m (1000 ft).
DISTRIBUTION: Norfolk Island.
CONSERVATION STATUS: Vulnerable.
DESCRIPTION: Crownshaft is green with brown tomentum and up to 1 m (3.3 ft) long. Short petiole. Leaf rachis is about 4 m (13 ft) long. Inflorescence is about 90 cm (3 ft) long. Fruit are ovoid to elliptical, up to 1.5 cm (0.6 in) long and bright red when ripe.
CULTIVATION: Subtropical to warm temperate areas. Tolerates cold.

Rhopalostylis baueri var. *cheesmanii*

Rhopalostylis sapida

Rhopalostylis baueri var. *baueri*

Rhopalostylis baueri var. *cheesmanii*

syn. *Rhopalostylis cheesmanii*
COMMON NAME: Raoul Island palm.
SIZE: Solitary grey-green trunk, up to 15 m (50 ft) tall and 20 cm (8 in) in diameter.
HABITAT: Understorey plant in wet forests on ridges and slopes.
DISTRIBUTION: Raoul Island, Kermadec Islands.
CONSERVATION STATUS: Rare.
DESCRIPTION: Crownshaft is green with brown tomentum. Is up to about 70 cm (28 in) long. Very short petiole. Leaf rachis is about 4 m (13 ft) long. Inflorescence is about 90 cm (3 ft) long. Fruit are more or less globose, about 1.6 cm (0.6 in) across and brick red when ripe.
CULTIVATION: Subtropical to warm temperate areas. Tolerates cold.

Rhopalostylis sapida

syn. *Eora sapida, Areca sapida*
COMMON NAME: Nikau palm.
SIZE: Solitary trunk, up to 10 m (33 ft) tall and 25 cm (10 in) in diameter.
HABITAT: A semi-emergent in moist dense forest and along watercourses, from sea level to 700 m (2300 ft).
DISTRIBUTION: New Zealand, Chatham Islands.
CONSERVATION STATUS: Indeterminate.
DESCRIPTION: Crownshaft is green and about 60 cm (2 ft) long. If present, petiole is very short. Leaf rachis is about 5 m (16 ft) long. Inflorescence is about 60 cm (2 ft) long. Fruit are ovoid to elliptical, up to 1.2 cm (0.5 in) long and brick red when ripe.
CULTIVATION: Young inflorescence and palm 'hearts' are edible. Suitable for subtropical to warm temperate areas. Tolerates cold.

ROYSTONEA

rŏy-'stō-nē-à

Roystonea is a genus with about 10–12 species, known under the collective common name of royal palms. Distributed throughout the Caribbean Islands, they also extend to Florida, Mexico, eastern Central America and northern South America. Most are lowland trees of open forest areas, but their original habitats have all but disappeared with agricultural clearing. They have been planted in many places throughout the tropics, especially in the New World. So much so, in fact, that it is now difficult to tell where original habitats finish and planting begins. Hybridisation has also made it difficult for the botanists to decide on the number of species in the genus.

Roystonea make wonderful tall trees with smooth, sometimes swollen trunks, prominent crownshafts and a rather large, spreading crown of pinnate leaves. Leaflets are long and narrow, tapering to a point, held in one plane or inserted at different angles, crowded or in groups, often giving a plumose appearance to the leaf. The huge, branching inflorescences arise below the crownshaft and carry both male and female flowers. Before the inflorescence opens, it is held in two large, smooth, green bracts that curve upwards, holding the bud like a horn. Flowers are arranged in triads, male flowers dominating the distal portions of the rachillae. Fruit are small and berry-like, most globose, but some species have ovoid or oblong-shaped fruit.

Royal palms are generally tropical in their requirements, but some can be grown in the subtropics and warm temperate zones. Grown from seed which usually germinates within three months, they will grow quickly given a warm tropical climate and a plentiful water supply. Growth is slower in cooler areas, and water and fertiliser needs are much reduced. Royal palms are widely used as avenue trees and feature trees.

Roystonea oleracea

Roystonea borinqueana

COMMON NAME: Puerto Rican royal palm.
SIZE: Stocky tree, up to about 18 m (60 ft) tall, 60 cm (2 ft) wide at the base, fatter in the middle.
HABITAT: On hillsides, in fields and forests.
DISTRIBUTION: Puerto Rico, Vieques, St Croix.
CONSERVATION STATUS: Not threatened.
DESCRIPTION: Large spreading crown. Leaves are up to about 3 m (10 ft) long. Leaflets are narrow, held in 2 planes or rows from the rachis, giving a plumose appearance. Flowers are very dense on rachillae. Fruit are ovoid to short, oblong, 1.2–1.5 cm (0.5–0.6 in) long and yellow-brown when ripe.
CULTIVATION: Needs a tropical climate and a good water supply.

Roystonea borinqueana

Roystonea elata

COMMON NAME: Florida royal palm.
SIZE: Slender trunk, 7–25 m (23–82 ft) tall, fatter in the middle than near the crown or base.
HABITAT: Lowland swampy areas.
DISTRIBUTION: Florida Everglades region.
CONSERVATION STATUS: Endangered.
DESCRIPTION: Large spreading crown. Leaflets are narrow, held in 2 planes or rows from the rachis, giving a plumose appearance. Leaflets are virtually without ribs, in contrast to other species. Flowers are not dense on rachillae. Fruit are almost globose, about 1 cm (0.4 in) in diameter.
CULTIVATION: Needs a tropical climate and a good water supply. Is adaptable to a variety of soil types.

Roystonea elata

Roystonea oleracea

COMMON NAME: Caribee royal palm, cabbage palm.
SIZE: Tallest of the royal palms, reaching 30 m (100 ft) or more. Bulging at the base and becoming narrower going up the trunk.
HABITAT: Lowlands and low hills.
DISTRIBUTION: Trinidad, Tobago, Barbados, Dominica, Guadeloupe, Martinique, Guyana, Venezuela.
CONSERVATION STATUS: Not threatened.
DESCRIPTION: Large spreading crown. Leaves are up to 7 m (23 ft) long. Leaflets are held in a single plane, not giving a plumose appearance. Bracts of inflorescence bud are very wavy. Fruit are oblong, 1.6–2 cm (0.6–0.8 in) long, turning purplish to black as they ripen.
CULTIVATION: Edible 'hearts'. Fruit is used as pig feed. A widely-cultivated palm that appears to be adaptable to warm temperate climates.

Roystonea oleracea

Roystonea regia

COMMON NAME: Royal palm, Cuban royal palm.

SIZE: Tall stout trunk, up to 25 m (80 ft) or more tall, usually slightly swollen midway up trunk.

HABITAT: Well-drained soils, up to 1000 m (3300 ft) elevations.

DISTRIBUTION: Cuba, Honduras.

CONSERVATION STATUS: Not threatened. *R. regia* var. *pinguis* is rare.

DESCRIPTION: Large spreading crown. Leaflets narrow, held in 2 planes or rows from the rachis, giving a plumose appearance. Inflorescence is rather shorter than in other species. Fruit are oblong, about 1.2 cm (0.5 in) and dull red to purplish when ripe.

CULTIVATION: Several varieties are described from different localities. Is adaptable to subtropical climates, and grows well in a variety of soil types. It is widely planted. Leaves and wood are used as building materials and ripening fruit is used as pig feed.

Roystonea regia

Roystonea venezuelana

Roystonea venezuelana

COMMON NAME: Venezuelan royal palm.

SIZE: Slender trunk, 25–30 m (80–100 ft) tall, slightly wider at the base. Trunk may be variously swollen.

HABITAT: Rainforest, mainly at low altitudes.

DISTRIBUTION: Venezuela.

CONSERVATION STATUS: Not threatened.

DESCRIPTION: Large spreading crown. Leaflets are narrow, held closely in 2 planes or rows from the rachis, giving a plumose appearance. Leaflet tips irregularly bifid. Underside of leaflets is slightly silvery. Fruit are oblong, sometimes broader, about 1.5–1.8 cm (0.6–0.7 in) long and purple-black when ripe.

CULTIVATION: Trunk wood is used in building construction. Needs a tropical climate and a good water supply.

SABAL

'ʒay-băl

Sabal is one of the larger genera of fan palms from the New World, distributed in the southeast of the United States, Mexico and the Caribbean, with an outlying species found in northern South America and Central America. There are about 15 species, some rather difficult to tell apart. Commonly known as palmetto palms, some species are widespread and weedy, thriving where native forests have been cleared for agriculture. Some occur naturally in swampy areas (e.g. *Sabal minor*) and others in sandy coastal or dry open areas.

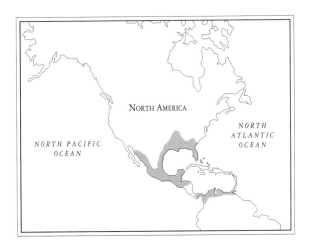

NORTH AMERICA

NORTH PACIFIC OCEAN

NORTH ATLANTIC OCEAN

Sabal palms have solitary above-ground or subterranean trunks. The trunk surface is covered with leaf bases, becoming bare with age. The sheath has fibrous margins and develops a split below the petiole. Petioles are often long and are not armed with spines. Leaf blades are shortly to rather prominently costapalmate, divided (to the middle or more) into many single-fold segments, the tips of which are bifid. Often there are thin threads between the leaf segments. Both sides of the leaf have a hastula where the leaf and petiole meet. The inflorescence arises among the leaves, is well branched and enclosed in a number of bracts in the bud stage. Flowers are solitary and contain both male and female parts. Fruit is globose to pear-shaped, smooth-skinned and usually single-seeded.

The palmettos are popular garden ornamentals. One cultivar, *Sabal* 'blackburniana' is widely grown. Easily propagated from seed, they grow slowly, but are generally sun-loving and hardy in a wide range of climates and soil types. A favourite for transplantation from the wild into gardens, trees can be buried deeper than they originally grew to help support the trunk. In the past, the palmettos have been used as a source of thatch and to make brooms, baskets and hats.

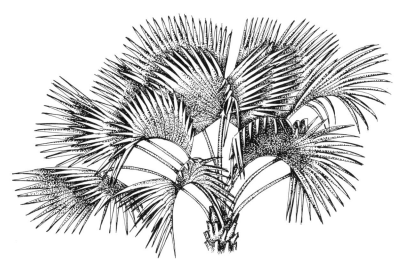

Sabal 'Blackburniana' cultivar

Sabal domingensis

Sabal domingensis

COMMON NAME: Latanier, palmetto palm.
SIZE: Massive trunk, up to about 10 m (33 ft) tall and 60 cm (2 ft) in diameter.
HABITAT: Commonly grows where forest has been cleared.
DISTRIBUTION: Haiti, Hispaniola, eastern Cuba.
CONSERVATION STATUS: Not threatened.
DESCRIPTION: Has 20–30 strongly costapalmate green leaves in crown, and about 90 segments per leaf. Inflorescence equals the leaves in length. Fruit are pear-shaped, black and about 1.1–1.4 cm (0.4–0.6 in) in diameter. Easily confused with *S. causiarum*, which has larger fruit and seeds.
CULTIVATION: Hardy in a wide range of climates.

Sabal mauritiiformis

COMMON NAME: Local names include palma de vaca, palma amarga, palma de guagara.
SIZE: Solitary trunk, up to about 25 m (82 ft) tall and 15–20 cm (6–8 in) in diameter.
HABITAT: Primary rainforests and in secondary growth. Generally from 0–400 m (0–1300 ft) elevations on soils derived from limestone.
DISTRIBUTION: Southern Mexico, Belize, Guatemala, southeastern Costa Rica, eastern Panama, Perlas Islands (Bay of Panama), north coastal South America (Colombia and Venezuela), Trinidad.
CONSERVATION STATUS: Not threatened.
DESCRIPTION: Trunk green and prominently ringed when young. Has 15–25 weakly costapalmate, green or blue-green leaves in crown and about 90–120 segments per leaf. Segments are joined in groups of 2 or 3. Inflorescence exceeds the leaves in length. Fruit are globose to pear-shaped, blackish and about 0.8–1.1 cm (0.3–0.4 in) long.
CULTIVATION: Suitable for tropical to subtropical regions.

Sabal causiarum

COMMON NAME: Puerto Rican hat palm.
SIZE: Massive solitary trunks, up to approximately 10 m (33 ft) tall and 35–60 cm (14–24 in) in diameter.
HABITAT: Sandy soil in subtropical moist forest from sea level to 100 m (330 ft).
DISTRIBUTION: Puerto Rico, Anegada, Haiti, Dominican Republic.
CONSERVATION STATUS: Not threatened.
DESCRIPTION: Has 20–30 strongly costapalmate green or blue-green leaves in crown. Has 60–120 segments per leaf. Inflorescence nearly exceeds the leaves in length. Fruit are usually globose, black, and about 1.5 cm (0.6 in) in diameter.
CULTIVATION: Widely planted. Hardy in a wide range of climates.

Sabal causiarum

Sabal mauritiiformis juvenile plant.

Sabal minor

COMMON NAME: Dwarf palmetto, bush palmetto, swamp palmetto.
SIZE: Small palm, up to 3 m (10 ft) tall. Trunk usually subterranean, 10–20 cm (4–8 in) in diameter.
HABITAT: On rich soils by rivers, water canals and on flood plains.
DISTRIBUTION: Southeastern mainland USA.
CONSERVATION STATUS: Not threatened.
DESCRIPTION: Has 4–10 weakly costapalmate green leaves in crown. Leaf blade is deeply divided into 15–65 segments per leaf. Inflorescence is erect and visible well above the leaves. Fruit are globose and slightly flattened, brown to black and about 0.6–1 cm (0.2–0.4 in) across.
CULTIVATION: Widely planted in tropical to temperate regions as a hardy palm.

Sabal minor

Sabal palmetto

Sabal palmetto

COMMON NAME: Palmetto palm, cabbage palm, cabbage palmetto.
SIZE: Stocky emergent palm, up to approximately 20 m (65 ft) tall and 20–35 cm (8–14 in) in diameter.
HABITAT: Various, including sandy coastal soils, river banks, beach sand dunes and seasonally-inundated swampy areas.
DISTRIBUTION: Peninsular Florida, coastal Georgia, Carolina (USA), Cuba, Bahamas.
CONSERVATION STATUS: Not threatened.
DESCRIPTION: Has 15–30 strongly costapalmate green leaves in crown. Has 50–95 segments per leaf. Inflorescences nearly equal, or slightly exceed, the leaves in length. Fruit are globose or slightly flattened and pear-shaped, black and about 0.8–1.4 cm (0.3–0.6 in) across.
CULTIVATION: Tolerates a wide range of soil types. Is said to be an indicator of poor soil in natural habitats. Tolerates extremes of temperature and withstands salt spray and brackish water.

SALACCA
ša-ˈlăk-à

Salacca is a genus closely related to the rattan genus, *Calamus*. Unlike the rattans, these are not climbing palms. However, in common with most rattans, they are armed with spines, have a clustering habit and have fruit covered with overlapping scales. Growing in tropical rainforests, they form part of the forest undergrowth. The 18 species (and others yet to be described and formally named) are distributed from lower Myanmar (Burma), Thailand, Peninsular Malaysia, Borneo, Sumatra, Java and the southern Philippine Islands. The greatest diversity is found in Borneo, Peninsular Malaysia and Sumatra.

The crown is usually at ground level and consists of a number of leaves which may be short or long, depending on the species. If there is a short trunk, it is usually obscured by the leaf bases. Sometimes plants may produce creeping stems in a stoloniferous type of growth. Most species of *Salacca* do not shoot from the leaf axil, but produce sucker shoots in a position opposite the leaf. Leaves are pinnate or entire, bifid and undivided, although marked with pinnate venations. Leaflets may be regularly arranged or grouped and fanned within the groups. They are armed with short bristles along the veins and margins, and in most species are powdery on the undersurface. The leaf rachis and petiole are usually spined, the latter sometimes densely so. Inflorescences arise from the leaf axils and break through the leaf sheath. They are sometimes short and spicate, but more often branching and covered by a number of papery bracts which become ragged. In *Salacca flabellata* and *S. wallichiana*, the inflorescence arches to the ground and takes root at the tip, developing into an independent plant. Most *Salacca* palms are dioecious. The male inflorescence bears flowers in pairs on catkin-like rachillae. The female inflorescence bears flowers singly or in dyads consisting of one fertile female flower and one sterile male flower. Fruit are single-, two- or three-seeded, globose to an irregular pear shape and covered in vertical rows of overlapping scales which are smooth or spined at the tips.

Several species are grown for their edible fruit. *S. zalacca* is the most important. Other species are *S. sumatrana*, *S. glabrescens*, *S. wallichiana* and *S. affinis*. Some natural hybrids have been used in commercial cultivation. Fresh seed usually germinates within a few weeks. A tropical climate, fertile, well-watered soil and organic matter encourages fast growth. *Salacca* palms display some cold tolerance and should be suitable for subtropical areas.

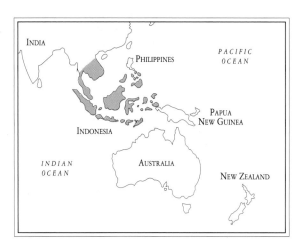

Salacca wallichiana

Salacca affinis

COMMON NAME: None known.
SIZE: Clumping, up to 6 m (19.5 ft) tall, no visible trunk.
HABITAT: Swampy ground, riversides and moist hill slopes.
DISTRIBUTION: Sumatra, Peninsular Malaysia, Borneo.
CONSERVATION STATUS: Not threatened.
DESCRIPTION: Leaves are 3–6 m (10–20 ft) long with broad tapering leaflets arranged in groups and in different planes along the rachis. Young leaves are reddish, turning dark green. Fruit are yellow, red or brown, 5–6.5 cm (2–2.6 in) long by 4–5 cm (1.6–2 in) wide.
CULTIVATION: Cultivated in a semi-wild condition in central Borneo. Has good ornamental potential. Fruit is edible, and tastes sweet or sour.

Salacca affinis

Salacca magnifica

Salacca dransfieldiana

Salacca dransfieldiana

COMMON NAME: None known.
SIZE: Clumping palm, up to 2 m (6.5 ft) tall. Very short stem, approximately 3 cm (1.2 in) in diameter.
HABITAT: Lowland rainforest.
DISTRIBUTION: Endemic to Kalimantan (Indonesian Borneo).
CONSERVATION STATUS: Rare.
DESCRIPTION: Leaves are entire, deeply bifid, pinnately veined, the blade about 70–100 cm (28–40 in) long and widest at the top, from 26–50 cm (10–20 in). The base is narrowly wedge shaped, glossy green above and whitish below. Occasionally leaves are pinnately divided near the base. Petiole around 40 cm (16 in) long. Has long, triangular spines which lie flat on the leaf sheath and rachis. Male inflorescence has 1–6 spikes, each 10–20 cm (4–8 in) long. Female inflorescences have 1–3 spikes. Fruit are ovoid to pear-shaped, about 4 cm (1.6 in) long.
CULTIVATION: Has good ornamental potential. Fruit are edible but astringent.

Salacca magnifica

COMMON NAME: None known.
SIZE: Stemless, clumping, up to 6.3 m (20 ft) tall.
HABITAT: Grows as an under-canopy palm. Found besides streams or in gullies between 2 ridges at an altitude of 900 m (3000 ft). Has also been collected close to sea level.
DISTRIBUTION: Endemic to Sarawak and Kalimantan (Borneo).
CONSERVATION STATUS: Rare.
DESCRIPTION: Has very large, entire, deeply bifid leaves, pinnately veined. Blade is up to 4 m (13 ft) long and widest at the top. It is about 70 cm (28 in) broad, has a narrowly wedge-shaped base, is paler green on the undersurface. Petiole is up to 2 m (6.5 ft) long. Upward-pointing spines on the leaf sheath, petiole and leaf rachis. Male inflorescence is branched, erect, about 45 cm (18 in) long. Female inflorescence is erect and consists of up to 6 spikes, around 30 cm (1 ft) long. Fruit are deep pink or yellowish brown, pear-shaped, up to 6 cm (2.4 in) long. Roots are white on the outside and black and very hard on the inside.
CULTIVATION: Has good ornamental potential. Can grow in full sun or partial shade. Fruits are edible and comparable in eating quality to other salaks.

Salacca wallichiana

Salacca wallichiana

COMMON NAME: Salak.

SIZE: Grows 6–7 m (20–23 ft) tall, height mostly made up of leaves. Stem is short or creeps on the ground.

HABITAT: Swampy or moist ground in or on the edge of rainforests.

DISTRIBUTION: Lower Myanmar (Burma), central and southern Thailand, Peninsular Malaysia.

CONSERVATION STATUS: Not threatened.

DESCRIPTION: Stem is up to about 0.5 m (1.5 ft) tall, about 12 cm (0.5 in) in diameter, or creeping along the ground for up to 2 m (6.5 ft), with many adventitious roots. Leaves are 5–7.5 m (16–25 ft) long, with leaflets arranged in different planes along the rachis. Spines on the petiole and rachis are arranged in rows and point upwards. Male and female inflorescences are similar, hanging down and often lying on the ground. Male inflorescence is up to 1 m (3.3 ft) long, female 1.5 m (5 ft) long. Male flowers are red, female pale pink to red. Fruits are orange, more or less egg-shaped with a pointed apex, and about 5 cm (2 in) long.

CULTIVATION: Cultivated in a semi-wild state in southern Thailand and eastern Peninsular Malaysia.

Salacca zalacca

Salacca zalacca

syn. *Salacca edulis*

COMMON NAME: Salak.

SIZE: Clumping palm, 4.5–7 m (15–23 ft) tall, with no visible trunk.

HABITAT: Swampy or moist ground in or on the edge of rainforests.

DISTRIBUTION: Indonesia.

CONSERVATION STATUS: Not threatened.

DESCRIPTION: Stems may grow as stolons along the ground. Petioles are about 2 m (6.5 ft) long and covered in long, flattened spines. Leaves have many long, tapering leaflets, often irregularly arranged in pairs along the rachis. Leaflets are whitish-green beneath and dark green on the upper surface. Male inflorescence is up to 1 m (3.3 ft) long, female up to 30 cm (12 in) long. Fruit are crowded onto the erect spike. Fruit are top-shaped, scaly, and brown to yellow in colour.

CULTIVATION: Widely cultivated in Indonesia and Malaysia. Grows best on the hot lowlands up to 1000 m (3300 ft) altitude. Commercial propagation is by seed although suckers can be grown. The first crop is produced when the plants are 4–5 years old. Fruit tastes both sweet and sour. The variety on Bali, var. *amboinensis*, is monoecious, being able to produce male and female flowers on the one plant. The dioecious variety grown elsewhere in Indonesia is usually var. *zalacca*.

Salacca zalacca: female; fruit and flowers.

SERENOA

še-ře-ˈnō-a̱

Serenoa repens represents this monotypic genus. Commonly known as the saw palmetto, it forms dense clumps by suckering. These suckers are vegetative shoots produced in quite an unusual way. Buds in the leaf axils of the prostrate or subterranean stem develop into either vegetative shoots (suckers) or inflorescences. In its natural habitat on the coastal sand dunes, coastal plains and pinelands of southeastern mainland USA, the saw palmetto often forms dense swards, which are regarded in some locations as an invasive weed.

Stems are subterranean, prostrate and creep along the ground surface. Less often, they are erect, and up to about 2 m (6.5 ft), sometimes more.

Saw palmetto is slow growing and tolerates frost. As a garden ornamental, it has gained some favour for its clumping and spreading habit and its hardiness to coastal winds and periods of drought. Propagation is by seed as division of the suckers is not usually successful.

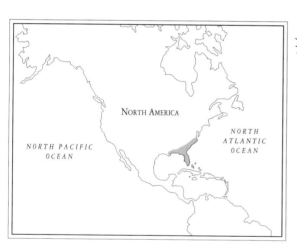

Serenoa repens

Serenoa repens

COMMON NAME: Saw palmetto.
SIZE: Clumps or dense swards, up to about 2 m (6.5 ft) tall.
HABITAT: Sand dunes, coastal plains and pinelands.
DISTRIBUTION: Southeastern mainland USA.
CONSERVATION STATUS: Not threatened.
DESCRIPTION: Stem covered with fibrous leaf bases. Petioles are armed with small teeth. Has a hastula on both sides of the leaf. Palmate blade is almost round, divided (to below the middle) into many stiffly-held segments, each shortly split at the apex. Leaves vary from blue-green or grey-green to green or yellow-green. Inflorescence is well branched and among the leaves. Flowers are bisexual, solitary or in pairs. Fruit are dark blue to black, ellipsoidal to globose and 2 cm (0.8 in) long.
CULTIVATION: This slow growing palm tolerates frost and grows in subtropical to warm temperate climates.

Serenoa repens

SOCRATEA

sŏk-'răt-ē-à

Socratea is a genus which was recently been revised (Henderson, 1990). It has been reduced from twelve to five species, distributed from Nicaragua to South America as far as Bolivia, Venezuela, the Guyanas and Brazil. Found in lowland rainforest between sea level and 1800 m (5900 ft), *Socratea* palms are tropical emergent or canopy palms with prominent stilt roots.

Trunks are usually erect and solitary, clustering in one species only. The base of the trunk is supported by long, spiny, stilt roots. Leaf sheaths are tubular, forming a well-defined crownshaft. Petioles are short. Leaves are few, unevenly pinnate and have a terminal leaflet. Leaflets are numerous, entire or divided into few segments. They have ribs radiating from the base, somewhat wedge-shaped like elongate *Caryota* leaflets in shape and often with praemorse ends. The split leaflets often give a plumose appearance to the leaf. Inflorescences arise among the leaves and mature below the leaves by the time they are open and flowering. Erect in bud and enclosed in about six bracts, they are simple-branched and pendulous when open and flowering. Rachillae bear spirally-arranged crowded triads of one female and two male flowers. Fruit are ellipsoid to almost globose and single-seeded.

Cultivation requires a warm tropical climate with good moisture and shade in the early stages of growth.

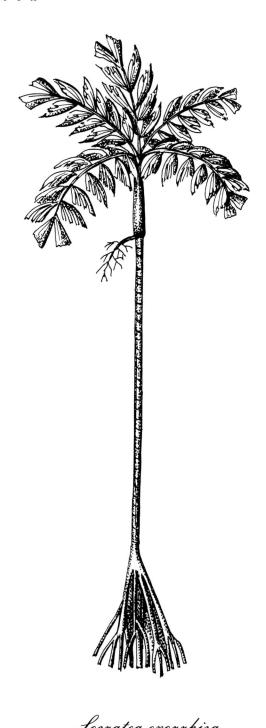

Socratea exorrhiza

Socratea exorrhiza

syn. *Socratea durissima*

COMMON NAME: None known.

SIZE: Solitary trunk, up to 20 m (66 ft) tall, but usually less, and 13–18 cm (5–7 in) in diameter.

HABITAT: Lowland rainforest from sea level to 1000 m (3300 ft).

DISTRIBUTION: From Nicaragua south to Bolivia, east through Venezuela, the Guyanas and Brazil.

CONSERVATION STATUS: Vulnerable in Costa Rica, not threatened elsewhere.

DESCRIPTION: Has up to 25 widely-spaced stilt roots, with spines up to 2 cm (0.8 in) long. Has about 7 spreading leaves in the crown. Rachis is about 1.4–2.8 m (4.5–9 ft) long. Has 15–25 leaflets on each side of the rachis, about 90 cm (3 ft) long and of various widths, asymmetrically wedge shaped, and with praemorse ends. Leaflets towards the middle of the leaf are further split into segments. Fruit are ovoid-cylindric, 2.5–3.5 cm (1–1.4 in) long and yellowish when ripe.

CULTIVATION: Palm is used for thatch. Trunks are also used, in housing construction and to make bows and spears. The palm 'heart' and leaves are reported to have insecticidal properties. Needs a warm tropical climate with good moisture and shade.

Socratea exorrhiza

Socratea exorrhiza

SYAGRUS

sy-'ăg-rŭs

Syagrus now includes the genera *Arikuryroba*, *Chrysallidosperma*, *Rhyticocos*, *Barbosa*, *Arecastrum*, *Langsdorffia*, *Platenia* and *Arikury*. This variable genus is closely related to *Cocos*. One of the most widely planted palms, *Syagrus romanzoffiana*, has been transferred from the genus *Arecastrum*. There are about 32 species distributed in South America, from Venezuela to Argentina, and one in the Lesser Antilles. Most species inhabit the dry regions of Brazil and Paraguay, in open grasslands or scrub forests, sometimes dominating the vegetation in huge colonies. Some species grow in the more humid coastal woodlands, in rainforests or in rocky areas along streams.

Small to tall in size, *Syagrus* palms may be solitary or clustering. Sometimes they have no apparent stem or the stem may be very short. Leaf bases tend to adhere to the stem for some distance below the crown and break down into an interwoven fibrous mass, eventually falling and leaving a clean, ringed trunk. Petioles may be short or long, their margins fibrous. Leaves are pinnate, leaflets regularly or irregularly arranged, often arising in different planes, giving a plumose appearance. Inflorescences arise among the leaves, are simple-branched to one order or,

occasionally, spicate. A large, usually woody, bract encloses the inflorescence in bud, then splits open lengthwise and persists well after flowering has occurred. Rachillae may be few to numerous and bear spirally arranged triads of flowers, each triad made up of one female and two male flowers. Fruit are small to relatively large, ovoid or ellipsoidal, and usually single-seeded, though occasionally two-seeded.

Syagrus palms are adaptable to various climates, from tropical to temperate. They are usually fast-growing plants suitable for drier locations. They show some frost tolerance. They also respond to generous watering and added fertiliser.

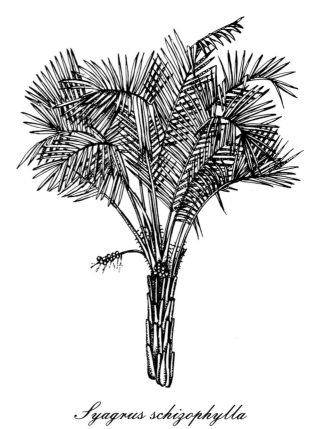

Syagrus schizophylla

Syagrus comosa

syn. *Cocos comosa*
COMMON NAME: None known.
SIZE: Solitary trunk, 2–7 m (6.5–23 ft) tall, 6–10 cm (2.5–4 in) in diameter. Sometimes clumping.
HABITAT: Woodlands and dryland scrub.
DISTRIBUTION: Brazil.
CONSERVATION STATUS: Unknown.
DESCRIPTION: Leaves are about 1.1 m (3.5 ft) long with about 80 leaflets on each side of the rachis, mostly in clusters of 2–4. Inflorescence is branched and about 60 cm (2 ft) long. Fruit are ovoid, up to 3 cm (1.2 in) long.

Syagrus coronata

syn. *Cocos coronata*
COMMON NAME: Licury palm.
SIZE: Solitary trunk, 5–9 m (16–30 ft) tall.
HABITAT: Woodlands and dryland scrub.
DISTRIBUTION: Brazil.
CONSERVATION STATUS: Not threatened.
DESCRIPTION: Leaf bases spiral down the trunk. Leaves are waxy, held stiffly upright and arching. Rachis is about 3 m (10 ft) long, with about 120 pairs of leaflets arranged in groups and arising in different planes, giving a plumose appearance. Fruit are ovoid, yellow and 2.5 cm (1 in) long.
CULTIVATION: Has an edible oily fruit. Leaves are used as a commercial source of wax. A tropical to subtropical climate is required, but it tolerates low rainfall and poor soils. Sensitive to cold.

Syagrus coronata

Syagrus romanzoffiana

syn. *Arecastrum romanzoffianum, Cocos plumosa*
COMMON NAME: None known.
SIZE: Trunk is 10–15 m (33–50 ft) tall and 40 cm (16 in) or more in diameter.
HABITAT: Woodlands, often together with *S. oleracea.*
DISTRIBUTION: Argentina, Paraguay, Uruguay, Bolivia, Brazil.
CONSERVATION STATUS: Not threatened.
DESCRIPTION: Sheathing leaf bases become fibrous. Petioles about 40 cm (16 in) long with fibrous margins. Rachis is about 3 m (10 ft) long, with around 150 pairs of leaflets arranged in groups and arising in different planes, giving a plumose appearance. Infructescence is generally large and pendulous. Fruit are ovoid and beaked, 2–3 cm (0.8–1.2 in) long and orange when ripe. Fruit are variable in size and shape, but the differences are insufficient for the recognition of different varieties.
CULTIVATION: Suitable for a very wide range of climates from tropical to cool temperate. Will withstand salt-laden or dry winds. Not suitable as an indoor plant. *S. romanzoffiana* hybridises easily with several other *Syagrus* species and with *Butia capitata.*

Syagrus comosa

Syagrus romanzoffiana

THRINAX

'thrȳ-năx

Thrinax includes seven species, three from the former genus *Hemithrinax*. A New World genus, these palms are found in the Caribbean islands and on the Atlantic coast of Belize and Mexico. Two species, *Thrinax parviflora* and *T. excelsa*, are endemic to Jamaica, while *T. radiata* and *T. morrisii* have a much wider range in the northern Caribbean, coastal northern Central America, Mexico and Florida. The three species formerly of *Hemithrinax*, *T. compacta*, *T. ekmaniana* and *T. rivularis* are endemic to Cuba. There is no common natural habitat of *Thrinax* palms. Localities vary from dry woodlands to montane rainforest and coastal woodlands and thickets.

Closely related to the genus *Coccothrinax*, *Thrinax* palms are small to moderate in size, solitary, with slender stems, smooth and obscurely ringed, or partially covered with a soft, fibrous, sometimes woolly material derived from leaf sheaths. There is often a mass of roots visible at the trunk base. There is an open crown of palmate leaves and no crownshaft. The leaf sheath splits both opposite and below the petiole and becomes fibrous. Petioles are long and slender. The leaf blade is an almost circular fan shape with irregularly folded segments divided (to about midway) into narrow pointed segments, the tips of which are usually bifid. The undersurface of the blade may be very scaly or white. The hastula is more prominent on the upper side of the leaf than on the underside.

Inflorescences arise among the leaves, project from a split in the leaf sheath, are well branched and are enclosed by numerous bracts in the bud stage. Flowers are bisexual, spirally arranged on the rachillae and each flower is on a short stalk. Fruit are very small, smooth-skinned, more or less globose, single-seeded and white when ripe.

Thrinax palms are found on alkaline soils derived from limestone or coral, the Cuban species on serpentine soils. Suitable for tropical to subtropical climates, they need partial shade when in juvenile stages. However, these palms will generally take full, open sun once they are well established.

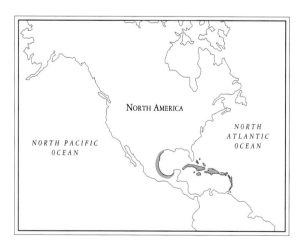

Thrinax morrisii

Thrinax parviflora

Thrinax morrisii

COMMON NAME: Key thatch palm, peaberry palm.
SIZE: Slender trunk, usually up to 1 m (3.3 ft) tall, occasionally up to 2 m (6.5 ft) tall, about 5 cm (2 in) in diameter.
HABITAT: Amongst limestone rocks.
DISTRIBUTION: Florida, Caribbean islands.
CONSERVATION STATUS: Not threatened.
DESCRIPTION: Leaf blade is about 1–1.5 m (3.3–5 ft) across, divided (to about halfway) into 40–50 segments. Undersurface silver. Petioles are slender, 1.2–1.8 m (4–6 ft) long. Leaf sheath is split and fibrous. Fruit are globose, white and 0.6 cm (0.25 in) in diameter.
CULTIVATION: Suitable for a wide variety of soils, including limestone-derived soils. Grows slowly. Tolerates salty winds and open sunny locations.

Thrinax parviflora

COMMON NAME: Thatch palm.
SIZE: Slender trunk, 3–9 m (10–30 ft) tall, 10–15 cm (4–6 in) in diameter.
HABITAT: Dry evergreen woodland or thicket.
DISTRIBUTION: Jamaica.
CONSERVATION STATUS: Not threatened.
DESCRIPTION: Leaf blade is about 1 m (3.3 ft) across, divided (to about halfway) into about 50 segments. Undersurface is slightly paler than the upper. Petioles are 60–100 cm (2–3.3 ft) long, with the sheath covered in a woolly tomentum. Fruit are globose, white, 0.6 cm (0.25 in) in diameter.
CULTIVATION: In its natural habitat it grows on soils derived from limestone. Grows slowly.

Thrinax morrisii

TRACHYCARPUS

ˌtrăk-ē-ˈkăr-pŭs

Trachycarpus palms are distributed from the Himalayas of northern India to northern Thailand and China. The popular cold-tolerating fan palm *Trachycarpus fortunei*, or Chinese windmill palm, hails from this genus. A revision of the genus by Martin Gibbons is currently in progress. There are six species described, two of which, *T. takil* and *T. wagnerianus*, are closely allied with *T. fortunei*, and when the genus is revised they may not justify separate species status. The plant known as *T. takil* occurs in a small location in northwest India and is probably a form of *T. fortunei*. *T. wagnerianus*, which is not known in the wild, is a distinctive form because of its small, stiff leaves. *T. caespitosus*, described as having multiple trunks, is unknown in the wild and may prove to be another variant of *T. fortunei*. Three species, *T. fortunei*, *T. martianus* and *T. nanus*, are briefly described here. A fourth species may soon be described from a population in northern Thailand.

Trachycarpus trunks may become bare with age, but are usually covered with a mat of fibres and ribbon-like threads from the disintegrating leaf bases. The petiole bases may also persist and can be a distinctive feature. The leaf has a slender petiole and a small to medium rigid blade which is usually divided to about halfway, the segments tapering to a bifid tip. The inflorescences are well branched and are covered in the bud stage by overlapping bowl-shaped bracts. Male and female flowers are usually on different plants, but hermaphroditic flowers may occasionally be seen. Fruit are small and blue-black with a white bloom when ripe. They are usually easy to grow from seed, although they grow very slowly. Their horticulturally useful feature is their cold-hardiness, *T. fortunei* even tolerating a cover of winter snow and temperatures as low as –15°C.

Trachycarpus fortunei

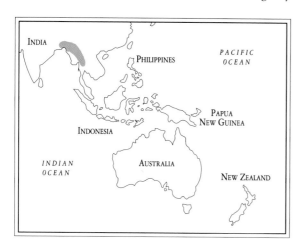

Trachycarpus fortunei

syn. *Chamaerops excelsa*, provisionally *Trachycarpus takil* and
T. wagnerianus
COMMON NAME: Chinese windmill palm, chusan palm.
SIZE: Single trunk, up to 9 m (30 ft) or more tall.
HABITAT: Unknown.
DISTRIBUTION: China.
CONSERVATION STATUS: Unknown. Large numbers in China.
DESCRIPTION: Trunk displays persistent dead leaves in a petticoat below
the crown. Has loosely-arranged fibres and persistent petiole bases.
Older part of the trunk may shed the fibrous covering to reveal a
smooth, ringed surface. Leaves are orbicular in outline with uneven and
variable depth of leaf split. Fruit are kidney-shaped.
CULTIVATION: Widely in cultivation in warm to cold temperate regions.
Very hardy in cold temperatures.

Trachycarpus martianus

Trachycarpus fortunei

Trachycarpus martianus

syn. *Trachycarpus khasyanus*
COMMON NAME: None known.
SIZE: Slender trunk, up to about 10 m (33 ft) tall.
HABITAT: Limestone hills and other soils up to 2400 m (7900 ft) altitude.
DISTRIBUTION: Nepal, northeastern India, northern Myanmar (Burma).
CONSERVATION STATUS: Unknown. Probably endangered.
DESCRIPTION: Dead leaves do not persist, but leaf bases do persist for
about 1 m (3.3 ft) or so below the crown and break down to a fibrous
material which is held rather closely to the trunk (in contrast to
T. fortunei which has loosely-held fibres). Rest of the trunk is smooth,
grey and closely ringed. Leaves are divided very evenly (to about
halfway) and have a bluish-grey undersurface. Fruit are oblong. Seeds
are oblong-oval and have a longitudinal groove on one side.
CULTIVATION: Little known in cultivation. Tolerates cold temperatures
and is known to grow in cool to warm temperate climates.

Trachycarpus nanus

COMMON NAME: None known.
SIZE: Subterranean, or with a short trunk.
HABITAT: Steep open hillsides and forests.
DISTRIBUTION: Yunnan province (south-western China).
CONSERVATION STATUS: Locally common, but probably endangered by
agriculture and grazing. It does not appear to be increasing in the wild.
DESCRIPTION: When growing in the open, has rigid blue-green leaves.
If grown in the shade, leaves are green and limp. Fibrous leaf bases
persist. Inflorescences and infructescences are held erect. Fruit and
seeds are kidney-shaped.
CULTIVATION: As yet little known in cultivation. It should prove as hardy
to cold as other species.

Trachycarpus nanus

TRITHRINAX

trў-ʹthrў-năx

Trithrinax currently includes five species, but the genus needs a modern revision. Distributed in Bolivia, Brazil, Paraguay, Uruguay and Argentina, they are found in dry locations. Several species are found in saline soils that test slightly alkaline. *Trithrinax biflabellata* grows in sandy marshes and along river banks.

Trithrinax palms are small to moderate in size, solitary or sometimes clustering. There is a rather compact crown of palmate leaves and no crownshaft. The leaf sheath is tubular, breaking down into a fibrous, often woody network, with the upper fibres becoming thick spines. This fibrous and spiny material covers the trunk, but may eventually fall off to reveal a clean, rough, trunk surface. Petioles have sharp margins and there is a hastula on both sides of the leaf where the petiole joins the blade. The leaf blade is an almost circular fan shape, regularly divided (to more than midway) into narrow pointed segments, the tips of which are usually bifid. Leaves may be slightly costapalmate. The undersurface of the blade may be lightly waxy and tomentose. Inflorescences arise among the leaves, are short and well branched, and are enclosed by several bracts in the bud stage. Flowers are bisexual, spirally arranged on the rachillae and each flower is on a short stalk. Fruit are very small, smooth-skinned, more or less globose, single-seeded and white when ripe.

Reportedly tolerating a variety of soil types, *Trithrinax* palms are slow growing, but resistant to drought and cold. Grown from seed, they are suitable for tropical to warm temperate climates. They have been useful plants to humans. The fibres are used for filters and weaving, and the leaves for thatch. You can make a fermented beverage from the fruit, extract their oil or eat them fresh.

Trithrinax acanthocoma

Trithrinax acanthocoma

COMMON NAME: Spiny fibre palm.

SIZE: Solitary trunk, up to 4 m (13 ft) tall and 7–10 cm (3–4 in) in diameter.

HABITAT: Dry areas.

DISTRIBUTION: Brazil.

CONSERVATION STATUS: Unknown.

DESCRIPTION: Trunk is covered in thick, brown, fibrous netting and spines 7–15 cm (3–6 in) long. Palmate leaf blade is about 1 m (3.3 ft) across. It has about 40 stiff segments dividing the blade, which is slightly silvery beneath, to about halfway. Inflorescence is up to 80 cm (32 in) long, with white flowers. Fruit are globose, greenish-yellow and about 2 cm (0.8 in) in diameter.

CULTIVATION: Grows slowly. Tolerates cold and dry periods.

Trithrinax acanthocoma

Trithrinax acanthocoma

VEITCHIA

'vēt-chē-à

Veitchia has about 18 species, distributed in Vanuatu, Fiji and the Philippine Islands. Their natural habitat varies from near sea level to 1000 m (3300 ft) altitudes, usually in moist forests where they may be understorey, semi-emergent or emergent. *Veitchia merrillii* is more unusual in that as well as being found in forests near the sea, it also grows in the seasonally-dry environment of steep karst limestone cliffs by the sea.

Veitchia are moderate to tall solitary palms with grey, ringed trunks which are smooth or covered with scales. Leaves are pinnate, the sheathing leaf bases forming a prominent crownshaft covered with deciduous grey to brown scaly tomentum. Petioles are short and leaves are arched. The leaflets taper from the middle towards the base and towards the apex, the tips being truncate or oblique and toothed, or pointed. The inflorescences are well branched panicles positioned below the crownshaft and covered by two bracts which split open and fall after the inflorescence emerges. Flowers are borne in triads of one female and two male flowers with the distal portions of the rachillae bearing only male flowers. Fruit are ovoid, sometimes beaked, small to moderately large, single-seeded, and yellow, red or orange-red at maturity.

Veitchia palms are elegant ornamental palms for the tropics with particularly attractive fruit. Although they will usually grow in subtropical climates, they are sensitive to cold and achieve fastest growth in tropical climates. Fresh seed germinates within a few months and young plants should be protected from direct sun and dry or cold wind.

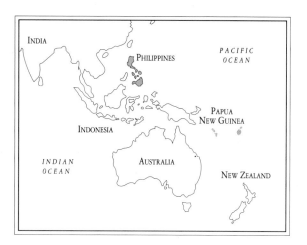

Veitchia macdanielsii

Veitchia joannis

COMMON NAME: None known.
SIZE: Solitary narrow trunk, up to approximately 30 m (100 ft) tall, or more, and approximately 35 cm (14 in) in diameter.
HABITAT: Dense or open forests from near sea level to 650 m (2100 ft).
DISTRIBUTION: Endemic to Fiji.
CONSERVATION STATUS: Rare.
DESCRIPTION: Has about 9 arching leaves in an open crown. Long narrow crownshaft is green with a grey tomentum. Petiole up to 25 cm (10 in) long, covered with brown scales. Leaf blades are about 3 m (10 ft) long, with up to 100 pairs of closely-spaced, pendulous leaflets. Inflorescence is about 60 cm (2 ft) long. Fruit are smooth-skinned, ovoid and beaked. They are 6 cm (2.4 in) long, 3 cm (1.2 in) wide and red to crimson at maturity.
CULTIVATION: Displays some cold tolerance and will grow in frost-free warm temperate areas.

Veitchia joannis

Veitchia montgomeryana

COMMON NAME: None known.
SIZE: Solitary slender trunk, up to 30 m (100 ft) tall and 20 cm (8 in) in diameter, expanded at the base.
HABITAT: Emergent palm in low altitude moist forests.
DISTRIBUTION: Vanuatu.
CULTIVATION: Under threat due to collection of palm 'hearts'.
DESCRIPTION: Has about 10 pinnate leaves in an open crown. Long narrow crownshaft is green with a grey tomentum. Petiole is up to 25 cm (10 in) long. Leaf blades are about 2.6 m (8.5 ft) long with about 60 pairs of closely spaced, slightly pendulous leaflets. Leaves are dotted with brown scales on the undersurface. Inflorescence is around 60 cm (2 ft) long and 80 cm (2ft 8 in) wide. Fruit are smooth-skinned, oblong and beaked. They are about 4.5 cm (1.8 in) long, 2.4 cm (1 in) wide and bright red at maturity.

Veitchia merrillii: in various stages of flowering and fruiting.

Veitchia merrillii

COMMON NAME: Christmas palm, Manila palm.
SIZE: Solitary trunk, up to 15 m (50 ft) tall and 25 cm (10 in) in diameter, expanded at the base.
HABITAT: Coastal forests in sandy soils. Also on limestone cliffs.
DISTRIBUTION: Endemic to the Philippines.
CONSERVATION STATUS: Not threatened.
DESCRIPTION: Compact crown has about 12–15 strongly arching leaves. Long crownshaft is green with a grey tomentum. Petiole 10–15 cm (4–6 in) long. Leaf blades are around 2 m (6.5 ft) long, with numerous closely spaced, pendulous leaflets. Inflorescence is 40–50 cm (16–20 in) long. Fruit are smooth-skinned, egg-shaped and beaked, about 3 cm (1.2 in) long and crimson at maturity.
CULTIVATION: A tropical to subtropical climate is suitable, but they are sensitive to cold. Can be grown in open sunny position from when young. Fruits at Christmas time in the Philippines.

Veitchia montgomeryana

VERSCHAFFELTIA

vĕr-shăf-ˈĕl-tē-à

Verschaffeltia splendida, a handsome ornamental, represents this genus. Its natural distribution is confined to the Seychelles Islands, where it is found on steep hillsides and ledges as scattered individuals or small colonies, at elevations of 300–600 m (1000–2000 ft).

Like *Phoenicophorium borsigianum*, to which it is related, *Verschaffeltia splendida* needs a warm tropical climate with good moisture and shade in the early stages of growth. Leaves are very large, entire and with a bifid tip. They are often split by the wind into pinnate segments. Propagation is from seed, which germinates readily in a few months. The trunks have been used in the Seychelles in building and the natural population of this palm has been affected.

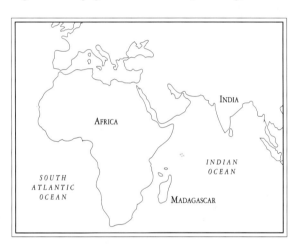

Verschaffeltia splendida

Verschaffeltia spendida

Verschaffeltia splendida

COMMON NAME: Latanier latte, stilt palm.
SIZE: Solitary trunk, up to 25 m (82 ft) tall and 20–30 cm (8–12 in) in diameter.
HABITAT: Steep hillsides from 300–600 m (1000–2000 ft).
DISTRIBUTION: Seychelles Islands.
CONSERVATION STATUS: Unknown.
DESCRIPTION: Trunk has rings of downward-pointing spines and stilt roots. Petioles, leaf sheaths and rachis bear black spines when young. Leaf blades are entire and with a bifid tip, about 2 m (6.5 ft) long, and 1 m (3.3 ft) wide. They are pinnately ribbed, with margins usually deeply divided, and often split by the wind. Inflorescences are among the leaves, are well branched and are 1–2 m (3.3–6.5 ft) long. Flowers in triads. Fruit are more or less globose, brownish green and 2–2.5 cm (0.8–1 in) in diameter and are single-seeded.
CULTIVATION: Needs a tropical climate with good moisture. Protection from wind will keep the leaves from splitting. Plants like open sun as they mature.

WALLICHIA

wŏl-ˈĭch-ē-ȧ

$\mathcal{W}$*allichia*, or Wallich palms, as they are commonly called, are attractive palms distributed from the Indian Himalayas to Myanmar (Burma), southern China and Thailand. Most of the seven species recognised are undergrowth plants of the humid tropical forest from sea level to mountain slopes up to 2000 m (6500 ft). One trunked species, *Wallichia disticha*, from India and Burma, grows on steep mountain slopes up to 1200 m (4000 ft).

Wallichia are solitary or clustering and sometimes become shrubby. *W. disticha* develops a moderate-sized trunk while the other species are smaller, some having a very short stem or no apparent stem. *W. disticha* has an unusual leaf arrangement of two vertical rows of leaves on opposite sides of the trunk. Other species have leaves spirally arranged. Leaves are pinnate, but with a terminal leaflet. Leaflets are regularly arranged or grouped and fanned within the group, narrow and tapering to a point, irregularly rhomboid or deeply lobed with jagged margins. They resemble leaves of *Arenga* or *Caryota* palms. *Wallichia* are hapaxanthic with a basipetal sequence of flowering, inflorescences being produced first from the top of the palm and successively down the palm at each leaf axil. Inflorescences are simple-branched and are unisexual — female and male inflorescences are separate and distinctly different on the same plant. Fruit are ellipsoidal, small, reddish or purplish, smooth-skinned and single-, two- or, occasionally, three-seeded. The fleshy mesocarp of the fruit contains irritant crystals as do the *Arenga* palms.

Suitable for tropical to warm temperate climates, wallich palms exhibit some cold tolerance.

Wallichia disticha

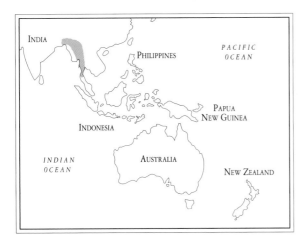

Wallichia densiflora

COMMON NAME: Wallich palm.

SIZE: Forms dense clumps, 2–3 m (6.5–10 ft) tall, usually with very short trunks.

HABITAT: Humid tropical forests in moist valleys up to 1400 m (4500 ft).

DISTRIBUTION: India, Nepal, Myanmar (Burma).

CONSERVATION STATUS: Unknown.

DESCRIPTION: Leaves are 2.5–3 m (8–10 ft) long. Large leaflets are a long oblong shape with wavy, jagged margins, green above, silvery beneath. Fruit are oblong, dull purple and about 0.2 cm (0.5 in) long.

CULTIVATION: Leaves are used to make a long-lasting thatch. Suitable for cultivation in subtropical to temperate climates.

Wallichia densiflora

Wallichia disticha

Wallichia disticha

COMMON NAME: Wallich palm.

SIZE: Solitary trunk, 3–6 m (10–20 ft) tall, 15–30 cm (6–12 in) in diameter.

HABITAT: Chiefly on eastern slopes in humid tropical forests to 1200 m (4000 ft).

DISTRIBUTION: India, Myanmar (Burma).

CONSERVATION STATUS: Unknown.

DESCRIPTION: Only species with a moderate-sized trunk. Leaves are 2.5–3 m (8–10 ft) long, arising in 2 rows on opposite sides of the stem. Leaflets narrow from a truncate apex to the base, with a large tooth on each side about the middle. They are green above, silvery beneath. Female inflorescence twice as long as the male. Fruit are oblong, irregular and reddish.

CULTIVATION: In eastern and northeastern India, starch is extracted from the stem for food. Suitable for tropical to subtropical climates.

WASHINGTONIA
wăsh-ĭng-ˈtōn-ē-a̍

Washingtonia is comprised of two closely-related species, *Washingtonia filifera* and *W. robusta*, native to Mexico and the southern states of mainland USA. They are desert fan palms occurring in oasis situations where they have access to underground water. Thus they are found colonising springs and seepages, and along streams and canyons. They are tall solitary palms that can be distinguished easily from each other by the size of the trunk (*W. robusta* has the narrower trunk). Young plants without trunks are more difficult to identify.

The Washington or cotton palms have stiff fan leaves which tend to persist after they die, and form a dense fibrous 'petticoat' under the crown, sometimes covering the trunk entirely. Leaves are costapalmate, divided (to about halfway or more) into many stiff segments, each pointed, drooping and split into two lobes at the tip. White thread-like fibres hang from between the segments. Leaf sheaths have a conspicuous cleft below the petiole and the sheath margins break down and become fibrous. Petioles are stout with sharp teeth along the margins. Inflorescences are well-branched panicles which arise among the leaves and extend beyond them. In the bud stage the inflorescences are enclosed by two sheathing bracts. The flowers are bisexual and are spirally arranged on the rachillae. Fruit are small and black, ellipsoidal to globose, and fall with the short pedicel (stalk) still attached.

They are suitable for a wide range of climates from dry arid (with cold night and winter temperatures) to humid tropical climates. They are fast-growing palms, popular as garden specimens or avenue trees. Seeds germinate readily and young plants develop a deep root system. They enjoy a sunny location and respond to plenty of water and added fertiliser. They are, however, not suitable as indoor plants.

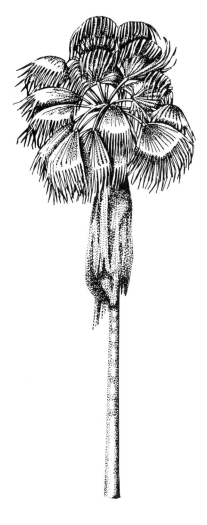

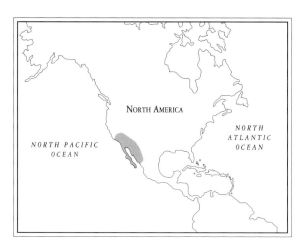

NORTH AMERICA

NORTH PACIFIC OCEAN

NORTH ATLANTIC OCEAN

Washingtonia robusta

Washingtonia filifera

COMMON NAME: Desert fan palm, American cotton palm, Washington palm.

SIZE: Solitary trunk, up to about 15 m (50 ft) tall and 60–80 cm (24–32 in) in diameter.

HABITAT: Desert and arid areas where underground water is available.

DISTRIBUTION: Southeastern California, western Arizona (USA), Baja California (Mexico).

CONSERVATION STATUS: Rare.

DESCRIPTION: Crown has stiff grey-green costapalmate leaves. Petioles are 1.5–2 m (5–6.5 ft) long, blades 1.5–2 m (5–6.5 ft) long. Cottony threads between the leaves do not persist as the tree ages. Inflorescence is 3–5 m (10–16 ft) long. Fruits are ovoid and brown to black.

CULTIVATION: Reported as more hardy in dry climates than *W. robusta*.

Washingtonia robusta

COMMON NAME: Mexican fan palm, Washington palm, cotton palm.

SIZE: Solitary trunks, up to 25 m (80 ft) or more tall and 25 cm (10 in) in diameter, more at the base.

HABITAT: Desert and arid areas where there is a source of underground water.

DISTRIBUTION: Baja California and Sonora (Mexico).

CONSERVATION STATUS: Unknown.

DESCRIPTION: Crown has stiff green, costapalmate leaves. Petioles are about 1 m (3.3 ft) long, blades 1 m (3.3 ft) long. Cottony threads between the leaves are absent on mature plants. Inflorescence is 2–3 m (6.5–10 ft) long. Fruits are almost globose and dark brown.

CULTIVATION: Suitable for a range of climates.

Washingtonia filifera

Washingtonia robusta: with petticoat.

Washingtonia robusta: juvenile plant.

WODYETIA
wŏd-'yĕt-ē-á

*W*odyetia is a monotypic genus, represented by *Wodyetia bifurcata* (the foxtail palm). It is endemic to the Melville Range on Cape York Peninsula, Queensland (Australia). This spectacular palm, only discovered in 1978 and formally described in 1983, has a restricted natural distribution. It grows in prolific stands in the relatively harsh environment of the slopes of an eroded granite range. Situated within a National Park, it is in open woodland among huge granite boulders, from 60–400 m (200–1300 ft) altitude, where the climate has a prolonged dry season.

Despite the illegality of seed collection from the wild, seed has been collected and exported, sometimes in large quantities. The palm is grown by nursery growers and collectors alike, and domestic specimens are now producing fruit. *W. bifurcata* is easy to germinate and thrives in a variety of climates from the equatorial tropics to warm temperate drier areas.

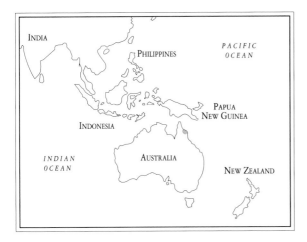

Wodyetia bifurcata

Wodyetia bifurcata

COMMON NAME: Foxtail palm, wodyetia palm.
SIZE: Solitary, ringed trunks, slightly bottle-shaped, up to 15 m (50 ft) tall, but usually much less.
HABITAT: Woodland slopes from 60–400 m (200–1300 ft) elevation.
DISTRIBUTION: Cape York Peninsula, Queensland (Australia).
CONSERVATION STATUS: Rare.
DESCRIPTION: Pinnate leaf has plumose appearance. Leaflets have ribbed margins and the ends are praemorse. Light green crownshaft. Well-branched inflorescence is below the crownshaft. Fruit are large, ovoid to globose, about 6 cm (2 in) long and orange to red when ripe.
CULTIVATION: Tropical to warm temperate climate. Tolerates seasonally-dry conditions and cold temperatures.

Wodyetia bifurcata

CYCAD GENERA
AND SPECIES

Macrozamia miquelii

BOWENIA

bōw-'ē-nē-à

Bowenia is a genus of two species, both delightful small fern-like plants distinguished from other cycads by their bipinnate leaves. The genus is very distinct among the cycads for this reason, and is not easily confused with other genera. *Bowenia serrulata* is known only from a few localities in central Queensland (Australia), the largest population being found in a relatively small area of moist sclerophyll forest near the coast. Interestingly, it appears to be colonising well in the planted pine forests that have replaced its native habitat in the same area. *B. spectabilis* grows on the shaded rainforest floor and in crevices of rocks and along creek banks. A third species may yet be described from the *Bowenia* population in the Tinaroo locality in Queensland. *Bowenia* appears to be an advanced genus of cycads from an evolutionary viewpoint. It has more in common with the American genus *Zamia* than with other Australian cycad genera, although it may have evolved in parallel with *Zamia* rather than in convergence.

Stems are subterranean, producing one or more short, slender branches that bear either leaves (one to several) or cones. The taproot is tuberous and large. Coralloid roots are also produced. Leaves are bipinnate, the leaf rachis branching several times, with the attached leaflets pinnately arranged and decurrent with the rachis. Petioles are long with the base somewhat thickened and hairy. Leaflets are flat, rhomboid to broadly lanceolate, with serrated tips in *B. serrulata*, and tapering to a point. Leaflets lack a midrib, but have numerous more or less parallel veins that divide dichotomously. Male and female cones are on very short peduncles, with spirally arranged sporophylls without spines, the megasporophyll with two ovules. Seeds have an outer fleshy covering which is a bright lavender colour when ripe.

Bowenia can be grown successfully up to coning in containers. Plants of both species can tolerate low light and can be grown indoors. A rich loam with plenty of humus and well-decomposed manure is a suitable potting mixture. A warm environment is required for growth and a humid atmosphere is preferred. Under optimal conditions plants grown from seed will produce cones in five years. *B. serrulata* is reported as requiring more light to harden new growth than does *B. spectabilis*.

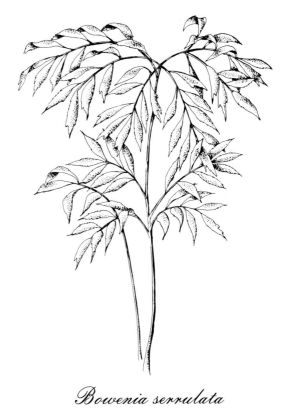

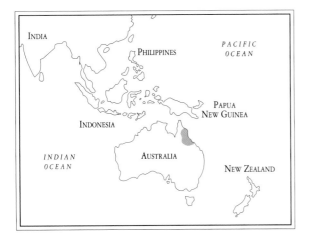

Bowenia serrulata

Bowenia serrulata

COMMON NAME: Byfield fern.
SIZE: Subterranean stem, leaf height up to
1.2 m (4 ft). Plant appears clumping.
HABITAT: Lower slopes of coastal foothills and
ranges. In the shade of eucalyptus trees in
open forest or rainforest. Localities receive
high rainfall.
DISTRIBUTION: Central eastern Queensland
(Australia).
CONSERVATION STATUS: Vulnerable.
DESCRIPTION: Underground stem is more or
less spherical and bears 5–20 short branches,
each developing leaves or, occasionally,
cones. Leaves are bipinnate, leaflets regularly
serrate and rhomboid (diamond-shaped).
CULTIVATION: Needs a tropical climate.
Tolerates low light.

Bowenia serrulata: leaflets have serrated margins.

Bowenia spectabilis

Bowenia spectabilis

COMMON NAME: None known.
SIZE: Subterranean stem, leaf height up to
2 m (6.5 ft). Plant does not appear clumping.
HABITAT: Rainforest. Coastal, up to 50 km
(30 miles) inland and to 700 m (2300 ft)
altitude.
DISTRIBUTION: Northeastern Queensland
(Australia).
CONSERVATION STATUS: Official status
unknown. Widespread and numerous.
DESCRIPTION: Underground stem is elongate,
with 1–5 short branches, each bearing leaves
or, occasionally, cones. Leaves are bipinnate,
leaflets are entire or (sometimes) irregularly
lacerate, and broadly lanceolate.
CULTIVATION: Needs a warm tropical humid
environment. Tolerates low light.

CERATOZAMIA

sĕr-ˌat-ō-ˈzăm-ē-à

Ceratozamia has ten species, distributed from Mexico to Belize and Guatemala. These delightful small cycads are found in various habitats ranging from the humid environment of dense tropical evergreen rainforest to the relatively drier pine and oak forest. Stevenson (1986) noticed a correlation between habitat and leaflet shape. The wetter the habitat, the larger and thinner the leaves and leaflets.

Ceratozamia stems are entirely subterranean or form a short above-ground trunk, which is covered with persistent leaf bases and cataphylls (scale leaves). Leaves are variously few to numerous, pinnate, the leaflets inserted near the edges of the rachis towards the upper side. Leaflets are variously shaped, narrowed at the base and articulate with the rachis. Small stipule-like outgrowths are present on the leaf bases and cataphylls. Some species have prickles on the petiole and rachis. In the seedling and juvenile stages of growth, all species of *Ceratozamia* appear identical. Male and female cones are on different plants (as in all cycads) and may have a short peduncle or be sessile. Sporophylls are valvate, peltate and are arranged in vertical columns. The sporophyll tips are characteristically two-horned.

Suitable for tropical to cool temperate climates, *Ceratozamia* palms are generally adaptable to the cool wet winters provided freezing temperatures are not sustained for long periods. *Ceratozamia latifolia*, *C. mexicana*, *C. robusta* and *C. hildae* are hardy ornamental species reasonably available in cultivation, although under threat in the wild. Other species are less common in cultivation and are also under threat of extinction in the wild. Plants do well in shaded or semi-shaded positions but will yellow in full sun. Although slow growing, plants of some species may reach maturity in five years and produce cones.

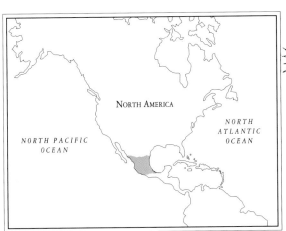

Ceratozamia mexicana

Ceratozamia hildae

COMMON NAME: Bamboo cycad.
SIZE: Stem is mostly subterranean and branching, eventually up to 30 cm (12 in) above ground.
HABITAT: Moist oak forest at about 900 m (1000 ft) altitude.
DISTRIBUTION: Mexico.
CONSERVATION STATUS: Rare. May be vulnerable because of exploitation.
DESCRIPTION: Leaves up to 1.5 m (5 ft) long. Leaflets have a papery texture, are clustered in groups of 3–12 along the rachis, lending a bamboo appearance to the leaf. Male cones are up to 25 cm (10 in) long, female cones up to 20 cm (8 in) long.
CULTIVATION: Tolerates cold and grows fast. Is adaptable to various climates and soils. Fresh seed germinates within 90 days.

Ceratozamia miqueliana

Ceratozamia miqueliana

COMMON NAME: None known.
SIZE: Trunk is subterranean.
HABITAT: Evergreen tropical rainforest and in the transitional zone between evergreen and deciduous forests, from 60–800 m (200–2600 ft) altitude.
DISTRIBUTION: Mexico.
CONSERVATION STATUS: Vulnerable.
DESCRIPTION: Has 5–9 leaves in a crown, each leaf 0.8–1.8 m (32 in–6 ft) long with 5–9 pairs of leaflets. Leaflets are 22–29 cm (9–11.5 in) long, 4–6.5 cm (1.5–2.5 in) wide, ovate to broadly lanceolate, and often dentate near the apex. Petiole armed with prickles. Male cones are about 15 cm (6 in) long, 3–4 cm (1.2–1.6 in) wide, and have a short peduncle. Female cones are about 10 cm (4 in) long, 6 cm (2.4 in) wide, and also have a short peduncle.
CULTIVATION: Not common in cultivation.

Ceratozamia hildae

Ceratozamia mexicana

COMMON NAME: None known.
SIZE: Trunk is up to about 1 m (3.3 ft) above ground and 20 cm (8 in) in diameter.
HABITAT: Tropical semi-deciduous rainforest.
DISTRIBUTION: Mexico.
CONSERVATION STATUS: Insufficiently known, but probably vulnerable because of reduction in habitat and exploitation.
DESCRIPTION: Leaves are 1.5–2 m (5–7 ft) long with 40–60 pairs of leaflets. Leaflets 30–40 cm (12–16 in) long, 1.5–2 cm (0.6–0.8 in) wide, linear lanceolate and subfalcate. They taper to a point. Seedling leaflets may be wider. Petiole armed with numerous short prickles. Male cones are solitary, green, variable in size, often about 40 cm (16 in) long, 7.5 cm (3 in) wide and with a peduncle 7.5–10 cm (3–4 in) long. Female cones are solitary, green, around 35 cm (14 in) long, 12 cm (5 in) wide, and with a peduncle about 10 cm (4 in) long.
CULTIVATION: Tolerates frost. Suitable for cool temperate climates. Does best in a wind-protected position because of its rather brittle leaflets.

Ceratozamia mexicana

CHIGUA

'chĭg-wă

Chigua is a newly-described genus of cycads from Colombia. It is the only endemic genus of cycads from South America (Stevenson, 1990). There have been two species described, both found in primary rainforest at low altitudes. They are in small numbers in their natural habitat and, in an attempt to prevent their eradication, their precise location has not been given by Stevenson.

Trunks are mostly subterranean with a crown of just two to three pinnate leaves. The leaf bases and cataphylls have stipules, and the petioles are long and armed with prickles. The rachis also has prickles in the lower portion. Leaflets are arranged alternately or almost opposite, are long and narrow in *Chigua bernalii*, and shorter and wider in *C. restrepoi*, both species displaying well-defined teeth along the leaflet margins. Characteristic is the presence of a prominent midvein and longitudinally dichotomizing lateral veins. Cones are, to date, known only in *C. restrepoi*. Cones of both sexes have hexagonal peltate sporophylls. Also characteristic of the genus is the conspicuous bump at each angle of the hexagon on the megasporophyll face.

Chigua restrepoi: leaf.

Chigua restrepoi

COMMON NAME: None known.
SIZE: Stem is subterranean, 40 cm (16 in) long and 15 cm (6 in) in diameter.
HABITAT: Primary rainforest at elevations of 150 m (500 ft).
DISTRIBUTION: Colombia.
CONSERVATION STATUS: Endangered.
DESCRIPTION: Has 2 or 3 leaves. Petiole is 60–80 cm (2–3 ft) long, armed with prickles. Rachis is 60–100 cm (2–3.3 ft) long with 20–30 pairs of lanceolate leaflets, each 15–25 cm (6–10 in) long and 3–5 cm (1.2–2 in) wide. Male cone is cylindrical, 5 cm (2 in) long. Female cone is also cylindrical and 15 cm (6 in) long. Cones of both sexes are covered with a reddish-brown tomentum and are on peduncles about twice the length of the cone.
CULTIVATION: Cultivated in only a few botanic garden collections.

Chigua restrepoi

CYCAS

'sȳ-kȧs

Cycas is a genus of perhaps 40–50 species of palm-like plants. The genus is in need of revision and several changes are to be expected in the taxonomy as more field work is done. Many named species may be proven to be synonyms, or may be classified as varieties rather than given species status. The genus *Cycas* is widely distributed with species found in Madagascar, across Asia from India to Japan, through Southeast Asia, New Guinea and northern Australia and across to the Polynesian Islands. Habitats vary from various forest types, including tropical rainforest, to dense or open woodlands and savanna. Some species are found on wet, well-drained hill slopes, while others are in hot, arid, desert-like locations where rain comes during only a few months of the year.

The pinnate leaves of *Cycas* resemble palm leaves, and the trunks, in a similar fashion to many palms, are covered in persistent leaf bases. The leaflets (but not the whole leaf) are tightly rolled inwards towards the rachis in the bud stage, unfurling as the leaf emerges upwards. Each leaflet has a single midrib, but no lateral veins. Male sporophylls form cones similar to the cones of other cycad genera. However, the female sporophylls (megasporophylls) are unmistakably different in that they do not form tightly enclosed cones. Instead they are spirally arranged in a mass that opens out and falls loosely downwards at maturity. Each megasporophyll resembles a leaf with the terminal section or blade often divided or toothed at the margins, the ovules (two to several) being attached at the lateral margins below the terminal blade. After the reproductive phase of growth is completed, the end of the trunk resumes vegetative growth, producing a whorl of new leaves.

Seed take 6–18 months to germinate. The seeds of many *Cycas* species contain a spongy layer enabling them to float, and thus be dispersed by water currents. *Cycas* species are best grown in full sunlight, but can also be grown in partial shade. They are generally suitable for a wide range of climates from tropical to temperate and many tolerate frost. A porous, well-drained soil site is required.

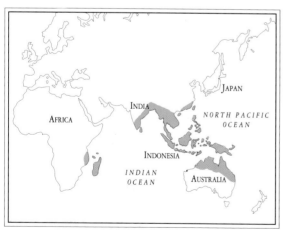

Cycas revoluta

Cycas media

syn. *Cycas normanbyana, C. kennedyana*

COMMON NAME: None known.

SIZE: Trunks are often 1–3 m (3.3–10 ft) tall, occasionally 6 m (20 ft), and 10–18 cm (4–7 in) in diameter, sometimes branching.

HABITAT: Rocky hillsides in open eucalypt forests, occasionally in rainforest.

DISTRIBUTION: Northeastern Queensland (Australia), Papua New Guinea.

CONSERVATION STATUS: Not threatened. Widespread and numerous.

DESCRIPTION: A highly variable species. Leaves are 90–180 cm (3–6 ft) long, almost flat in cross-section, green to blue-green, with short spines near the base of the petiole. Leaflets are in 80–150 pairs, 16–26 cm (6.5–10.5 in) long, 0.6–1 cm (0.25–0.4 in) wide, flat in cross-section and tapering at the base and the tip. Male cones are ovoid, 15–25 cm (6–10 in) long and 8–15 cm (3–6 in) wide. Megasporophylls are 20–30 cm (8–12 in) long, red or grey and tomentose. Blade is narrow and triangular, has regular teeth, an apical spine and 4–10 ovules attached. Seeds are ovoid to almost globose and 3.1–3.8 cm (1.2–1.5 in) long.

CULTIVATION: Once established, this cycad tolerates hot, dry conditions. Grows in a tropical to warm temperate climate. Prefers dry winters and wet summers.

Cycas pruinosa: Lake Argyle, Western Australia.

Cycas media

Cycas pruinosa

COMMON NAME: None known.

SIZE: Trunks are up to 2 m (6.5 ft) high and 25–40 cm (10–16 in) in diameter.

HABITAT: Hill slopes and cliffs.

DISTRIBUTION: Northern Western Australia.

CONSERVATION STATUS: Rare. Numerous in local populations.

DESCRIPTION: Leaves are 90–100 cm (36–40 in) long, grey-green or glaucous blue-green, and U- or V-shaped in cross-section. Leaflets have revolute margins. There are 120–240 per leaf, angled forward on the rachis. Leaflets are 11–20 cm (4.5–8 in) long and 0.2–0.4 cm (0.08–0.16 in) wide, including long pointed tips. Megasporophylls are 27–30 cm (11–12 in) long, rust coloured and pruinose (covered with a frost-like bloom). Blade is about 15 cm (6 in) long, has 20–30 teeth along the margins and a pointed apex. Usually has 4 globular to ovoid ovules per sporophyll, brown to bluish. Male cone is 38–50 cm (15–20 in) long and 9 cm (3.5 in) wide, and tapers to a point.

Cycas revoluta

COMMON NAME: Sago palm, Japanese sago palm, sotetsu (Japan).
SIZE: Trunk is up to 3 m (10 ft) long and 40 cm (16 in) in diameter, but more often half this size. Forms clumps from suckers. Some miniature or bonsai forms are grown.
HABITAT: Seasonally (summer) wet hill slopes.
DISTRIBUTION: Nansei Islands (Japan), South China.
CONSERVATION STATUS: Not threatened. Widespread and numerous.
DESCRIPTION: Leaves are 1–1.5 m (40–60 in) long, dark glossy green. Leaflets are 15–20 cm (6–8 in) long, 0.4–0.6 cm (0.16–0.24 in) wide, with revolute margins. Leaflets are occasionally bifid. Male cones are oblong to cylindrical, generally 25–35 cm (10–14 in) long, on a short peduncle. Megasporophyll is 10–20 cm (4–8 in) long and densely tomentose. Blade has 12–18 pronounced teeth, with 4–6 ovules attached.
CULTIVATION: Edible starch has been extracted from the trunk. Dried leaves, used by florists, have been an export item from Japan. Is suitable for tropical to cool temperate climates, but does best in subtropics. Tolerates frost. May take 13 years or more to produce a cone or seeds.

Cycas taiwaniana

COMMON NAME: None known.
SIZE: Trunk is up to 3 m (10 ft) tall. Forms clumps from suckers.
HABITAT: Along river banks and mountain cliffs.
DISTRIBUTION: Taiwan, southern China.
CONSERVATION STATUS: Indeterminate. Probably not threatened.
DESCRIPTION: Leaves 1–1.5 m (40–60 in) long, dark glossy green. Leaflets are 12.5–17.5 cm (5–7 in) long, 0.6–0.7 cm (0.24–0.28 in) wide and flat in cross-section. Male cones are long, cylindrical, and on a short peduncle. Megasporophyll blade is slightly longer than broad, deeply cut along the margins into long teeth, with 3–4 ovules.
CULTIVATION: Suitable for tropical to cool temperate climates, but does best in subtropics. Tolerates frost, but is not as hardy as _C. revoluta_. Likes an open sunny position. Grows faster than _C. revoluta_.

Cycas revoluta: male cone.

Cycas rumphii

COMMON NAME: None known.
SIZE: Trunk is up to 6 m (20 ft) tall, occasionally up to 15 m (50 ft), often branched, covered in persistent leaf bases.
HABITAT: Coastal forests.
DISTRIBUTION: Andaman Islands, Nicobar Islands, Cocos Islands, Sri Lanka, southern India, Malay Peninsula, Moluccas, New Guinea.
CONSERVATION STATUS: Not threatened. Widespread and numerous.
DESCRIPTION: This highly variable species may be found to encompass several distinct species or varieties. Leaves 1–2 m (3.3–6.5 ft) long with 50–70 leaflets. Leaflets have flat margins, are 20–30 cm (8–12 in) long and 1.5–1.7 cm (0.6–0.7 in) wide. Male cone is oblong to ellipsoid, reddish, tomentose, with a short peduncle. Megasporophyll is short, with an oval-shaped blade and minutely serrated or toothed margins. Has 6–10 ovules. Seeds are large, 5–7 cm (2–2.8 in) long.
CULTIVATION: Needs a tropical climate.

Cycas taiwaniana: the megasporophylls in a tight terminal mass.

Cycas rumphii

DIOON

dȳ-'ō-ŏn

*D*ioon is a genus of ten species distributed throughout Mexico and Honduras from sea level to over 3000 m (10 000 ft) altitudes. In recent years, these handsome cycads have received the close scrutiny of botanists and several species have become popular in cultivation. Habitats range from tropical rainforests to dry rocky mountains.

Trunks are generally above ground, sometimes tall, and covered with persistent leaf bases. Leaves are numerous, pinnate, with the leaflets inserted towards the edges of the rachis on the upper side, individual leaflets lacking a midrib. Unlike some of the other cycad genera, *Dioon* leaflets are not narrowed at the point of attachment with the rachis. Some species, such as *Dioon spinulosum*, have leaflets which are relatively broad where they attach to the rachis. *Dioon* is dioecious, as are all cycads, male and female cones being borne on separate plants. Cones may be sessile or with a short peduncle and appear to be terminal on the main stem. Female cones of *D. spinulosum* and *D. mejiae* become large and heavy, and become pendant on the trunk. Only one cone is produced at each coning period. Sporophylls

are arranged spirally, with the ends truncate or shortly tapering to a point and overlapping. Vegetative growth continues from the stem tissue at the base of the cone.

Dioon species are slow growing and may take ten years or more before producing their first cone. They are generally suited to warm temperate, subtropical and tropical climates, the most common in cultivation being *D. spinulosum* and *D. edule*. The former is faster growing, but less frost tolerant than the latter. Although from tropical regions, *Dioon* species are generally hardy plants which can tolerate periods of cold temperatures and frosts. The narrow-leaved species appear to be more suited to dry conditions and open sun than the broad-leaved species.

Dioon edule

NORTH AMERICA

NORTH PACIFIC OCEAN

NORTH ATLANTIC OCEAN

Dioon califanoi

COMMON NAME: None known.
SIZE: Trunk is up to 4–5 m (13–16.5 ft) tall.
HABITAT: Steep slopes shaded by trees, 1800–2200 m (5900–7200 ft) altitude.
DISTRIBUTION: Mexico.
CONSERVATION STATUS: Endangered.
DESCRIPTION: Keeled leaves are held stiffly erect in an upright V shape, with leaflets inserted obliquely on the upper surface of the rachis. Leaflets are generally spineless, closely spaced and somewhat overlapping. Has large female cones, 30–50 cm (12–20 in) long. Seeds are large.
CULTIVATION: Grows well in open sun in dry areas.

Dioon califanoi: female.

Dioon edule

COMMON NAME: Chamal (Mexico).
SIZE: Trunks are mostly subterranean and up to 3 m (10 ft) long (usually only short above the ground), and 20–30 cm (8–12 in) in diameter.
HABITAT: In areas transitional between tropical deciduous forest and oak forest from sea level to 1500 m (0–5000 ft).
DISTRIBUTION: Mexico.
CONSERVATION STATUS: Insufficiently known. Probably vulnerable.
DESCRIPTION: Leaves are numerous, 70–140 cm (28–56 in) long, usually flat in cross-section. Leaflets are linear-lanceolate, 6–12 cm (2.4–4.8 in) long and 0.6–0.9 cm (0.25–0.35 in) wide. They are generally inserted at right angles to the rachis, have margins without spines except in juvenile leaflets, and may be overlapping towards the leaf apex. Female cones are ovate, 20–40 cm (8–16 in) long and 15–20 cm (6–8 in) wide. Male cones are a similar length but narrower.
Note: The above description is for *D. edule* var. *edule.* The variety *angustifolium* has narrower leaflets (0.4–0.6 cm (0.15–0.25 in) wide) which are generally inserted at an acute angle to the rachis.
CULTIVATION: Suitable for various climates from dry to wet subtropical to warm temperate. Tolerates frost.

Dioon edule

Dioon spinulosum: the female cone becomes pendant.

Dioon merolae

COMMON NAME: None known.
SIZE: Trunk is 4–5 m (13–16.5 ft) tall, and 15–20 cm (6–8 in) in diameter.
HABITAT: Pine-oak forest and tropical semi-deciduous forest.
DISTRIBUTION: Mexico.
CONSERVATION STATUS: Insufficiently known. Probably vulnerable.
DESCRIPTION: Leaves have a distinctive flat appearance. Leaflets are linear-lanceolate, overlapping, obliquely inserted on the rachis except near the base. Median leaflets are 7–9 cm (2.8–3.6 in) long and 1–1.2 cm (0.4–0.5 in) wide, with 1 or 2 spines on upper margins. New leaves very tomentose. Female cones are 30–50 cm (12–20 in) long, about 25 cm (10 in) wide. Male cones are shorter and narrower.

Dioon spinulosum

COMMON NAME: Gum palm.
SIZE: Large trunk, generally 3–6 m (10–20 ft) tall, but can be taller.
HABITAT: Among limestone rocks in evergreen forest, up to 300 m (1000 ft .
DISTRIBUTION: Mexico.
CONSERVATION STATUS: Indeterminate. Probably vulnerable.
DESCRIPTION: Leaves in cross-section are a flat to upside-down V shape. Leaflets are broad compared with other species, median leaflets 15–20 cm (6–8 in) long and 1–1.5 cm (0.4–0.6 in) wide, spines on the upper margins. Lower leaflets reduced to spines. Female cones are large, ovoid-cylindrical, 50–80 cm (20–36 in) long and up to 25 cm (10 in) wide. They are on a peduncle and become pendulous.
CULTIVATION: Suitable for wet subtropical climates. Grows fast.

Dioon merolae

ENCEPHALARTOS

ĕn-ˈkĕf-ăl-ˌărt-ŏs

Encephalartos is a genus of about 52 species of trunked, palm-like cycads endemic to Africa. Many are quite spectacular in their habit, with robust trunks, dense crowns of foliage and vividly-coloured cones. Immensely admired as garden specimens, the pressure from collectors on natural stands of many of these wonderful cycads has led to their proclamation as threatened species. There is a ban on collecting plants or seeds from the wild in South Africa. Their survival in the wild is still uncertain as they continue to be plundered for illegal trade. Survival of these threatened species, as with many other cycads of other genera, may depend on cultivation of seed.

Trunks may be subterranean or above ground, and are covered with persistent leaf bases. Pinnate leaves may be few to numerous, with a straight rachis and leaflets inserted near the edge of the rachis close to the upper surface of the leaf. Leaflets lack a midrib and are narrowed to their point of attachment with the rachis, but are quite varied in shape and size from one species to another. Some leaflets are toothed, others entire with an unbroken margin. Leaflets often reduce in size towards the leaf base and become a series of prickles. Female cones may have a short peduncle or are sessile, while male cones are always borne on a short peduncle. Sporophylls are spirally arranged with truncate ends. This terminal portion of the sporophyll is often distinctive, particularly in the megasporophyll. Two ovules are attached to each megasporophyll and cones may carry 500 or more seeds in the larger species.

The starchy pith of *Encephalartos* stems has long been used by local African tribes as a source of food. The seed endosperm is poisonous, but the fleshy outer covering does not carry any toxin and is often eaten by birds and small animals.

Encephalartos natalensis

Encephalartos varies in cold hardiness from species to species. Giddy (1984) hypothesised a relationship between leaflet width, leaflet colour and adaptability to climate. In general, the narrow leaflet species, particularly those coloured blue-green, tolerate cold and frost better than those with broader leaflets of bright or dark green colour. The same generalities can be applied to their ability to adapt to dry climates. The narrow leaflet species with bluer leaves tend to be found in the lower rainfall areas of southern Africa. In general, *Encephalartos* cycads are adapted to seasonal warm temperate climates. Many prefer winters in which temperatures are low and do not grow well in areas where the climate lacks marked seasons. Therefore, tropical regions with warm to hot temperatures all year round do not suit these cycads.

Encephalartos cycads take about 10–15 years to grow to sexual maturity and produce cones. Their growth rates vary and can be measured by determining the stem distance between successive growth flushes. The magnificent *Encephalartos tegulaneus* from Kenya has been measured as growing 10 cm (4 in) between annual leaf flushes. Other species may gain only half this height and, of course, those with below-ground stems are more difficult to measure. People growing *Encephalartos* should bear in mind that some species hybridise in the wild and in cultivation.

Encephalartos ferox

syn. *Encephalartos kosiensis*

COMMON NAME: Chihanga, chipissana and untopanin (Mozambique), isiqiki somkhovu (South Africa).

SIZE: Trunks are usually only short above the ground, but can be up to 2 m (6.5 ft) tall, and up to 25–35 cm (10–14 in) in diameter.

HABITAT: Coastal scrub and sand dunes.

DISTRIBUTION: Natal Province (South Africa), Mozambique.

CONSERVATION STATUS: Vulnerable.

DESCRIPTION: Leaves are 1–2 m (3–6.5 ft) long, usually straight. Leaflets are dark green, close to regularly arranged, reduced to prickles near the leaf base. Median leaflets are flat, 15 cm (6 in) long and 3.5–5 cm (1.4–2 in) wide. Leaflet margins and tips are spiny and dentate, giving the leaf a 'holly' appearance. Cones often borne in multiples. Male cones are 40–50 cm (16–20 in) long and 7–8 cm (2.8–3.2 in) wide. Female cones are 25–50 cm (10–20 in) long and 20–40 cm (8–16 in) wide. Cones are usually scarlet, occasionally pink to yellow. Seeds have dark red fleshy covering.

CULTIVATION: Will grow in tropical to subtropical and warm temperate climates, but does not tolerate frosts. Grows rapidly and can cone within 12 years from seed germination. Grows best in warm to hot temperatures with a good water supply and added fertiliser.

Encephalartos ferox.

Encephalartos laevifolius

Encephalartos laevifolius

COMMON NAME: None known.

SIZE: Trunk is 3–4 m (10–13 ft) tall and 30–40 cm (12–16 in) in diameter. Often branches and suckers. Has a small leaf base pattern on trunk.

HABITAT: Rocky outcrops from 1300–1800 m (4300–5900 ft) altitude. High rainfall area.

DISTRIBUTION: Eastern Transvaal (South Africa), Swaziland.

CONSERVATION STATUS: Endangered.

DESCRIPTION: Sharp pointed cataphylls are clearly evident at trunk apex. Leaves are straight, dark green, 1 m (3.3 ft) long, V-shaped in cross-section. Bare petiole is up to 25 cm (10 in) long. Median leaflets are 12–15 cm (4.8–6 in) long, 0.5–0.6 cm (0.2–0.25 in) wide and have a spiny tip. Has up to 5 male cones, each 30–40 cm (12–16 in) long and 10 cm (4 in) wide. Usually has 3 female cones, each 20–30 cm (8–12 in) long and 10–15 cm (4–6 in) wide. Seeds have orange-yellow fleshy covering.

CULTIVATION: Tolerates frost, grows slowly.

Encephalartos natalensis

COMMON NAME: None known.

SIZE: Trunks are 4–6 m (13–20 ft) long, 25–40 cm (10–16 in) in diameter.

HABITAT: Rocky outcrops.

DISTRIBUTION: Natal Province (South Africa).

CONSERVATION STATUS: Rare.

DESCRIPTION: Leaves are straight, 1.5–3 m (5–10 ft) long, glossy green. Median leaflets 15–25 cm (6–10 in) long, 2.5–4 cm (1–1.6 in) wide. Occasionally some leaflets are toothed, but they are usually not. Leaflets reduce to prickles towards the base. Produces up to 5 yellow cones. Male cones are 45–50 cm (18–20 in) long and 10–12 cm (4–4.8 in) wide. Female cones are 50–60 cm (20–24 in) long and 25–30 cm (10–12 in) wide. Seeds have orange-red fleshy covering.

CULTIVATION: Relatively fast growing, prefers full sun.

Encephalartos natalensis

Encephalartos transvenosus, the modjadji cycad.

Encephalartos transvenosus

COMMON NAME: The modjadji cycad.

SIZE: Trunks are tall, often 7–8 m (23–26 ft), recorded up to 13 m (43 ft). Trunk diameter is 40–65 cm (16–26 in). Has a distinctive leaf base pattern on trunk.

HABITAT: Steep mountain slopes at about 1000 m (3300 ft), often covered by mist. High rainfall area with cool moist summers.

DISTRIBUTION: Transvaal (South Africa).

CONSERVATION STATUS: Rare. Forests of this cycad are protected by tribal law by the Lovedu, who are ruled by the Rain Queens.

DESCRIPTION: Often has dormant buds along trunk. Apex of trunk covered with brown woolly hairs. Leaves are 1.5–2.5 m (5–8 ft) long with dense overlapping leaflets, glossy dark green, reducing to prickles near the base. Median leaflets are about 18 cm (7 in) long and 3 cm (1.2 in) wide, with 1–3 teeth on both margins. Bare, yellow petiole, 14 cm (5.5 in) long. Up to 5 orange cones. Male cones are 40–60 cm (16–24 in) long, 13–15 cm (5.2–6 in) wide. Female cones are very large; 65 cm (26 in) long and 25 cm (10 in) in diameter. Seeds have orange-red fleshy covering.

CULTIVATION: Relatively fast growing. Plants are quite large in 4–5 years and will cone in as little as 11 years from seed. Do not tolerate frost. They prefer a position sheltered from open sun and winds.

Encephalartos villosus

COMMON NAME: None known.

SIZE: Mostly subterranean stem, not more than 30 cm (1 ft) above ground, 30 cm (1 ft) in diameter. Often clumping.

HABITAT: Low forest with summer-dominant rainfall and mild, dry winter.

DISTRIBUTION: Transkei, Natal, Kwazulu and Transvaal (South Africa), Swaziland.

CONSERVATION STATUS: Rare.

DESCRIPTION: A highly variable species. Apex of stem is very woolly. Leaves are 1.5–3 m (5–10 ft) long, glossy dark green, gently curved. Leaflets reduce in size towards the base, finally becoming tiny prickles. No bare petiole. Median leaflets are up to 25 cm (10 in) long and 2 cm (0.8 in) wide. Leaflets are curved, with a few teeth on both margins. Has yellow to orange cones with peduncles on both sexes. Male cones 60 cm (2 ft) long, 10 cm (4 in) wide. Female cones 40 cm (16 in) long, 20 cm (8 in) wide. Cone scales overlap in female. Seeds have scarlet fleshy covering.

CULTIVATION: Needs a subtropical to temperate climate. Prefers shade and protection from frosts.

Encephalartos villosus

LEPIDOZAMIA

lĕp-id-ō-'zăm-ē-à

Lepidozamia has two species, both endemic to the east coast of Australia. They are quite spectacular, large, trunked cycads usually found in wet sclerophyll forest or in rainforest.

Trunks can be tall, occasionally branched, and are covered in persistent leaf bases. The pinnate leaves are

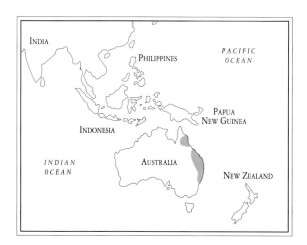

large, numerous, glossy dark green, with the leaflets inserted on the rachis midline towards the upper side of the leaf. The rachis is not twisted and the base of the petiole is swollen and at first tomentose. Leaflets curve and droop downwards. Successive crowns of leaves are separated by a broad series of cataphylls. New leaves are a bronze colour before turning green. Male and female cones are on different plants (as in all cycads), arise from the leaf axils on very short stalks or without stalks. Sporophylls of both male and female cones are spirally arranged, and overlapping, with the ends tomentose and laterally spreading, but without spines (as in the *Macrozamia* cycads). Two (occasionally one or three) ovules are borne on the megasporophylls. The seeds are large and covered with a red or yellowish fleshy layer.

Fresh seeds germinate in 4–12 months. *Lepidozamia* cycads make good garden and pot plants, although they require space to adequately display their leaves. They tolerate frost, *Lepidozamia peroffskyana* more so than *L. hopei.*

Lepidozamia peroffskyana

Lepidozamia hopei

COMMON NAME: None known.
SIZE: Trunk is 2–20 m (6.5–66 ft) tall.
HABITAT: Hilly country in or near rainforest.
DISTRIBUTION: Northeast Queensland (Australia).
CONSERVATION STATUS: Unknown. Locally abundant.
DESCRIPTION: Leaves 2–3 m (6.5–10 ft) long. Petiole 30–60 cm (1–2 ft) long. Has 160–200 (or more) leaflets, each 20–40 cm (8–16 in) long and 1.5–3 cm (0.6–1.2 in) wide, tapering to a pointed tip and slightly narrowed at the base. Cones are surrounded at the base by several tomentose cataphylls. Male cones are 50–60 cm (20–48 in) long and 10–12 cm (4–5 in) wide. Female cones are ovoid, contracted at the base, 40–60 cm (16–24 in) long and 20–25 cm (8–10 in) wide.
CULTIVATION: Best in shade or semi-shade. Needs tropical to warm temperate climates.

Lepidozamia peroffskyana

Lepidozamia hopei

Lepidozamia peroffskyana

COMMON NAME: None known.
SIZE: Trunk is 2–7 m (6.5–23 ft) tall, usually 0.6–1.8 m (2–6 ft), and up to 35 cm (14 in) in diameter. Sometimes branched.
HABITAT: Hilly country in wet sclerophyll forest, in and near rainforest and near the sea shore.
DISTRIBUTION: Southeast Queensland and northeast New South Wales (Australia).
CONSERVATION STATUS: Unknown. Locally abundant.
DESCRIPTION: Leaves 2–3 m (6.5–10 ft) long. Petiole 30–60 cm (1–2 ft) long. Has 160–200 (or more) leaflets, each 10–32 cm (4–13 in) long and 0.7–1.4 cm (0.3–0.6 in) wide, tapering to a pointed tip and slightly narrowed at the base. Note that leaflets are narrower and lighter green than in *L. hopei*. Cones are surrounded at the base by several tomentose cataphylls. Male cones are 50–60 cm (20–48 in) long and 10–12 cm (4–5 in) wide. Female cones are ovoid, contracted at the base, 40–60 cm (16–24 in) long and 20–25 cm (8–10 in) wide.
CULTIVATION: Plants collected from the wild may be infested with the destructive weevil *Tranes internatus*. Are adaptable to subtropical to cool temperate climates.

MACROZAMIA

măk-rō-ˈzăm-ē-à

Macrozamia is a genus of approximately 22 species, perhaps as many as 25, endemic to Australia and distributed in warm temperate and subtropical areas, barely reaching the Tropic of Capricorn. Most species are in eastern Australia, with one found in Central Australia and another in southwestern Australia. Habitats are generally sclerophyll forest or woodlands, usually rather dry locations on poor, sandy, rocky and frequently siliceous soils. Many communities of *Macrozamia* cycads have been eradicated from properties carrying stock because they contain a poison that causes a condition known as the 'staggers' when eaten by cattle or sheep.

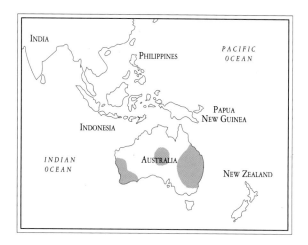

Over a century ago, the botanist Miquel divided the genus into two. Section *Macrozamia* contains the large plant species that typically have many leaves and sometimes an above-ground trunk. Section *Parazamia* contains the smaller plant species that have fewer leaves and a stem which is almost completely subterranean. In all species, the leaf bases persist on the above-ground portion of the trunk. Leaves are usually simple-pinnate, but leaflets can be forked in some species. Leaflets are inserted towards the upper side of the rachis. The rachis may be straight, curved or twisted and the leaf bases are usually expanded and silky, or covered with woolly long hairs. Cataphylls are present and are silky or woolly when young. Male and female cones are on separate plants, are more or less cylindrical, and are pedunculate, arising from the leaf axils. Sporophylls are spirally arranged and bear spines on the outer terminal surface. The female sporophylls are greatly thickened towards the ends, closely fitting and somewhat overlapping.

Macrozamia cycads are suitable for subtropical to warm temperate climates with several of the New South Wales species tolerating a cool temperate climate. Fresh seed germinates after about 4–12 months. Plants respond to added fertiliser and adequate moisture, provided the soil does not become soggy. A sunny location with partial shade is best, but plants can tolerate open sun.

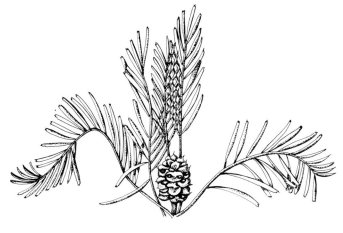

Macrozamia fawcettii

Macrozamia communis: female.

Macrozamia communis

COMMON NAME: Burrawang palm.
SIZE: Trunk is mostly subterranean, but can be up to 1.2 m (4 ft) above ground, occasionally more, and 30–60 cm (1–2 ft) in diameter.
HABITAT: Dry or wet sclerophyll forest on sandy to loamy soils.
DISTRIBUTION: Eastern New South Wales (Australia).
CONSERVATION STATUS: Not threatened. Locally abundant.
DESCRIPTION: Has 20–100 leaves, each about 1–2 m (3.3–6.5 ft) long. Has 70–130 leaflets, each up to 35 cm (14 in) long and 1.2 cm (0.5 in) wide. Lowest leaflets are reduced to spines. Petiole 12–60 cm (5–24 in) long, spine-free. Male cones are cylindrical, 20–45 cm (8–18 in) long and 8–12 cm (3–5 in) wide. Female cones are cylindrical, same length as male and 10–20 cm (4–8 in) wide, with the longest spines 4–10 cm (1.6–4 in) long. Seeds are covered in scarlet or yellow flesh when ripe.
CULTIVATION: Tolerates frost. Prefers a semi-shaded position, but will tolerate a sunny position.

Macrozamia fawcettii

COMMON NAME: None known.
SIZE: Stem is mostly subterranean, 10–20 cm (4–8 in) in diameter.
HABITAT: Dry or wet sclerophyll forest on very sandy soil.
DISTRIBUTION: Northeastern New South Wales (Australia).
CONSERVATION STATUS: Not threatened.
DESCRIPTION: Has 2–12 leaves, each 60–110 cm (24–44 in) long. Rachis is spirally twisted. Has about 30–70 leaflets, each 50–120 cm (20–48 in) long and about 1 cm (0.4 in) wide, with a few small teeth at the tips. Petiole is round, sometimes flattened and grooved, and about 25 cm (10 in) long. Male cones are 15–25 cm (6–10 in) long and 4–6 cm (1.5–2.5 in) wide, female cones 12–18 cm (5–7 in) long and 7–9 cm (3–3.5 in) wide, with longest spines 1.5–2.5 cm (0.6–1 in). Seeds are covered in a bright red to dark red flesh when ripe.
CULTIVATION: Tolerates low temperatures. Prefers a semi-shaded position.

Macrozamia heteromera: the female cone falling apart.

Macrozamia fawcetti: female.

Macrozamia heteromera

COMMON NAME: None known.
SIZE: Stem is mostly subterranean, 8–15 cm (3–6 in) in diameter, unbranched.
HABITAT: Dry sclerophyll forest on sandy soils in flat country.
DISTRIBUTION: Inland northeastern New South Wales (Australia).
CONSERVATION STATUS: Rare.
DESCRIPTION: Has 2–10 leaves, erect at first, then spreading. Each is 45–80 cm (18–32 in) long, V-shaped in cross-section. Rachis is curved throughout. Has 80–130 leaflets, once or twice divided. Leaves vary in colour from blue to green. Petiole 5–12 cm (2–5 in) long. Male cones are cylindrical, 12–20 cm (5–8 in) long and 4–5 cm (1.6–2 in) wide. Female cones are cylindrical, 10–25 cm (4–10 in) long and 8–12 cm (3–5 in) wide, with the longest spines 1–2 cm (0.4–0.8 in). Seeds are covered in scarlet flesh when ripe.
CULTIVATION: Tolerates frost. The blue form tolerates full sun, the green form prefers semi-shade.

Macrozamia lucida: male.

Macrozamia lucida

COMMON NAME: None known.
SIZE: Stem is mostly subterranean, 10–20 cm (4–8 in) or more in diameter.
HABITAT: Wet sclerophyll forest or rainforest, usually on slopes.
DISTRIBUTION: Southern Queensland (Australia).
CONSERVATION STATUS: Rare.
DESCRIPTION: Has 2–15 leaves, each 80–110 cm (32–44 in) long. Rachis is curved and usually not (or scarcely) twisted. Has 50–100 leaflets, up to 35 cm (14 in) long and 1.2 cm (0.5 in) wide. Petiole 25–30 cm (10–12 in) long. Male cones are about 15 cm (6 in) long and 4 cm (1.6 in) wide. Female cones are 15–20 cm (6–8 in) long and 7.5–9 cm (3–3.5 in) wide. Seeds are covered in orange-red flesh when ripe.
CULTIVATION: Prefers a shaded position.

Macrozamia moorei

COMMON NAME: None known.

SIZE: Massive above-ground trunk, 2–5 m (6.5–16.5 ft) tall, 60–80 cm (24–32 in) in diameter.

HABITAT: Flat to undulating hilly country.

DISTRIBUTION: Central southern Queensland (Australia).

CONSERVATION STATUS: Indeterminate. Locally abundant. Probably not threatened.

DESCRIPTION: Up to 150 leaves, each about 1.5–3 m (5–10 ft) long. Rachis is not twisted. Has 150–250 leaflets, each up to 40 cm (16 in) long and 1 cm (0.4 in) wide. About 40 of the lowest leaflets reduce to spines, leaving almost no spine-free petiole. Male cones are cylindrical, 30–45 cm (12–18 in) long and 8–10 cm (3–4 in) wide. Female cones are cylindrical, 40–90 cm (16–36 in) long and 12–19 cm (5–7.5 in) wide, with the longest spines 2.5–7 cm (1–3 in). Seeds are covered in scarlet flesh when ripe.

Note: *M. johnsonii*, from northern New South Wales, described by Jones and Hill in 1992, was previously included in *M. moorei*.

CULTIVATION: Relatively fast growing. Tolerates frost and full sun.

Macrozamia moorei

Macrozamia riedlei: Western Australia.

Macrozamia pauli-guilielmi: male.

Macrozamia pauli-guilielmi

COMMON NAME: Pineapple zamia.

SIZE: Stem is mostly subterranean, 10–20 cm (4–8 in) in diameter.

HABITAT: Sclerophyll forest.

DISTRIBUTION: Southeastern Queensland and northeastern New South Wales (Australia).

CONSERVATION STATUS: Not threatened. Locally numerous.

DESCRIPTION: Has 2–12 leaves, each 40–110 cm (16–44 in) long. Rachis spirally twisted several times. Has 50–200 leaflets, each up to 30 cm (1 ft) long and 0.7 cm (0.3 in) wide, sometimes with 2 or 3 apical teeth. Petiole 5–35 cm (2–14 in) long. Male cones 8–25 cm (3.5–10 in) long and 4–6 cm (1.5–2.5 in) wide, female cones 10–25 cm (4–10 in) long and 7–8.5 cm (3–3.5 in) wide, with the longest spines 1.5–4 cm (0.6–1.6 in). Seeds are covered in orange to red flesh when ripe.

CULTIVATION: Prefers a shaded position.

Macrozamia riedlei

COMMON NAME: Zamia.

SIZE: Trunk is mostly subterranean, but can be above ground, 1–5 m (3.3–16.5 ft) tall and 60–120 cm (2–4 ft) in diameter.

HABITAT: Dry and wet sclerophyll forest on sandy and lateritic soils.

DISTRIBUTION: Southwestern Australia.

CONSERVATION STATUS: Rare.

DESCRIPTION: A variable species, with 50–100 leaves, each 1.5–2 m (5–6.5 ft) long. Petiole 20–30 cm (8–12 in) long, spine-free. Has 100–150 leaflets, pointed forward towards the leaf apex and held upward so the leaf is V-shaped in cross-section, at least in the distal portion. Longest leaflets are 20–30 cm (8–12 in), the lowest leaflets reduced to spines. Female cones 25–40 cm (10–16 in) long and 15–25 cm (6–10 in) wide, the longest spines 1.5–6 cm (0.6–2.5 in). Seeds are covered with a red flesh when ripe.

CULTIVATION: Tolerates full sun but prefers semi-shade.

Macrozamia stenomera

Macrozamia stenomera

COMMON NAME: None known.

SIZE: Stem is mostly subterranean, 8–15 cm (3–6 in) in diameter.

HABITAT: Dry sclerophyll forest on stony hillsides up to 1200 m (4000 ft).

DISTRIBUTION: Northwestern New South Wales (Australia).

CONSERVATION STATUS: Rare.

DESCRIPTION: Has 2–10 leaves, each 40–80 cm (16–32 in). Rachis twisted, particularly near the tip. Has 70–120 leaflets, each dichotomously divided 1–4 times, giving a bushy appearance to the leaves. Female cones 10–25 cm (4–10 in) long and 8–12 cm (3.5–5 in) wide, longest spines 1–2 cm (0.4–0.8 in). Seeds are covered in a yellow or red flesh when ripe.

CULTIVATION: Tolerates low temperatures and heavy frosts. Prefers a semi-shaded position with well-drained soil.

MICROCYCAS

mȳc-rō-'sȳ-kăs

Microcycas is a monotypic genus of cycads found only on the island of Cuba. It is a rare species found on the slopes of the canyons and foothills of the Sierra del Rosario in western Cuba. Some colonies are in lowland areas and others in montane areas up to 240 m (785 ft) above sea level. Less than 600 plants are reported as surviving in the wild. *Microcycas calocoma* shares many botanical characteristics with the arborescent *Zamia* cycads of tropical America, and there is a distinct possibility that after more research it will be returned to the genus *Zamia*.

Microcycas calocoma is among the tallest of living cycads with individuals in the wild often 10 m (33 ft) or more in trunk height and 30–37 cm (12–15 in) in trunk diameter. After pollination, seeds take about ten months to mature and fall. Seed has been distributed from the Fairchild Tropical Gardens in Florida to many botanical gardens around the world. *Microcycas* is reputed to grow quickly under optimal conditions in a tropical climate, but it is very sensitive to cold.

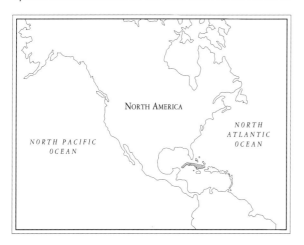

Microcycas calocoma: male plant.

Microcycas calocoma

COMMON NAME: None known.
SIZE: Trunks are up to 10 m (33 ft) or more tall, 30–37 cm (12–15 in) in diameter.
HABITAT: Slopes and hillsides from lowlands to 240 m (785 ft).
DISTRIBUTION: Cuba.
CONSERVATION STATUS: Endangered.
DESCRIPTION: Has 10–40 bright green pinnate leaves, each 1–2 m (3.3–6.5 ft) long. Each leaf has 50–80 pairs of narrow, tapering, reflexed leaflets, each 8–20 cm (3.2–8 in) long. Terminal leaflets are about the same length as those in the midsection. Cones of both sexes are 40–70 cm (16–28 in) long, on a short peduncle, and with 500–1500 hexagonal scales in about 20 rows. Cones are covered with a tawny pubescence and each scale has a knob-like apex. Seeds are 2.5–3 cm (1–1.2 in) long, covered with a salmon pink flesh.
CULTIVATION: Needs a tropical climate.

Microcycas calocoma: male.

STANGERIA

stăn-'gĕr-ē-à

Stangeria is one of the two genera in the family Stangeriaceae, according to Stevenson's classification (1992). The genus is monotypic, *Stangeria eriopus* being the single species. It is fern-like in appearance but quite variable in size. Distribution is along the east coast of South Africa, but usually at least 2–3 km, and no more than 50 km, inland. It grows in forests in deep or partial shade, and in open sun in grassland. Soil types in habitat vary from sandy or granitic to heavy black clay, and are all slightly acid. Annual rainfall varies from over 1000 mm (40 in) to around 750 mm (30 in) with a summer dominance.

Differing from other cycads in the leaf venation, *Stangeria eriopus* is fern-like in that the leaflets have a single prominent midrib and many branching lateral veins. The root system is composed of an underground tuberous root which may be 10 cm (4 in) or more across, and is usually multi-headed. Coralloid roots are also produced. Each of the above-ground growing points produces a new leaf, one at a time, and is capable of eventually producing a cone. The leaves are pinnate and vary in number and size according to growing conditions. In the open, they may reach a length of 25–30 cm (10–12 in), while in the deep shade of their forest habitat they may be up to 2 m (6.5 ft) long. Leaflet number also varies from five to twenty, with opposite or nearly opposite pairs. Lower leaflets have short stalks while upper ones are directly attached to the rachis, and the leaflet margins may be smooth and regular, slightly undulate or sometimes serrated. Each growing point potentially produces a stalked cone. Female cones are elliptic to egg-shaped, up to 18 cm (7 in) long and 8 cm (3 in) in diameter, covered with a pale green to silvery soft velvet which becomes dark green to brown. This covering eventually falls away and the cone falls open to reveal the seeds, each covered with bright red flesh. Male cones are cylindrical, apically tapering, covered with a silvery green velvet, becoming brown to yellow-brown. Both male and female cones have overlapping scales which appear to be arranged in vertical rows.

Seedlings should be situated in shade and watered freely to achieve luxuriant foliage. Container depth should be at least 30 cm (1 ft) to allow unhindered root development. The potting mix or garden soil should be one which drains easily yet is rich in organic matter. A sandy soil with high humus content and testing slightly acid is recommended. Plants require regular watering and protection from frost. Well-established plants will tolerate some dry periods. Mulching around the plant is recommended. *Stangeria* is relatively fast growing, taking around seven to eight years from seed germination to production of the first cone.

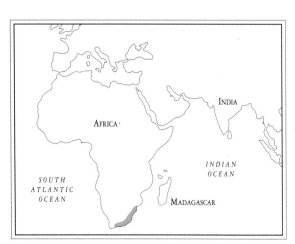

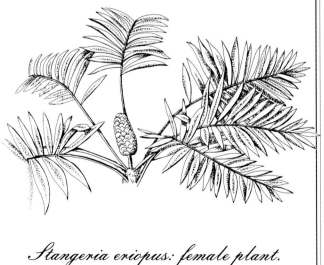

Stangeria eriopus: female plant.

Stangeria eriopus: female.

Stangeria eriopus

COMMON NAME: None known.

SIZE: Stem is below ground. Has 4–5 leaves, each up to 2 m (6.5 ft).

HABITAT: Near coastal grasslands and forests.

DISTRIBUTION: South Africa.

CONSERVATION STATUS: Endangered.

DESCRIPTION: Has pinnate, fern-like leaves 30 cm–2 m (1–6.5 ft) long. Has 5–20 leaflets, in opposite or near-opposite pairs. Lower leaflets have short stalks. Leaflets have midribs and branching lateral veins, with margins varying from smooth to undulate or (sometimes) serrated. Female cones are elliptical to egg-shaped and up to 18 cm (7 in) long. Male cones are cylindrical, apically tapering, 10–25 cm (4–10 in) long. Cones of both sexes are covered with a silvery green tomentum. Seed are about 2 cm (0.8 in) by 1.4 cm (0.6 in).

CULTIVATION: Needs a subtropical to temperate climate.

Stangeria eriopus: male cone.

ZAMIA

'ză̄m-ē̇-à

Zamia has about 44 species, distributed throughout Florida and Georgia in the USA, the West Indies (except the Lesser Antilles), Mexico and south through Central America to Colombia, Venezuela, Ecuador, Peru, Bolivia and Brazil. Habitats vary greatly. They range from coastal sand dunes to steep mountain slopes in rainforests, from sea level to elevations of 2500 m (8200 ft). One species, *Zamia roezlii*, can grow in mangrove swamps, while another, *Z. pseudoparasitica*, is an epiphyte. The genus is in much need of revision. Its distribution in Central and South America is also not well known. A number of species are as yet undescribed.

Zamia cycads usually have either a subterranean or a short above-ground trunk. The trunk is naked as leaf bases do not persist. Besides the normal taproot all species have coralloid roots. Short cataphylls (scale leaves) 1–2 cm (0.4–0.8 in) long alternate with leaves from the crown. Leaves are generally few (two to fifteen), pinnate, the leaflets generally oblong and with parallel and branched veins, and no midrib. Leaflets are usually flat and smooth, narrowed at the base and articulate with the rachis. In some species, leaflets have toothed or serrated margins and can appear very fern-like. Small stipule-like outgrowths are present on the leaf bases, and the petiole is well developed. Some species have prickles on the petiole and rachis. Male and female cones are borne on different plants and may have a peduncle or be sessile. Sporophylls do not overlap, are peltate and are arranged in vertical columns. The cones of both sexes are cylindrical, the male usually narrower, particularly at the apex. The sporophyll tips in the female are characteristically hexagonal, with six inclined facets surrounding a single central facet. Seeds have a red to orange-red outer fleshy covering.

Zamia seed germination is often poor and fresh seed will start to lose its viability after a few months. Germination is improved by removing the fleshy outer covering of the seed. A more labour-intensive method to improve germination (Hooft, 1970) is to first remove the fleshy covering from the seed, then puncture and carefully peel away the hard seed coat with a knife. The excised seed must be treated with a fungicidal dust or solution, and then placed in a dish of wet vermiculite or sand, covered and kept at room temperature away from direct sunlight. Germination should start within 48 hours. Transplanting seedlings should be very carefully done, ensuring the whole tuber is covered. Damaged tap roots will usually rot. Zamias grow relatively slowly in the first year or two, but may cone within three to five years from the seedling stage. They are generally suitable for a wide range of climates from tropical to cool temperate, but grow best in the tropics and subtropics.

Zamia furfuracea

Zamia fischeri

COMMON NAME: None known.
SIZE: Stem is underground, often producing multiple heads. Plants 30–100 cm (1–3.3 ft) tall.
HABITAT: Evergreen oak forest and semi-evergreen forest from 180–900 m (600–3000 ft).
DISTRIBUTION: Mexico.
CONSERVATION STATUS: Indeterminate. Probably vulnerable.
DESCRIPTION: Has 6–30 (or more) fern-like leaves, each up to 45 cm (18 in) long. Has many narrow-lanceolate leaflets, 5–14 cm (2–5.6 in) long and 0.7–4.5 cm (0.3–1.8 in) wide, tapering at the base and with toothed, acute, asymmetrical tips. Leaflets have a papery to almost membranous texture and 10–20 veins. Female cones are grey, egg-shaped, up to 7 cm (2.8 in) long and 4.5 cm (1.8 in) in diameter. Male cones are cylindrical, 6 cm (2.4 in) long and 2 cm (0.8 in) in diameter.
CULTIVATION: Best grown in shade or partial shade.

Zamia fischeri

Zamia furfuracea

COMMON NAME: Cardboard palm.
SIZE: Short above-ground trunk, 10–20 cm (4–8 in) tall. Plants are 30–90 cm (1–3 ft) high.
HABITAT: Stable coastal sand dunes.
DISTRIBUTION: Mexico.
CONSERVATION STATUS: Unknown, probably vulnerable.
DESCRIPTION: Has 8–30 leaves forming a dense crown. Leaves are strongly furfuraceous when young. Has 10–20 (or more) leaflets, each broadly lanceolate, 8–16 cm (3.2–6.5 in) long and 1.8–4.5 cm (0.7–1.8 in) wide. Leaflets are leathery, margins have short teeth or are serrated, and they have many parallel and dichotomously-branched veins. Male cones cylindrical, 9–12 cm (3.6–4.8 in) long, 1.8–2 cm (0.7–0.8 in) in diameter. Female cones cylindrical, 18–23 cm (7.2–9.2 in) long, 6.5–7 cm (2.6–2.8 in) in diameter, often on a peduncle longer than the cone.
CULTIVATION: Is often used as an indoor plant. Outside it can be grown in full sun or partial shade. Resistant to salty sea air. Will hybridise with *Z. loddigesii* and *Z. spartea*.

Zamia furfuracea: male.

Zamia integrifolia

syn. *Zamia floridana, Z. silvicola, Z. umbrosa, Z. erosa, Z. media, Z. tenuis*

COMMON NAME: Wild sago, Florida arrowroot, Indian bread root, koonti, contie.

SIZE: Stem is underground.

HABITAT: Various: coastal sand dunes, pinelands subject to periodic fires, closed-canopy oak hammocks.

DISTRIBUTION: Florida and southeastern Georgia (USA), Bahamas, Cuba, Cayman Islands.

CONSERVATION STATUS: Vulnerable.

DESCRIPTION: Pinnate leaves are up to 1 m (3.3 ft) long. With 6–20 pairs of leaflets, flat and oblong with inconspicuous teeth near the tip. Cones of both sexes are cylindrical, sometimes tapering to a sterile pointed apex, 7–16 cm (3–6.5 in) long and covered with a dense tomentum, particularly in the female.

CULTIVATION: Suitable for tropical to cool temperate climates and tolerant of frosts. Seedlings are best grown in shade. Older plants require a sunny location to encourage cone production. Stems have been used as a source of edible starch, after thorough washing to remove the toxins.

Zamia integrifolia: with female cones.

Zamia loddigesii

Probable synonyms are *Zamia lawsoniana* and *Z. sylvatica*

COMMON NAME: None known.

SIZE: Plant height is variable, from 0.5–1 m (1.5–3.3 ft) or more tall. Stem is underground.

HABITAT: Dry deciduous tropical forest, often oak forest, from 500–750 m (1600–2500 ft).

DISTRIBUTION: Mexico.

CONSERVATION STATUS: Insufficiently known. Probably not threatened.

DESCRIPTION: Has 1–6 (or more) leaves, each 40–100 cm (16 in–3.3 ft) long. Leaflets have various shapes; linear lanceolate to oval, sometimes falcate, gradually tapering, toothed, with 7–25 veins, frequently dichotomous. Lower side of leaf is sometimes tomentose. Petiole is armed with prickles. Female cones are brown to grey, cylindrical to egg-shaped, up to about 11 cm (4.4 in) long and 4 cm (1.6 in) in diameter. Male cones are cylindrical, about 8 cm (3.2 in) long and 1.8 cm (0.7 in) in diameter.

CULTIVATION: Prefers an open sunny position.

Zamia loddigesii

Zamia pumila

syn. *Zamia debilis, Z. latifoliolata*

COMMON NAME: None known.

SIZE: Stem is generally underground, but can be short above ground, up to about 15 cm (6 in).

HABITAT: Pine and oak forests.

DISTRIBUTION: Dominican Republic, Puerto Rico, Cuba.

CONSERVATION STATUS: Insufficiently known.

DESCRIPTION: Pinnate leaves are 60–120 cm (2–4 ft) long. With 2–13 pairs of leaflets, each 9–19 cm (3.5–7.5 in) long and 1–2 cm (0.4–0.8 in) wide. Leaflets are lanceolate, gradually widening, asymmetrical, and have 30–40 veins, a fairly blunt tip (sometimes tapering) and many teeth. No prickles on petiole. Female cones, usually produced singly, are dark reddish brown, cylindrical and up to 12 cm (5 in) long. Male cones are shorter and cylindrical. Usually 3–5 cones are produced at one time.

CULTIVATION: Tolerates frosts.

Zamia pumila

Pests and Diseases
of Palms and Cycads

Healthy, well-grown palms and cycads are usually not troubled by many pests and diseases. Cycads, because of their rather less succulent foliage, are less affected by disease than palms. A warm and humid environment around the plant which is conducive to plant growth also encourages the multiplication of many insects and the growth of fungi. In the tropics, as in the hothouse, we are thus more likely to strike problems. Palms grown in monoculture are also more likely to sustain damage because fungal diseases and insects which use the palm as a host are accommodated in a virtually unlimited fashion. Palms and cycads growing in conditions that do not encourage growth (e.g. cold temperatures, dry atmosphere, draughts, dry soil, wet and badly aerated soil) are also more vulnerable to damage from their immediate environment as well as from pests and diseases.

The biological controls provided by nature should be encouraged where possible and practical. Providing space around plants so they can benefit from the free movement of air is just as important in the nursery as it is in the plantation. Chemicals also have a role to play when biological and environmental manipulations may be insufficient.

COMMON PESTS AND DISEASES

APHIDS

Palm aphids (*Cerataphis palmae*) can heavily infest young foliage. These tiny sap-sucking insects are dark and ringed with a white wax, much like a scale insect. Sooty mould will often grow on the excretions of the palm aphid. Individual plants can be wiped clean with a sponge and soapy water as an alternative to a contact insecticide.

SCALES

Sap-sucking scale insects on palms, and sometimes on the new growth of cycads, may be caused by a number of species. Often found in colonies on foliage and stems, they are of various shapes and sizes, usually round or oval with hard shell-like covers, and sometimes accompanied by sooty mould. As with other sap-sucking insects they can be sponged off an individual plant or treated with a contact insecticide or white oil emulsion spray. If left unattended, scales can cause a great deal of damage by yellowing the foliage.

MEALY BUGS

These are small sucking insects, covered with a white fluffy wax, which can infest the undersides of palm leaves. In large numbers, they appear like a white fungal growth. Infestations can be heavy enough to cause leaf wilt. They secrete a sugary 'honey dew' on which sooty

White wax infestation on *Macrozamia communis*.

mould develops. Ants are also attracted to the honey dew and feed upon it. The ants can transfer the mealy bugs from one plant to another and spread the infestation. They also assist in spreading the root-feeding mealy bug by constructing galleries among the roots of the plants and giving access to the mealy bugs. Individual plants can be hand cleaned with a sponge. A contact insecticide may be required for larger numbers of plants.

SPIDER MITES

Infestations build up on the undersides of palm leaves and can cause yellowing and necrotic patches if left uncontrolled. The red spider mite is the most common of these almost microscopic insects. The first sign of attack may be the appearance of brown speckles on the foliage. A fine webbing can sometimes be discovered on the undersides of the leaf. A dry atmosphere indoors provides an environment very suitable for the red spider mite. Their life cycle is very short — just ten days — and so infestations can build quickly. Contact insecticides or specific miticides may need to be used.

CATERPILLARS

The larvae (caterpillars) of many moths and butterflies chew the succulent leaves of palms. A few of these larvae also feed on new cycad growth and can virtually strip the new leaves. Plants can be regularly checked (the caterpillars removed by hand), or they can be sprayed with insecticides specifically designed to kill chewing insects.

WEEVILS

Cycads in southern Africa are often affected by the weevil *Antliarhinus zamiae*, which can destroy the seed endosperm. Affected seed should be burned. Plants can be protected against potential attacks by a contact insecticide on developing cones. In Australia, the weevil *Tranes internatus* can cause the death of cycads by eating away the inside of their trunks or eating the more-easily-devoured seedlings.

TERMITES

These insects can cause major losses amongst palms and sometimes also in cycads. They attack the plant from below the ground, invading roots and progressively causing damage up the trunk. By the time termite damage is noticed, the plant is usually too badly damaged to be saved. Affected soil may require treating with a contact insecticide to destroy colonies of termites that have become established in that area.

RATS

Asian plantations of the African oil palm, *Elaeis guineensis*, suffer reduced yields of fruit because of the ravages of hungry rats. On Lord Howe Island, off the east coast of Australia, the harvest of kentia palm (*Howea forsteriana*) seed is also reduced by rats, which feed on the fruit in the trees. In Malaysia, many types of control have been tried over the last few decades, including setting rat baits and introducing snakes. The latest control measure, introducing barn owls (a natural predator of rats) into plantations, is proving effective and unobtrusive.

FUSARIUM WILT

Reported as a problem in date palms in California, this fungus (*Fusarium oxysporum*) is spread easily by pruning tools if they are not sterilised between uses on plants. Systemically attacking the conductive tissues of the palm, the fungus will first cause leaves to die and will gradually kill the whole plant. It can lie dormant in the soil for years and suddenly in warm weather can enter the plant's roots. There is no effective treatment for fusarium wilt.

PHYTOPHTHORA ROOT ROT

Some palms are sensitive to *Phytophthora cinnamomii*, which is a root fungus with a wide range of host plants. *Syagrus romanzoffiana* and *Caryota* spp. can sometimes be attacked by this pathogen when they are in poorly-drained soils. Palms should not be replanted in the same soil unless it has been treated with an appropriate fungicide. The fungus will remain dormant in dead plant material and therefore all plant rubbish from the area should be removed and burned.

LETHAL YELLOWING

This is a disease caused by a mycoplasma-like organism which has caused the devastation of palms in the Caribbean, Florida and, recently, Texas. It has not spread to palms in the Asia–Pacific area, but the potential is present if infected plants are introduced. Thought to be spread by an insect vector, the leaf hopper bug (*Myndus crudus*), this disease is particularly virulent in coconuts. Meerow (1992) lists 25 palm species susceptible to lethal yellowing. The disease can cause a mature palm's death in about four months. The first sign may be a wilting and yellowing leaf or the premature death of an inflorescence. In coconuts, the developing fruit suddenly drops off the palm. In affected areas, those palms known to be susceptible should not be planted. Four-monthly treatments of palms with injections of tetracycline antibiotics into the trunk will prevent the disease. Coconut varieties resistant to lethal yellowing have been developed.

Glossary

Acaulescent: Without an above-ground stem (or trunk).

Acropetal (of flowering): Progressing from the base towards the apex.

Acute: Sharply pointed, but without being drawn out to the point.

Anther: Pollen-containing part of the stamen.

Armed: Bearing spines, sharp teeth, prickles etc.

Articulate: (of leaflets) Having a narrowed base which tends to abscise before the leaf.

Basipetal (of flowering): Progressing from the apex towards the base.

Bifid: Divided into two equal parts.

Bipinnate (of leaves): Doubly pinnate, the rachis itself dividing and the secondary rachis bearing leaflets.

Bisexual: Containing functional male and female parts.

Bract: A modified leaf acting as a protective organ and associated with an inflorescence, a flower or with cycad cones.

Branching (of the inflorescence): The following terms are used to describe the degree of branching, not the number of branches.

simple-branched or simply branched — branching to one order

moderate-branched or moderately branched — branching to two or three orders

well branched — branching to four orders.

Cabbage: Apical leaf bud of the crown, or 'heart of palm' (edible).

Caespitose: Clustered, clumping, with several to many stems.

Campo: Extensive, nearly level, grassy plain in South America.

Carpel: The organ of the flower which encloses the ovules.

Cataphyll: A rudimentary leaf form, such as a scale.

Catkin-like: Describes a thick, cylindrical rachilla on which the flowers are densely crowded.

Caudex: Term often used for the trunk of cycads (not used in this book).

Circinate: Rolled up into a circle or ring shape (in cross-section).

Cirrus: A whip-like climbing organ with reflexed spines that is an apical extension of the leaf rachis (plural: cirri).

Coralloid (of roots): Coral-like, always near the surface of the soil or just above the soil (characteristic of cycads).

Costa: An extension of the petiole into the blade of a palmate leaf.

Costapalmate (of the leaf shape): Shaped like a fan or the palm of a hand, with a midrib which is an extension of the petiole.

Crown: The cluster of leaves at the top of the stem.

Crownshaft: The cylinder-shaped collection of tubular leaf sheaths at the top of the stem, each sheath wrapped around the one beneath.

Decompound (of leaves): To compound (divide) a second or further time.

Decumbent (of stems): Reclining, but with the apex turned upwards.

Decurrent (of leaflets): The lower margins extending along the rachis and near-parallel to the rachis. In cycads, decurrent leaflets are less likely to abscise before the leaf itself.

Dentate: Toothed.

Dichotomous: Forking (of stem, root etc.) into two equal branches.

Dioecious: When male and female flowers are borne on different plants.

Distal: Situated farthest away from the place of attachment.

Divaricate (of branching): Spread widely.

Dyad (of flowers): A pair.

Ellipsoidal: Shaped like a solid ellipse.

Elliptic or elliptical: Shaped like an ellipse.

Endemic: Restricted in distribution to a particular area.

Endocarp: The innermost layer of the fruit wall that encloses the seed.

Endosperm: The energy storage tissue of the seed which is used for the developing embryo and seedling.

Eophyll: First seedling leaf.

Epicarp: The outermost layer of the fruit wall.

Falcate: With one margin longer than the other: sickle-shaped.

Flagellum: A whip-like climbing organ formed from a modified inflorescence (plural: flagella).

Frond: Leaf of a non-flowering plant such as a fern or cycad. (Not used in this book)

Genus: The usual major subdivision of a family or subfamily, usually consisting of more than one species. The species which make up the genus are very similar to one another and are considered very closely related. The genus designation is the first part of the scientific name of a species (plural: genera).

Glabrous: Smooth-surfaced, without hairs or scales, etc.

Glaucous: Covered with wax, giving a grey or bluish-grey bloom.

Hapaxanthic: (of stems) Those stems that flower only once and then die.

Hastula: An outgrowth or flap of tissue at the insertion of the blade on the petiole (in palmate leaves).

Homogenous (of seed endosperm): Uniform throughout, without interruptions of the seed coat into the endosperm. (SEE ruminate)

Hybrid: A plant resulting from the cross between plants of two different taxa, such as between two species of the same genus, between two species of different genera, or between two subspecies of the same genus.

Imbricate: To overlap.

Indumentum: A covering of hairs or scales.

Induplicate (of leaflets): V-shaped in cross-section.

Inflorescence: That part of the plant which includes all the flowering branches.

Infructescence: The same parts as the inflorescence, but when they are in fruit.

Internode: The stem between the point of attachment of two leaves.

Involute: Rolled inwards from the edge.

Irregular (of arrangement of leaflets): Leaflets not arranged directly opposite on either side of the leaf rachis.

Knee (in rattans): A swelling on the leaf sheath at the base of the petiole.

Lamina (of leaf): Surface of the blade.

Lanceolate (of leaf or leaflet): Narrow and tapering at both ends.

Leaflet: Division of a pinnate leaf. (See pinna.)

Linear (of leaf or leaflets): Very narrow, many times longer than wide, with the sides parallel or nearly so.

Median (of leaves): At or about the middle section of the rachis.

Megasporophyll: Structure on the female cycad plant containing the ovules.

Mesocarp: The middle layer of the fruit wall, usually fleshy or fibrous, sometimes oily.

Microsporophyll: Structure on the male cycad plant containing the pollen.

Monocarpic: Fruiting only once before dying.

Monoecious: Bearing both male and female flowers on the one plant.

Monotypic (of a genus, family etc.): Containing only one species.

Node: That point on a stem where the leaf is or was attached.

Notched (of a leaf or leaflet): A cut or indentation in the edge.

Ocrea: An extension of the leaf sheath beyond the point of insertion of the petiole.

Ovoid or ovate: Egg-shaped.

Palmate: Shaped like the palm of a hand, with ribs or veins radiating from one point.

Panicle: An inflorescence with many branches, in which each successive branch becomes smaller.

Paniculate: Descriptive of an inflorescence that is a panicle.

Pectinate: With teeth like a comb.

Peduncle: The lower unbranched stalk of an inflorescence.

Peltate (of leaves): Having a petiole attached to the lower surface at a distance from the margin.

Pericarp: The walls of the fruit: epicarp, mesocarp and endocarp.

Persistent: Applied to plant parts that remain attached to the plant after they (the parts) die or cease to function.

Petiole: The leaf stalk, below where the leaflets are attached and above the leaf sheath. (See rachis.)

Pinna: Term sometimes used instead of leaflet (not used in this book) (plural: pinnae).

Pinnate (of a leaf): Leaflets or lateral ribs arranged an each side of a central axis (leaf rachis), feather-like.

Pleonanthic (of stems): Those that flower more than once, not dying after one flowering.

Plicate: Folded into pleats.

Plumose: Having a feathery appearance.

Praemorse: Jagged-toothed.

Prickle: Epidermal projection that is spine-like.

Prophyll: The first bract borne on the inflorescence.

Proximal: Situated closest to the place of attachment.

Pytxis: Young, emerging foliage leaf.

Rachilla: The branch that bears the flowers (plural: rachillae).

Rachis: That part of the leaf from which the leaflets arise; that is, the axis of a leaf beyond the petiole. (See petiole, sheath.)

Radicle: The first root developed from an embryo.

Recurved or reflexed: Curved backwards.

Reduplicate (of leaflets): Upside-down V-shaped in cross-section.

Regular (of arrangement of leaflets): Leaflets arranged in pairs directly opposite on either side of the leaf rachis.

Revolute: Rolled under (backwards) towards the underside.

Rhizome: Underground stem.

Ruminate (of endosperm or seed): Streaked due to indentations of the seed coat into the endosperm.

Scurfy: With small, flattened, papery scales.

Segment (of leaves): A division of a palmate leaf.

Senescent: Growing old: becoming dysfunctional due to age.

Serrate: Toothed like a saw.

Sessile: Without a stalk.

Sigmoid: S-shaped.

Sheath (of the leaf): The base of the leaf that wraps around the stem. It is always tubular at first, but may split while or after it matures. (See rachis, petiole.)

Species: The basic category of classification designated to signify a single kind of plant or animal. The species designation is the second part of the scientific name of a species. (See genus.)

Spicate: Spike-like, the inflorescence when it is not branched.

Spine: Sharp projection.

Sporophyll: Modified leaf structure carrying the reproductive parts in cycads.

Stipule: One pair of lateral outgrowths or appendages at the base of a petiole.

Stolon: Above-ground, prostrate stem that usually roots at the nodes.

Stoloniferous: Describing stems that grow as stolons.

Stomata: Pores in the surface of leaves for the exchange of gases.

Subfalcate: Nearly, or almost, falcate.

Syncarpous: With united carpels.

Sympatrically: Growing in the same or overlapping areas.

Taxon: Term used to denote any taxonomic category, such as species, genus, etc (plural: taxa).

Tomentose: Covered with tomentum.

Tomentum: Covering of felt-like, dense short hairs, scales, wool or down.

Triad: A cluster or group of three flowers, one female flanked by two male.

Truncate (of leaflets): The apex appearing as though cut off nearly straight across.

Undulate: Wavy.

Valvate: Two parts that meet exactly and do not overlap.

Venation: The arrangement of veins in a leaf.

BIBLIOGRAPHY

PALM AND CYCAD CULTIVATION

Boyer, K., 1992. *Palms and Cycads Beyond the Tropics*, Palm and Cycad Societies of Australia, Brisbane, Australia. (Especially good on climate requirements outside the tropics.)

Doughty, S. C., 1991. 'The cycad garden: Repotting cycad seedlings after germination', *The Cycad Newsletter*, XIV(1):12–20 and XIV(2):4–11.

Giddy, C., 1984. *Cycads of South Africa*, 2nd ed., Struik Publishers, Cape Town, pp. 21–26.

Giddy, C., 1990. 'Conservation through cultivation', *Memoirs of the New York Botanical Gardens*, 57:89–93. (Explains techniques of cycad pollination and propagation.)

Jones, D., 1984. *Palms in Australia*, Reed Books, Australia, chapters 4–6.

Jones, D., 1993. *Cycads of the World*, Read Books, Australia, chapters 7-10

Hodel, D. R., 1992. Chamaedorea *Palms: The Species and Their Cultivation*, The International Palm Society, Kansas, chapter 9.

Stewart, L., 1981. *Palms for the Home and Garden*, Angus&Robertson, Australia, chapters 4–6.

Tang, W., 1986. 'Cycad seeds and seedlings', *The Cycad Newsletter*, IX(2).

Walkely, S., 1992. '*Cycas* pollination', *Encephalartos*, 31:22–23.

PALMS

Bailey, L. H., 1935. 'The royal palms — preliminary survey', *Gentes Herbarum*, 3(7):343–387.

Bailey, L. H., 1935. 'Certain ptychospermate palms of horticulturists', *Gentes Herbarum*, 3(8):410–437.

Bailey, L. H., 1937. '*Erythea* — the Hesper palms', *Gentes Herbarum*, 4(3):85–118.

Bailey, L. H., 1937. 'Notes on *Brahea*', *Gentes Herbarum*, 4(3):119–125.

Bailey, L. H., 1942. 'Palms of the Seychelles Islands', *Gentes Herbarum*, 6(1):3–48.

Bailey, L. H., 1942. 'Palms of the Mascarenes', *Gentes Herbarum*, 6(2):49–80.

Balick, M. J., 1979. 'Amazonian oil palms of promise: a survey', *Advances in Economic Botany*, 33(1):11–28.

Balick, M. J., 1986. 'Systematics and economic botany of the *Oenocarpus-Jessenia* (Palmae) complex', *Advances in Economic Botany*, 3:1–140.

Balint, D., 1988. '*Iguanura* — The forgotten genus from the Old World tropics', *Palms and Cycads*, 21:6–14.

Balint, D., 1990. 'The genus *Areca* in Sarawak', *Palms and Cycads*, 28:2–9.

Balint, D., 1991. 'The genus *Pinanga*: The remarkable palms of Sarawak', *Palms and Cycads*, 30: 2–9

Blombery, A. and Rodd, T., 1982. *An informative, practical guide to Palms of the World, their cultivation, care and landscape use*, Angus & Robertson, Sydney.

Braun, A., 1968. *Cultivated Palms of Venezuela*, The International Palm Society, Kansas, USA.

Chazdon, R. L., 1985. 'The palm flora of Finca La Selva', *Principes*, 29(2):74–78.

Chazdon, R. L., 1988. 'Conservation-conscious collecting: concerns and guidelines', *Principes*, 32(1):13–17.

Chazdon, R. L. and Marquis, R. J., 1985. 'Key to seedling palms of Finca La Selva', *Principes*, 29(2):79–82.

Corner, E. J. H., 1966. *The Natural History of Palms*, Weidenfeld and Nicolson, London.

Dahlgren, B. E. and Glassman, S. F., 1961. 'A revision of the genus *Copernicia* 1. South American species', *Gentes Herbarum*, 9(1):3–40.

Dahlgren, B. E. and Glassman, S. F., 1963. 'A revision of the genus *Copernicia* 2. West Indian species', *Gentes Herbarum*, 9(2):43–232.

Davis, A. T., 1988. 'Uses of semi-wild palms in Indonesia and elsewhere in South and Southeast Asia', *Advances in Economic Botany*, 6:98–118.

De Granville, J. and Henderson, A., 1988. 'A new species of *Asterogyne* (Palmae) from French Guiana', *Brittonia*, 40(1):76–80.

De Guzman, E. and Fernando, E. S., 1986. 'Philippine Palms', in *Guide to Philippine Flora and Fauna*, 4:147–233.

Dowe, J., 1987. Pinanga — *Essence of the Malayan palm flora*, Palm and Cycad Societies of Australia, *Pinanga* issue, 16:10–15.

Dowe, J., 1989. 'Palms of the South-West Pacific', *Palm and Cycad Societies of Australia*, pp. 77-82, 110–126.

Dowe, J., 1990. 'Ecological status and endangerment of

Australian palms', *Palms and Cycads*, 26:2–7.

Dransfield, J., 1972. 'The genus *Borassodendron* (Palmae) in Malesia', *Reinwardtia*, 8:351–363.

Dransfield, J., 1972. 'The genus *Johannesteijsmannia* H.E. Moore Jr.', *Gardens Bulletin of Singapore*, 26:63–83.

Dransfield, J., 1974. 'Notes on *Caryota no* Becc. and other Malesian *Caryota* species', *Principes*, 18(3):87–93.

Dransfield, J., 1979. *A Manual of the Rattans of the Malay Peninsula Forest Department*, Ministry of Primary Industries, Malaysia.

Dransfield, J., 1980. 'Systematic notes on *Pinanga* (Palmae) in Borneo, *Kew Bulletin*, 34:769–788.

Dransfield, J., 1983. '*Kerriodoxa*, a new coryphoid palm genus from Thailand', *Principes*, 27(1):3–11.

Dransfield, J., 1984. 'The genus *Areca* (Palmae: Arecoideae) in Borneo', *Kew Bulletin*, 39:1–22.

Dransfield, J., 1984. 'The Rattans of Sabah', *Sabah Forest Record No.13*, Forest Department, Sabah.

Dransfield, J., 1986. *Palmae. Flora of Tropical East Africa*, A. A. Balkema, Rotterdam.

Dransfield, J., Johnson, D. and Synge, H., 1988. *The Palms of the New World, a conservation census*, IUCN–WWF Plants Conservation Programme, Publication No. 2.

Dransfield, J. and Johnson, D., 1989. 'The conservation status of palms in Sabah', *Malayan Naturalist*, 43(1& 2):16–19.

Dransfield, J. and Uhl, N. W., 1986. '*Ravenea* in the Comores', *Principes*, 30(4):156–160.

Dransfield, J. and Uhl, N. W., 1986. 'An outline of a classification of palms', *Principes*, 30(1):3–11.

Duke, N. C., 1991. '*Nypa* in the Mangroves of Central America: Introduced or Relict?', *Principes*, 35(3):127–132.

Endt, D., 1987. '*Rhopalostylis sapida* on the Great Barrier Island, New Zealand', *Principes,* 31(4):165–168.

Essig, F. B., 1977. 'A preliminary analysis of the palm flora of New Guinea and the Bismarck Archipelago', *Papua New Guinea Botany Bulletin*, No. 9.

Essig, F. B., 1978. 'A Revision of the Genus *Ptychosperma* Labill. (Arecaceae)', *Allertonia*, 1:415–478.

Fernando, E. S., 1983. 'A revision of the genus *Nenga*', *Principes*, 27(2):55–70.

Fernando, E. S., 1988. 'The mottled-leaved species of *Pinanga* in the Philippines', *Principes*, 32(4):165–174.

Fernando, E. S., 1989. 'The genus *Heterospathe* (Palmae: Arecoideae) in the Philippines', *Kew Bulletin*, 45(2):219–234.

Furtado, C. X., 1940. 'Palmae Malesicae VIII — The genus *Licuala* in the Malay Peninsula', *Gardeners' Bulletin Straits Settlement*, 11:31–73.

Furtado, C. X., 1949. 'The Malayan species of *Salacca*', *Gardeners' Bulletin Straits Settlement*, 12:378–403.

Gibbons, M., 1993. *The Palm Identifier*, Simon & Schuster, Australia.

Gibbons, M., 1993. 'Tracking the *Trachycarpus* trail', *Principes*, 37(1):19–25.

Gillett, G. W., 1971. '*Pelagodoxa* in the Marquesas Islands', *Principes*, 15(2):45–48.

Glassman, S. F., 1977. 'Preliminary taxonomic studies in the palm genus *Attalea* H. B. K.', *Fieldiana, Botanical*, 38:31–61.

Glassman, S. F., 1977. 'Preliminary taxonomic studies in the palm genus *Orbignya* Mart.', *Phytologia*, 36:89–115.

Glassman, S. F., 1977. 'Preliminary taxonomic studies in the palm genus *Scheelea* Karsten', *Phytologia*, 37(3):219–250.

Glassman, S. F., 1979. 'Re-evaluation of the genus *Butia* with a description of a new species', *Principes*, 23(2):65–79.

Glassman, S. F., 1987. 'Revisions of the palm genus *Syagrus* Mart. and other selected genera in the Cocos alliance', *Illinois Biological Monographs*, 56:1–230, University of Illinois Press, Chicago.

Hambali, G. G, Mogea, J. P. and Yatazawa, M., 1989. '*Salacca* germplasm for potential economic use', Proceedings of the First PROSEA International Conference, p. 260.

Harrison, E., 1986. 'The Raphias of Mtunzini', *The Palm Enthusiast*, 3(3):22–7.

Hay, A. J. M., 1984. 'Palmae', in Johns, R. J. and Hay, A. J., (eds), *A Guide to the Monocotyledons of Papua New Guinea*, Department of Forestry, P. N. G. University of Technology, Papua New Guinea, pp. 195–318.

Henderson, A., 1990. 'Arecaceae. Part 1. Introduction and the Iiarteinae', *Flora Neotropica*, Monograph 53, New York Botanical Garden.

Henderson, A. and Steyermark, J. A., 1986. 'New palms from Venezuela', *Brittonia*, 38(4):309–313.

Hodel, D., 1980. 'Notes on *Pritchardia* in Hawaii', *Principes*, 24(2):65–81.

Hodel, D., 1992. Chamaedorea *Palms, the species and their cultivation*, The International Palm Society, Kansas.

Hodel, D., 1992. 'Additions to *Chamaedorea* palms: new species from Mexico and Guatemala and miscellaneous notes', *Principes*, 36(4):188–202.

Hodel, D., 1993. 'A Tale of Two (Three?) *Neodypsis*', *The Palm Journal*, Jan., pp. 8–18.

Irvine, A., 1983. '*Wodyetia*, a new arecoid genus from Australia', *Principes*, 27(4):158–167.

Johnson, D., 1988. 'Worldwide endangerment of useful palms', *Advances in Economic Botany*, 6:268–273.

Johnson, D., 1991. *Palms for Human Needs in Asia. Palm utilization and conservation in India, Indonesia, Malaysia and the Philippines*, WWF Project 3325.

Jumelle, H. and Perrier de la Bâthie, H., 1945. 'Palmiers', in Humbert, H., (ed.), *Flore de Madagascar et des Comores*, Tananarive.

Kiew, R., 1976. 'The genus *Ignuanura* Bl. (Palmae)', *Gardens Bulletin of Singapore*, 28(2):191–226.

Kiew, R., 1979. 'New species and records of *Iguanura* (Palmae) from Sarawak and Thailand', *Kew Bulletin*, 34(1):143–145.

Kiew, R., 1989. 'The conservation status of palms in Peninsular Malaysia', *Malayan Naturalist*, 43(1& 2):3–15.

Kiew, R., 1989. 'Utilization of palms in Peninsular Malaysia', *Malayan Naturalist*, 43(1& 2):43–67.

Kiew, R. and Davison, G. W. H., 1989. 'Relations between wild palms and other plants and animals', *Malayan Naturalist*, 43(1& 2):37–42.

Kimnach, M., 1977. 'The species of *Trachycarpus*', *Principes*, 21:155–160.

Lott, R. H. and McIntyre, S., 1991. 'Seed predation and dispersal in a tropical palm *Normanbya normanbyi* (W. Hill) L. H. Bailey', *Palms and Cycads*, 32:6–16.

McKamey, L., 1983. *Secret of the Orient: Dwarf Rhapis excelsa*, Grunwald Printing Co., Texas.

Meerow, A. W., 1992. *Betrock's Guide to Landscape Palms*, Florida.

Mogea, J. P., 1980. 'The flabellate-leaved species of *Salacca* (Palmae)', *Reinwardtia*, 9(4):461–479.

Mogea, J. P., 1981. 'Notes on *Salacca wallichiana*', *Principes*, 25(3):120–123.

Moore, H. E., 1957. 'The genus *Reinhardtia*', *Principes*, 1(4):127–145.

Moore, H. E., 1957. 'Synopses of various genera of Arecoideae. 21. *Veitchia*', *Gentes Herbarum*, 8(7):483–536.

Moore, H. E., 1962. '*Allagoptera* and *Diplothemium*', *Principes*, 6(1):37–39.

Moore, H. E., 1963. 'An annotated checklist of cultivated palms', *Principes*, 7(4):119–182.

Moore, H. E., 1970. 'The genus *Rhopaloblaste* (Palmae)', *Principes*, 14(3):75–92.

Moore, H. E., 1971. 'Additions and corrections to "*An annotated checklist of cultivated palms*"', *Principes*, 15(3):102–106.

Moore, H. E., 1973. 'The major groups of palms and their distribution', *Gentes Herbarum*, 11(2):27–141.

Moore, H. E., 1978. 'The genus *Hyophorbe* (Palmae)', *Gentes Herbarum*, 11(4):212–245.

Moore, H. E., 1979. 'Arecaceae', pp. 392-438 in Smith, A. C., *Flora Vitiensis Nova 1*, Pacific Tropical Garden, Lawaii, Kauai, Hawaii.

Moore, H. E., 1979. 'Endangerment at the specific and generic levels in palms', *Principes*, 23(2):47–64.

Moore, H. E. and Chazdon, R. L., 1985. 'Key to palms of Finca La Selva, Costa Rica', *Principes*, 29(2):82–84.

Moore, H. E. and Fosberg, F. R., 1956. 'The palms of Micronesia and Bonin Islands', *Gentes Herbarum*, 8(6):423–478.

Moore, H. E. and Guého, L. J., 1984. 'Flore des Mascareignes', *189 Palmiers*, 1–34.

Moore, H. E. and Uhl, N. W., 1984. 'The Indigenous palms of New Caledonia', *Allertonia*, 3:313–402.

Okolo, E. C., 1992. 'The genus *Raphia* and its uses in Nigeria', *Mooreana*, 2(1):29–33.

Palms of Indonesia, (the English translation of *Palem Indonesia*), 1987, Palm and Cycad Societies of Australia.

Partomihardjo, T., Mirmanto, E., Riswan, S. and Whittaker, R. J., 1992. 'Ecology and distribution of Nibung (*Oncosperma tigillarium*) within the Krakatau Islands, Indonesia', *Principes*, 36(1):7–17.

Pearce, K. G., 1989. 'Conservation status of palms in Sarawak', *Malayan Naturalist*, 43(1& 2):20–36.

Pearce, K. G., 1989. 'Utilization of palms in Sarawak', *Malayan Naturalist*, 43(1& 2):68–91.

Piggott, C. J., 1990. *Growing oil palms, an illustrated guide*, Incorporated Society of Planters, Kuala Lumpur.

Price, P., 1987. '*Livistona drudei*, a north Queensland coastal palm', *Principes minor*, 29:10–11.

Quero, H. J., 1981. '*Pseudophoenix sargentii* in the Yucatan Peninsula, Mexico', *Principes*, 25(2):63–72.

Rauwerdink, J. B., 1986. 'An essay on *Metroxylon*, the Sago Palm', *Principes*, 30(4):165–180.

Read, R. W., 1961. 'Madagascar's Three-sided palm — *Neodypsis decaryi*', *Principes*, 5:71–74.

Read, R. W., 1968. 'A study of *Pseudophoenix* (Palmae)', *Gentes Herbarum*, 10(2):169–213.

Read, R. W., 1975. 'The genus *Thrinax* (Palmae: Coryphoideae)', *Smithsonian Contr. Bot.*, 19:1–98.

Read, R. W., 1979. 'Palmae', in Howard, R. A., (ed.), *Flora of the Lesser Antilles 3*, Arnold Arboretum, Harvard University, pp. 320-368.

Rosengarten, F., 1986. 'Coconut', *Principes*, 30(2):47–62.

Russel, T. A., 1965. 'The *Raphia* palms of West Africa', *Kew Bulletin*, 19(2):173–196.

Savage, A. and Ashton, P., 1991. 'Tourism is affecting the stand structure of Coco-de-Mer', *Principes*, 35(1):47–48.

Stevenson, G. B., 1974. *Palms of Southern Florida*, published by the author.

The IUCN Plant Red Data Book, IUCN, Morges, Switzerland.

Tucker, R., 1979. 'Pinanga', Palm and Cycad Societies of Australia, *Pinanga* issue, 16:2–9.

Tucker, R., 1984. 'Growing *Pigafetta filaris*', *Palms and Cycads*, 3:2–4.

Tucker, R., 1988. *The Palms of Subequatorial Queensland*, Palm and Cycad Societies of Australia.

Tucker, R., 1989. '*Bowenia* in north Queensland', *Palms and Cycads*, 25:2–6.

Tucker, R., 1992. 'Experiences with *Cytostachys renda*', *Mooreana*, 2(1):11–16.

Tucker, R., 1992. '*Pritchardia* in Hawaii: a traveller's view', *Mooreana*, 2(1):17–28.

Tucker, R., 1992. 'Vegetataive Proliferation in *Asterogyne martiana*', *Mooreana*, 2(2):22–24.

Uhl, N. W. and Dransfield, J., 1987. *Genera Palmarum*, L. H. Bailey Hortorium and The International Palm Society, Lawrence, Kansas.

Wessels Boer, J. G., 1968. *The Geonomoid Palms*, N. V.

Noord-Hollandsche Uitgevers Maatschappij, Amsterdam.

White, A., 1988. *Palms of the Northern Territory and their distribution*, Palm and Cycad Societies of Australia.

Whitmore, T. C., 1973. *Palms of Malaya*, Oxford University Press, London.

Wood, B. J., 1986. *A brief guide to oil palm science*, Incorporated Society of Planters, Kuala Lumpur.

Zona, S., 1990. 'A monograph of *Sabal* (Arecaceae: Coryphoideae)', *Aliso*, 12(4):583–666.

Zona, S., 1991. 'Notes on *Roystonea* in Cuba', *Principes*, 35(4):225–233.

Zanoni, T., 1991. 'The royal palm of the island of Hispaniola', *Principes*, 35(1):49–54.

CYCADS

Butt, L., 1988. 'Cycads of Australia, *Macrozamia riedlei*', *Encephalartos*, 15:32.

Butt, L., 1990. *An Introduction to the Genus Cycas in Australia*, Palm and Cycad Societies of Australia.

Butt, L., 1991. *An Introduction to the Zamiaceae in Australia*, Palm and Cycad Societies of Australia.

Carruthers, W., 1893. 'On *Cycas taiwaniana* sp. *nov.* and *C. seemanii*', *British Journal of Botany*, 31:1–3, t.330, 331.

Chamberlain, C., 1935. *Gymnosperms: Structure and Evolution*, University of Chicago Press, Chicago.

De Luca, P., Sabato, S. and Torres, M. V., 1982. 'Distribution and variation of *Dioon edule* (Zamiaceae)', *Brittonia*, 34(3):355–62.

De Luca, P., Sabato, S. and Torres, M. V., 1981. '*Dioon merolae* (Zamiaceae): A new species from Mexico', *Brittonia*, 33(2):179–85.

De Luca, P., Sabato, S. and Torres, M. V., 1984. '*Dioon tomasellii* (Zamiaceae): A new species with two varieties from western Mexico', *Brittonia*, 36(3):22–7.

Eckenwalder, J. E., 1980. 'Taxonomy of the West Indian Cycads', *Journal of the Arnold Arboretum*, 6(4):701–22.

Giddy, C., 1984. *Cycads of South Africa*, 2nd ed., Struik Publishers, Cape Town.

Giddy, C., 1990. 'Conservation through cultivation', *Memoirs of the New York Botanical Garden*, 57:89–93.

Gilbert, S., 1984. *Cycads: Status, Trade, Exploitation and Protection 1977–1982*, World Wildlife Fund, USA.

Goode, D., 1989. *Cycads of Africa*, Struik Publishers, Cape Town.

Gregory, T. J. and T. T., 1984. 'A brief review of the genus *Dioon* (Zamiaceae)', *The Cycad Newsletter*, 8(4):1–15.

Grobbelaar, N., 1992. 'A more realistic conservation

strategy for the South African cycads', *Encephalartos*, 32:15–18.

Guide to Philippine Flora and Fauna, Vol. IV, 1986. Section 'Palms' by Guzman, E. and Fernando, E., pp. 147–232.

Hall, A.V., de Winter, M., de Winter, B. and van Oosterhout, S. A. M., 1980. *Threatened Plants of Southern Africa*, S.A. National Science Programme Report No. 5.

Harden, G. J., (ed.), 1990. *Flora of New South Wales*, Vol. 1, pp. 74–8.

Hodel, D. R., 1992. Chamaedorea *Palms: The Species and Their Cultivation*, The International Palm Society, Kansas.

Hill, K. D., 1992. 'A preliminary account of *Cycas* (Cycadaceae) in Queensland', *Telopea*, 5(1):177–205.

Hill, R. S., 1978. 'Two new species of *Bowenia* Hook. *ex* Hook. *f.* from the Eocene of Eastern Australia', *Aust. J. Bot.* 26:837–46.

Hooft, J., 1970. '*Zamia* from seed', *Carolina Tips*, 33(2):1–11, reprinted in *Encephalartos*, (1990) 22:16–17.

Johnson, L. A. S., 1959. 'The families of cycads and the Zamiaceae of Australia', *Proceedings of the Linnaeus Society of New South Wales*, 84(1):64–117.

Johnson, L. A. S., 1961. '*Zamiaceae*', Contributions from the New South Wales National Herbarium, *Flora Series*, 2:21–41.

Johnson, L. A. S. and Wilson, K. L., 1990. 'General traits of the cycadales' in *The Families and Genera of Vascular Plants*, Vol. 1, Springer-Verlag Berlin, Heidelberg.

Jones, D. L., 1991. 'Notes on *Macrozamia* Miq. (Zamiaceae) in Queensland with the description of two new species in section *Parazamia* (Miq.) Miq.',

Astrobaileya, 3(3):481–7.

Jones, D. L. and Hill, K. D., 1992. '*Macrozamia johnsonii*, a new species of *Macrozamia* section *Macrozamia* (Zamiaceae) from northern New South Wales', *Telopea*, 5(1):31–4.

Kemp, M., 1987. 'Focus on *Encephalartos horridus*', *Encephalartos*, 7:8–13.

Kennedy, P., 1986. 'Visiting the NSW Macrozamias with Loran Whitelock', *Encephalartos*, 6:18–22.

Kennedy, P., 1992. '*Macrozamia stenomera*', *Principes minor*, 55, 4 pages.

Kennedy, P., 1992. '*Lepidozamia peroffskyana*', *Principes minor*, 57, 6 pages.

Kennedy, P., 1992. '*Macrozamia heteromera*', *Principes minor*, 59, 5 pages.

Kennedy, P., 1993. '*Macrozamia communis*', *Principes minor*, 60, 7 pages.

Knorstog, K. J., 1990. 'Studies of cycad reproduction at Fairchild Tropical Garden', *Memoirs of the New York Botanical Garden*, 57:63–81.

Landry, G. P., 1990. '*Ceratozamia hildae*, the bamboo cycad', *The Cycad Newsletter*, 13(1):3–7.

Landry, G. P., 1991. '*Microcycas calocoma*', *The Cycad Newsletter*, 14(2):14–19.

Lindblad, P., 1990. 'Nitrogen and carbon metabolism in coralloid roots of cycads', *Memoirs of the New York Botanical Garden*, 57:104–13.

Maconochie, J. R., 1978. 'Two new species of *Cycas* from northern Australia', *Journal of the Adelaide Botanic Gardens*, 1(3):175–8.

Miyano, L., 1989. 'Cycad landscaping', *Encephalartos*, 19:16–17.

Moretti, A. and Sabato, S., 1988. 'Systematics and evolution of *Dioon* and *Ceratozamia*', *Fairchild Tropical Garden Bulletin*, 43(1):22–7.

Osborne, R., 1986. 'Focus on *Encephalartos woodii*', *Encephalartos*, 5:4–10.

Osborne, R., 1987. 'Focus on *Encephalartos ferox*', *Encephalartos*, 9:14–21.

Osborne, R., 1987. 'Focus on *Encephalartos villosus*', *Encephalartos*, 10:16–23.

Osborne, R., 1989. 'Focus on *Encephalartos laevifolius*', *Encephalartos*, 19:2–8.

Osborne, R., 1989. 'Focus on *Encephalartos transvenosus*', *Encephalartos*, 20:10–17.

Osborne, R., 1990. 'Micropropagation in cycads', *Memoirs of the New York Botanical Garden*, 57:82–88.

Pant, D. D., 1990. 'On the Genus *Glandulataenia*, nov. from the Tiassic of Nidhpuri, India', *Memoirs of the New York Botanical Garden*, 57:186–199.

Pant, D. D., 1991. 'Cycads of Asia', *Encephalartos*, 26:15.

Peters, H. A., 1986. '*Zamia*', *Encephalartos*, 5:14–15.

Sabato, S., 1990. 'West Indian and South American Cycads', *Memoirs of the New York Botanical Garden*, 57:173–185.

Stevenson, D. W., 1980. 'Form follows function in cycads', *Fairchild Tropical Garden Bulletin*, January.

Stevenson, D. W., 1982. 'A new species of *Ceratozamia* (Zamiaceae) from Chipas, Mexico', *Brittonia*, 34(2):182–184.

Stevenson, D. W., 1990. 'Morphology and Systematics of the Cycadales', *Memoirs of the New York Botanical Garden*, 57:8–55.

Stevenson, D., 1990. '*Chigua*, A new genus in the Zamiaceae. With comments in its biographical significance', *Memoirs of the New York Botanical Garden*, 57:169–172.

Stevenson, D. W., 1991. 'The Zamiaceae in the southeastern United States', *J. Arnold Arboretum*, Supplementary Series, Vol. 1:367–384.

Stevenson, D. W., 1992. 'A formal classification of the extant cycads', *Brittonia*, 44:220–223.

Stevenson, D. W, and Osborne, R., 1993. 'The World List of Cycads', *Encephalartos*, 33:19–25.

Stevenson, D. W., Sabato, S. and Vázquez Torres, M., 1986. 'A new species of *Ceratozamia* (Zamiaceae) from Veracruz, Mexico with comments on species relationships, habitats, and vegetative morphology in *Ceratozamia*', *Brittonia*, 38(1):17–26.

Tang, W., 1985. 'Cycad trade and conservation', *Encephalartos*, 4:22–23.

Tang, W., 1986. 'Pollinating cycads', *Encephalartos*, 8:16–19.

Tang, W., 1986, 'Cycad seeds and seedlings', *The Cycad Newsletter*, 9(2):4–8.

Tang, W., 1990. 'Maturity in cycads', *Encephalartos*, 24:24–27.

Tang, W., 1991. 'Growth rates of cycad trunks', *The Cycad Newsletter*, 14(3):13–16.

Tucker, R., 1989. '*Bowenia* in north Queensland', *Palms and Cycads*, 25:6.

Vorster, P. and E., 1985. 'Focus on *Stangeria eriopus*', *Encephalartos*, 2:8–11.

Vorster, P., 1987. 'Hybridization in *Encephalartos*', *Encephalartos*, 10:10–15.

Vovides, A. P., 1992. *The Cycads of Veracruz, Mexico*, El Eco de Virginia, Virginia, USA.

Vovides, A. P., 1985. 'Systematic studies on Mexican Zamiaceae II. Additional notes on *Ceratozamia kuesteriana* from Tamaulipas, Mexico', *Brittonia*, 37(2):226–231.

Whitelock, L., 1985. 'In search of cycads in Australia', *Palms and Cycads*, 6:4–11.

Walkely, S., 1992. '*Cycas* pollination', *Encephalartos*, 31:22–23.

Photographic Credits

Illustrations

All black and white illustrations © Margaret Hodgson.

Photographs

Photographs are in page order (l) left; r (right), c (centre); t (top); b (bottom); m (middle). Species names have been used to identify photographs. Unless otherwise stated, all photographs © Lynette Stewart. In all other cases, copyright remains with individual photographers or institutions.

Front cover *Cyrtostachys renda*, Lynette Stewart; p 8 *Rhopalostylis sapida*, K Boyer (b l); p 9 *Metroxylon warburgii*, J Dowe; p 19 The palm house at Kew Gardens, Kew Gardens; p 21 *Encephalartos horridus*, K Hill; p 22 *Pritchardia affinis*, R Tucker; p 23 *Wodyetia bifurcata*, J Dowe; p 27 *Howea forsteriana*, I Hutton; p 31 *Phoenix reclinata*, D & V Morris; p 43 *Arenga australasica*, R Tucker (b c); p 52 *Bactris gasipaes*, J Dowe (t r); p 53 *Balaka seemanii*, J Dowe (b r); p 55 *Basselinia pancheri* , A de Does (t r); p 55 *Basselinia pancheri* inflorescence, A de Does (b r); p 61 *Borassus flabellifer*, C Thompson; p 65 *Butia eriospatha*, J Dowe (b c); p 68 *Calamus manan*, J Dransfield (b l); p 68 *Calamus moti,* J Dowe (b r); p 71 *Carpentaria acuminata*, J. Dowe; p 85 *Clinostigma exorrihizum*, J Dowe; p 95 *Dictyosperma album*, J Dowe; p 104 *Hedyscepe canterburyana*, K Boyer; p 106 *Heterospathe woodfordiana*, C McQueen (m r); p 108 *Howea forsteriana*, J & J Marley (t r); p 111 *Hyophorbe verschaffeltii*, J Dowe, (t r); p 115 *Iguanura wallichiana* var *wallichiana*, J Dowe, (b r); p 118 *Kentiopsis oliviformis*, B Laughland; p 128 *Licuala lauterbachii*, J Dowe (m l); p 134 *Livistona muelleri*, R Tucker (m b); p 134 *Livistona rotundifolia*, C Thompson, (b r); p 138 *Metroxylon salomonense*, J Dowe (m l); p 138 *Metroxylon sagu*, O Murang (t r); p 143 *Nypa fruticans*, J Dowe (t); p 143 *Nypa fruticans* inflorescence, J Dowe (b r); p 151 *Phoenix dactylifera*, J Dowe (m l); p 157 *Pinanga disticha*, J Dowe (m b); p 159 *Pinanga simplicifrons*, J Dowe (c); p 161 *Pritchardia martii*, R Tucker (b l); p 161 *Pritchardia remota*, R Tucker (c t); p 161 *Pritchardai thurstonii*, K Boyer (b r); p 167 *Raphia australis*, J Dowe (t r); p 167 *Raphia hookeri*, J Dowe (b c); p 175 *Rhopalostylis baueri* var *cheesmanii*, K Boyer (t r); p 175 *Rhopalostylis sapida*, K Boyer (b l); p 183 *Salacca dransfieldiana*, G Hambali (t r); p 183 *Salacca magnifica*, G Hambalia (b l); p 184 *Salacca zalacca*, G Hambali (b l); p 187 *Socratea exorrhiza*, A Henderson (t r); p 193 *Trachycarpus nanus*, M Gibbins (b r); p 197 *Veitchia joannis*, J Dowe, (t c); p 211 *Cycas pruinosa*, K Hill (t r); p 216 *Encephalartos ferox*, C Giddy (b l); p 216 *Encephalartos laevifolius*, C Giddy (m r); p 217 *Encephalartos natalensis*, C Giddy (t r); p 217 *Encephalartos transvenosus*, K Hill (c l); p 217 *Encephalartos villosus*, C Giddy (b r); p 221 *Macrozamia heteromera*, C Thompson (c); p 221 *Macrozami a lucida*, J Dowe (c r); p 222 *Macrozamia moorei*, J Dowe (c l); p 222 *Macrozamia riedlei*, L. Butt (t c); p 222 *Macrozamia stenomera*, C Thompson (c r); back cover *Cycas pruinosa*, K Hill.

INDEX OF BOTANICAL NAMES

(Numbers in *italics* refer to illustrations, numbers in **bold** refer to main entries)

CYCAD SPECIES

General Index